SCHIZOPHRENIA
AND THE
NEED-FEAR DILEMMA

SCHIZOPHRENIA AND THE NEED-FEAR DILEMMA

by DONALD L. BURNHAM, M.D.,
ARTHUR I. GLADSTONE, Ph.D.
and
ROBERT W. GIBSON, M.D.

INTERNATIONAL UNIVERSITIES PRESS, INC.

NEW YORK

TABLE OF CONTENTS

ACKNOWLEDGMENTS

Our foremost debt springs directly from our decision to focus our study principally on relationships. We needed the help of the participants in the relationships to be studied. They responded most generously by giving not only willing consent but active collaboration. This meant allowing us access to the deep personal significance of many of these relationships, involving, as they often did, the gamut of emotions of extraordinary intensity. Since a relationship may become either the tenuous bridge to hope, reorganization, and reintegration into shared reality or the final disillusioning seal on a doom to irreversible despair, disorganization, and alienation, it is small wonder that both participants may experience it as the severest possible test of personal worth. For the privilege of studying relationships that had this bedrock meaning, we are profoundly grateful.

We enjoyed the assistance of an entire institution, Chestnut Lodge, and the stimulation of its excellent clinical program. Dr. Dexter M. Bullard, Medical Director, established the Chestnut Lodge Research Institute, initiated the application to the Ford Foundation for funding of the study, and gave unfaltering encouragement to all phases of our work. Dr. Marvin L. Adland, Associate Medical Director, provided a vital liaison between our research endeavors and the clinical program of the hospital. He made it possible for us to be an integral part of the hospital community so that we hardly ever felt like foreign intruders viewed suspiciously by the natives. At the same time we were allowed remarkable freedom to observe whatever aspects of the clinical program engaged our research interests. Dr. Adland also arranged advantageous opportunities for us to present our ideas and preliminary findings to the staff.

Dr. Otto A. Will, Director of Psychotherapy, facilitated our receiving the full cooperation of the psychotherapy staff. Collectively and individually, the therapists provided us with invaluable information concerning their therapeutic relationships with their patients. In this regard, we are particularly indebted to Drs. Charles A. Baker, Clay F. Barritt, Robert N. Butler, John L. Cameron, John P. Fort, Milton G. Hendlich, Harry L. Hinson, John S. Kafka, Berl Mendel, César Meza, Ping-nie Pao, Clarence G. Schulz, Joseph H. Smith, Helm Stierlin, and the late Yvonne Van der Reyden.

Many members of the nursing, social service, and activities staffs— in fact, of all departments of the hospital—gave us valuable assistance.

Our debt to the patients is incalculable. They were the *raison d'être* of the entire study and made manifold direct and indirect contributions to it. Beyond this, they provided inspiring proof of the capacity of courage, good will, and good humor to survive in the grimmest of life situations.

Throughout the study we benefited from formal and informal consultations with many members of the Chestnut Lodge staff. Dr. Harold F. Searles and the late Dr. Frieda Fromm-Reichmann were especially helpful.

Our major source of extramural consultation was a series of exchange visits with a research team from the Austen Riggs Center comprising Drs. Stuart C. Miller, Eugene Talbot, and Robert B. White. They afforded valuable criticism of our research and illuminating comparisons with their sociopsychological studies of different types of patients in a different clinical setting. Statistical consultation was provided by Dr. Ardie Lubin.

In addition to the authors, our research staff consisted of Mrs. Jane Burkhardt, research assistant, and Mrs. Verdelia Scott and Mrs. Bernice Smith, whose exceptional secretarial talents made it possible for them to assist in a research capacity as well. Even more valuable than their individual contributions was the remarkable capacity of this trio to function as a team, to say nothing of their ability to sustain an atmosphere conducive to unharried study.

We were equally fortunate in the assistance afforded us in the writing phase of the study. Mrs. Marcie Giberman performed outstandingly as secretary and research assistant at NIMH. Additional typing assistance was provided by Mrs. Virginia Clarkson at the Sheppard and Enoch Pratt Hospital.

We also are grateful for the skillful editorial assistance of Miss Norma Fox of International Universities Press.

We have striven to preserve the anonymity of the persons described in this book. All names of patients are fictitious, as are all but two of the names of staff members. In addition, such possibly identifying information as places and dates have been altered.

Our study was generously supported by a grant from the Ford Foundation to the Chestnut Lodge Research Institute. Much of Dr. Burnham's writing was done at the National Institute of Mental Health where he is a research psychiatrist, and where he was fortunate in having received the professional support and criticism of Dr. Robert A. Cohen, Director of Clinical and Behavioral Research.

We wish to express our gratitude to the following:

The Commonwealth Fund and Harvard University Press for permission to reprint from Andras Angyal, *Foundations for a Science of Personality*, 1958.

The William Alanson White Psychiatric Foundation, Inc., for permission to reprint, with slight alteration, Donald L. Burnham, "Identity Definition and Role Demand in the Hospital Careers of Schizophrenic Patients," *Psychiat.*, 24:96-122, Supplement to May, 1961.

The American Medical Association for permission to reprint, with slight alteration, Donald L. Burnham, "Separation Anxiety," *Arch. Gen. Psychiat.*, 13:346-358, October, 1965, copyright 1965.

Edward B. Marks Music Corporation for permission to reprint the lyrics of "Paper Doll," composed by Johnny S. Black.

DONALD L. BURNHAM
ARTHUR I. GLADSTONE
ROBERT W. GIBSON

FOREWORD

To THE PSYCHIATRIST one of the rewarding aspects of increasing age is a sense of participation in history, a personal realization that there is a recognizable growth and unfolding of concepts which promise a more powerful theory of personality development, a deeper under-standing of human behavior. As a new resident 30 years ago, I was taught to view schizophrenia as a psychobiological reaction to stress. But the nature and mode of action of relevant types of stress, the char-acter of the developmental tasks which each person must accomplish before he reaches maturity, the specific effects of individual, interper-sonal, social and cultural experiences, and the possible psychobiological mechanisms and processes which led to the particular developments observed were but dimly apprehended.

It was my good fortune, in subsequent years, to have been a member of the Chestnut Lodge staff when Stanton and Schwartz carried out the trail-blazing study reported in *The Mental Hospital* (1954). It has been equally gratifying to have had some administrative responsibility for the intramural research program at the National Institute of Men-tal Health where the disciplines represented range from those which study the influences of culture, social structure, and life experience on the one hand, to the nature of the cellular and subcellular processes involved in the behavior of living systems on the other. Vicariously I have been on many voyages of discovery: the work of Clausen and Kohn on social relations in schizophrenia; of Wynne on family transactions; of Shakow on psychological processes; of Silverman on cognitive controls; of Rosenthal and Pollin on genetic studies; and of Kety on biological processes are only selected examples. There is a beginning convergence of findings from these diverse vantage points, although we cannot yet see beyond the horizon.

This book gives eloquent expression to the conception of schizophrenia which springs from the development of psychoanalytic ego psychology. Reading it has been a particularly rewarding experience for me because of the meaningful way in which it brings together what at first glance appear to be disparate clinical phenomena, and also because I have had the privilege of frequent association with the authors as they developed their point of view and can therefore share with them the satisfaction they must feel at its explication. I first met two of them almost 20 years ago when, at different times, they were on duty at the U. S. Naval Hospital at Bethesda. I came to know them later as students in the Washington Psychoanalytic Institute and as colleagues at Chestnut Lodge; now they have taken leadership responsibilities on the Washington scene—Burnham as former Director of Research at Chestnut Lodge, Editor of *Psychiatry,* and Research Psychiatrist at the National Institute of Mental Health; Gibson as Medical Director at Sheppard and Enoch Pratt Hospital; and both of them as Training and Supervising Analysts in the Washington Psychoanalytic Institute, where Burnham also served as Director of the Educational Program. Gladstone I knew by reputation, and then personally when he came to take part in the research which the book reports.

The authors' decision to study the interpersonal relationships of schizophrenic individuals followed quite naturally from the earlier work of Stanton and Schwartz on the social structure of the mental hospital, and was strategically influenced by an almost unique characteristic of Chestnut Lodge—its veritable immersion in the life of the schizophrenic. I know of no other psychiatric hospital where so much time of so many people is devoted to attempts to define the nature and to understand the meaning of the schizophrenic individual's behavior, where ideas developed in the course of these efforts so dominate the organization of the entire institution, and where the members of the staff often come to feel so deeply personal an involve-

ment that they may consider themselves at fault when a patient who
has been ill for many years fails to improve while in their care.

Beyond the illumination which the concept of the need-fear dilemma
casts on the schizophrenic patient's interpersonal relations, the book
makes a contribution to the view of the individual as an open system
to be studied in transactions with other systems. The authors do not
look upon the schizophrenic person as a deteriorated individual, cut
off from others by an autistic barrier, and out of touch with reality.
Instead they have tried to define the possible nature of the defect, and
have viewed many of the "symptoms" as adaptive efforts which the
patient makes in his attempt to organize his world. Obviously not all
of these ideas are completely original. I recognize the influence of my
teachers: Meyer, Fromm-Reichmann, and Sullivan. Some of these
concepts were modified in turn by my generation. The present authors
have taken what they have considered as solid constructs in the older
teachings, have added from their own experiences, and have integrated their views with those of others in related fields in their efforts
to elaborate the central thesis which is here advanced. The detailed
clinical histories make explicit their sophisticated understanding of
behaviors which are often designated as "inappropriate" because they
cannot be deciphered by means of common sense. The authors have
gone beyond labeling single instances as items of psychodynamic or
psychopathologic import, and have defined them in process terms as
stages in individual personality development.

Looking back, one wonders how we failed to identify some of these
transactions years ago. There were certain facts of which we were all
aware which pointed in the direction the authors and other investigators have taken, but we failed to follow them to their logical conclusion. In the first week of our residency, Adolf Meyer told us how
important it was to avoid or postpone hospitalization as long as possible and, if that failed, to keep it as brief as could be since it so often
led to deterioration. So we avoided, postponed, or kept it as brief as
possible, and never tried to identify what circumstances or factors led
to deterioration. I remember vividly meeting with the parents and
siblings of a schizophrenic youth; they wanted to see both the boy and
myself every day during his hospitalization. With the support of the
Chief Resident, I firmly denied this request, ordered the siblings away
lest they be unfavorably influenced, arranged to meet the parents indi-

vidually at the most infrequent intervals possible, and kept them away from the patient—all this in the name of treatment—because it was clear that the family interaction strongly influenced the patient's behavior, and that the parents always quarreled and contradicted each other when they were seen together. Particularly after we started analytic training, we spoke of the intense feelings aroused in our work with patients; but we rushed with these to our analysts or our supervisors and discussed them only as manifestations of our own neuroses, hopefully to be understood, but in any event to be squelched as soon as possible.

It seems to me that despite the fact that we spoke in interactional and interpersonal terms, we still had not broken free from the notion of the disease *in* the patient. Although we were familiar with the concepts of ambivalence, identification, introjection, and projection, our understanding of the vicissitudes of the integration of conflicting drives, affects, goals, and ideals in the personality as a whole was much more hazy than is the case with students of today. We paid more attention to biology and psychology, and very little to developments in the fields of sociology, particularly to the studies of social systems which we now realize have great relevance for our understanding of human behavior.

One of the most commendable aspects of this book is the clear way in which it shows how certain aspects of an individual's functioning within an individual personality system may be related to his functioning in the hospital social system. Coming at the problem independently and from a different direction, the authors' work complements the studies of Wynne, Lidz, and Jackson, who have contributed so much to our understanding of the family systems of schizophrenic individuals. The probability that concepts from studies such as these may be linked with those derived from current work on cognitive controls, on the genetic aspects of certain behavior patterns, and the rapidly growing knowledge of regional biochemical processes is an exciting prospect for behavioral research.

In addition to its obvious great interest to researchers, the Appendix on the Relationship Questionnaire will make particularly rewarding reading for the clinician, who often finds that attempts to quantify his data have a tendency to deprive it at the same time of its emotional meaning. It describes an instrument for the systematic study of issues which arise regularly in the course of intensive psychotherapy carried out in a hospital setting. It illustrates graphically the attitudinal differences of the various staff members, each of whom may have a significant impact on the patient's attitudes and behavior. The history of its design, refinement, and testing is a case study of a research methodology which has much to offer in its application to the clinical situation.

It should be noted that the authors are not proposing a primary etiological theory of schizophrenia. We certainly do not know, nor do we need to know for the purposes of this level of explanation, just how the ego defect develops. It may be inherited, constitutional, experiential, or the result of some biological imbalance. What the authors attempt to explain is the nature of the human experience of the schizophrenic individual, and they offer a structural psychological theory to account for his observed behavior and reported feelings, relating these to vicissitudes in the course of personality development. Any theory of schizophrenia which purports to be complete must include a consideration of these issues, and must take into account the schizophrenic's adapted as well as his maladapted behavior.

Finally, what is the clinical significance of the book? It seems to me that it fulfills a need eloquently stated by David Stafford-Clark in his 1959 Mental Health Research Fund Lecture on "The Foundations of Research in Psychiatry." After describing some biological studies, he went on to say:

> We must never forget that communication remains the ultimate key to the treatment of schizophrenia. . . . However skillful and appropriate our physical treatment . . . may become as a result of the refinement in our knowledge and understanding both of the biochemical processes which may underlie it and the electrophysiological processes whose secondary disturbance ultimately brings about the illness, it remains true that we can treat patients successfully and restore them to true health and happiness only if we can gain contact with them at a human and personal level, and give them thereby the bridge over which they may cross back to normal harmony and understanding with their fellows.

This book is a rich contribution to the understanding which is necessary for the achievement of such contact, and it makes an important additional point; namely, that the traffic on the bridge moves in two directions.

—ROBERT A. COHEN, M.D.
Director of Clinical and Behavioral Research
National Institute of Mental Health

SCHIZOPHRENIA
AND THE
NEED-FEAR DILEMMA

I

INTRODUCTION

DONALD L. BURNHAM

THIS BOOK REPORTS the collaborative efforts of the authors (DLB, RWG, and AIG), two psychoanalysts and a social psychologist, to study the staff-patient relationships of a group of hospitalized chronic schizophrenic patients. Our approaches to this study underwent numerous shifts and modifications which are reflected in the final form of the book.

Our choice of patients' relationships as a focus for our study had several determinants, one of which is the prominence of disturbed relationships in schizophrenia. The schizophrenic person suffers severe disability in establishing and maintaining satisfactory relationships, and the chronic phases of illness are characterized by withdrawal and desocialization. There is evidence that many of these difficulties may have their origins in disturbed early child-parent relationships. Furthermore, many treatment methods, especially psychotherapy and milieu therapy, emphasize personal relationships as a major therapeutic vehicle. This is especially true at Chestnut Lodge, which was the locus of our study.

It seemed appropriate, perhaps even imperative, that a clinical research project take its impetus and much of its form from the clinical program already in existence. For over three decades Chestnut Lodge had developed a program, philosophy, and tradition strongly emphasizing intensive psychotherapy and the doctor-patient relationship in the treatment of schizophrenic patients. This began with a determination to test the applicability of psychoanalytic concepts and technical principles to the treatment of psychoses (Bullard, 1939, 1940). It

3

continued with the teaching and practice of Sullivan (1956) and Fromm-Reichmann (1939, 1941).

In addition, the importance of patient relationships within the hospital, and of the hospital as a social organization with capacities to influence patients both beneficially and detrimentally, was increasingly recognized. The publication by Stanton and Schwartz of *The Mental Hospital* (1954) was a landmark in this development.

Among the clinical staff, interest in the study of the therapeutic use of relationships remained high, as evidenced, for instance, in the writings of Searles (1965) and Will (1960, 1961). There was lively interest in how events and relationships in the total hospital milieu might influence events in psychotherapy and vice versa. Preliminary observations indicated that events in these two spheres of patient-staff interaction might correlate in various patterns. For example, the patient might regress in one sphere while progressing in the other. Or he might approach and cling in one relationship while fearfully avoiding closeness in others. In still another pattern, feelings aroused in the doctor-patient relationship might be displaced to relationships with ward staff members. These were but a few of the intricacies of staff-patient relationships which had aroused clinical staff interest (Cohen, 1957).

Our research group was made further aware of the centrality of relationships in the clinical staff's thinking and operations when we conducted an interview survey of the concepts employed by the medical staff in its employment of psychotherapy to treat schizophrenia. Each therapist was asked, "What do you regard as your basic ideas and operating assumptions of the nature of schizophrenia and the psychotherapeutic approach to it?" (Burnham, 1957). Although what emerged from the answers to this question in interviews of an hour or longer was by no means a uniform ideology or coherent "Chestnut Lodge approach," there was a remarkable emphasis upon relationships, not only regarding treatment but in connection with the genesis and manifestations of schizophrenia as well. For example, the majority of the therapists interviewed considered disturbances of early child-parent relationships as a major etiologic factor. Each of the therapists mentioned disordered relationships as a salient feature of the clinical picture of schizophrenia. In addition, each considered relationships, doctor-patient and other staff-patient, as the primary means of assisting the patient to recovery. Still further significance was attached to changes in relationships as an index of improvement. To some extent the doctor-patient relationship was assigned primacy, and other staff-patient relationships were expected to be more or less modeled upon it. A view of relationships patterned in dyads was more frequent than more complex views of group process.

With this as background, we, the authors, set ourselves the research task of making a comprehensive and systematic study of the relationships with hospital staff members of a small group of schizophrenic patients. Several early decisions were made as to the scope and design of the study. One was that the study would interfere as little as possible with the normal operations of the hospital, but would examine these operations in their natural state. In other words, we would make no attempt to set apart a special group of patients for study nor would we introduce experimental variations in staff assignments, treatment techniques, or other aspects of the clinical program.

We chose to study a group of chronic schizophrenic male patients who were housed on the third floor of the main building of Chestnut Lodge.[1] Our choice of chronic patients was based largely upon two considerations. One was the belief that it was in the treatment of such patients that the Chestnut Lodge program offered the greatest opportunities for unique observations, as contrasted, say, with the treatment of borderline patients being conducted in numerous other hospitals. The second consideration was that these patients were likely to remain in the hospital and on the same ward long enough to permit study of their relationships over a substantial period of time. Augmenting both of those considerations was Chestnut Lodge's strong emphasis on sustained and very active treatment of even extremely chronic patients, in contrast to less abundantly staffed institutions where chronic patients of necessity may be relegated to custodial care.

The choice of male patients was based partly on the unverified impression that previous studies of the social interaction of schizo-

[1] At the time of our study, the main building, the largest of four which house patients, had living quarters for patients on the top three floors. Administrative and medical offices were located on the first floor, and a dining room used separately by staff and patients was in the basement. This building, along with others which include offices, nurses' quarters and a recreation center, is located on a tract of 96 acres on the outskirts of a small city.

phrenic patients, not only at Chestnut Lodge but elsewhere, had focused more upon women than upon men.

Another, though not overriding factor in our choice of Third Floor patients, was that Dr. Gibson, a member of the research team, was clinical administrator of that ward. Thus it was decided that he would function as both participant and observer, as had Dr. Stanton in his earlier work.

There was an average of 12 patients on Third Floor during the five years of our study. However, for various reasons they were not the same 12 for the entire period. Details of turnover rates, discharges, and transfers are presented in Chapter V. It also should be noted that since our various methods of study were developed and applied at different times, some patients were studied by one or another method for a longer period of time than by other methods. The patients all were white males from upper and upper-middle socioeconomic class families. Their ages ranged from 17 to 53 at time of admission, averaging approximately 29. Each patient included in the central focus of our study was unequivocally diagnosed as schizophrenic and had been overtly ill for several years prior to admission to Chestnut Lodge.

In addition to our choice of patients for study, we faced decisions as to which of the patient's relationships in the hospital were to be studied. These relationships included those with a psychotherapist, the Third Floor administrator, a social worker, nurses, psychiatric aides, activities workers, housekeeping employees, and other patients. For several reasons we wished to study a reasonably comprehensive sample of these relationships. One reason was that a study limited to only one or two of these relationships might yield an unrepresentative, narrow view of the patient's interpersonal behavior. Another was that we were interested in phenomena concerning the tendency of many schizophrenic patients to diffuse, split, and otherwise scatter their adaptive efforts among many relationships because of inability to contain and to integrate their intense conflicts within single relationships. At the same time, since we obviously could not observe an unlimited number and variety of relationships, we had to select certain relationships for more detailed observation than others.

We decided to limit our systematic collection of data to staff-patient relationships. Important patient-patient relationships would not be overlooked, but neither would they be studied methodically. From among each patient's relationships with staff members, we chose for ordered study those with his psychotherapist, ward administrator, and the ward nurses and aides. Less regularly we would collect information concerning more peripheral relationships, such as those with activities staff members and the social worker.

The normal Third Floor staff complement comprised one or two graduate nurses, several student nurses, and approximately 10 aides. This meant regular, methodical collection of information about each patient's relationships with from 15 to 18 different staff members. Since during the period of our study the staff assigned to Third Floor did not remain constant but was changed relatively frequently, the total number of relationships studied over the entire period was even greater. More details of patient and staff population of Third Floor, and such information as turnover rate, are provided in Chapter V.

After deciding which relationships to study, our next task was to find or to devise suitable means of collecting information about them, and ordering it in meaningful form. This involved countless hours of discussion among the authors, clinical staff members, and consultants on numerous questions of methodology and conceptualization.

Throughout our study we were concerned with developing and revising concepts and theories which would enhance the meaning of our observations and the reports others made to us. The theoretical framework which eventually emerged is presented in Chapter II. It grew in a fashion not always clear in its developmental stages, and reflects not only the direct results of our study methods but cumulative clinical experience, reading, and discussion as well.

At the outset in our discussion of concepts to be employed, we were impressed by a need for more precise specification of the nature of the schizophrenic patient's difficulty in establishing and maintaining relationships. We felt that the terms *desocialized* and *withdrawn* were too broad. Specific problems in relationships, such as excessive dependency, unneutralized aggression, and sexual conflicts, required integration into an overall theory.

In addition to wishing to specify more clearly the schizophrenic person's relationship disabilities, we found ourselves interested in many other questions. Some of these were: What are the developmental stages of a relationship? What are the ingredients of a significant relationship? What makes a particular relationship constructive for a patient? What factors in individual psychotherapy, ward social climate, and hospital organization promote growth of satisfactory relationships? To attempt to answer these questions required conceptual refinement of what we meant by the term *relationship* and how it connected with the schizophrenic person's psychological disabilities.

Our efforts to develop a conceptual framework were also dictated by methodological considerations. In order to compare one patient's relationships with those of another, or with his own at another time, it would be necessary for us to collect information within a reasonably standardized framework. It was important that the framework include aspects of relationships which were both relevant and accessible to study.

The question of accessibility involved important methodological decisions as to how data were to be collected. Two principal types of data collection were available to us, each with certain advantages and disadvantages. One was to depend upon reports from regular hospital personnel and patients; they would be asked to remember and report their interactions with each other by means of interviews, questionnaires, and similar devices. The other was to make direct observations, either by special observers or by use of sound and visual recording instruments. Several considerations prompted us to rely primarily upon reports rather than upon direct observations. One was our decision to obtain information about a large number of possibly diverse relationships. A second was the lack of research personnel sufficient to function as observers over extended periods. This combination made direct observation unfeasible as a primary method of data collection. It was, however, employed to supplement and check the validity of the methods we used more extensively. A third consideration in favor of reports was that hopefully some of them would include the private, not directly observable, thoughts, feelings, and intentions of the participants in relationships.

It was decided to obtain regular reports from each staff participant in the staff-patient relationships we had selected for study. We debated at length whether to seek reports from the patient participants. Initially we decided against this, with the thought that not only did several of them have great difficulty in communicating, but that requesting reports on their relationships might interfere with the natural course of these relationships. Later we reversed this decision and had partial success in obtaining reports from patients through both interviews and questionnaires. These reports permitted us to compare patient and staff views of the same relationship.

We employed a variety of techniques for obtaining reports from the different participants. In collaboration with the psychotherapists of Third Floor patients, we designed an outline for interviewing each therapist at three-month intervals. These interviews were sound-recorded and transcribed. They covered such aspects of the doctor-patient relationship as the interest and approach-avoidance moves of each participant, feelings expressed, efforts to influence each other, the goals and intentions of each, and his apparent assumptions about the other's goals and intentions within the relationship. Part of the interview was left open for the therapist to tell us whatever he wished regarding the patient, himself, and the relationship between them. Whenever the patient's behavior and his relationships seemed to be changing significantly, additional interviews with the therapist were held. Several of the therapists made available their dictated or written notes on therapy sessions with the patients. Some sound recordings of therapy sessions were obtained. Transcriptions of the therapists' presentations at regular clinical staff conferences also were available. Later a questionnaire was designed for the therapists' use in reporting at three-month intervals particular aspects of the doctor-patient relationship. In the long run, however, it proved a less valuable source of information than the interviews and similar forms of report.

In his role of administrator of Third Floor, Dr. Gibson employed a variety of techniques for reporting his relationships with patients as well as his observations of other staff-patient interactions. He dictated daily descriptions of the general ward scene and of salient events and specific problems with particular patients. He recorded the principal interactions of patients and staff members at weekly Third Floor staff-patient meetings. His weekly meetings with the Third Floor staff were sound-recorded and indexed according to the patients and problems discussed. At approximate two-month intervals, assisted by a checklist reminder of salient interactional features, he made a detailed report of his latest interaction with each patient.

A similar variety of techniques, including several types of interviews, was employed to obtain reports from Third Floor nurses and aides. Soon, however, we found ourselves engaged in the major task of creating a new research instrument in the form of a questionnaire. We needed a standardized form for data collection and were unable in our survey of preexisting forms to find any which suited our purposes. Scales such as the Lorr IMPS for rating the patient's behavior did not provide a report of the staff member's participation in the relationship. We conducted preliminary trials with the Interpersonal Checklist devised by Leary and associates (1957), but found it inappropriate for reports on the type of relationships we were studying.[2] The problems encountered in the construction, repeated revision, attempted validation, and use of a new questionnaire were plentiful, and are discussed in detail in the Appendix.

Here we would emphasize mainly that the task of questionnaire construction involved us all the more deeply in attempts to refine concepts and theories of schizophrenia. We wanted an instrument which would assess aspects of relationships which were especially relevant not only to the psychological handicaps of the schizophrenic patient but also to the treatment program at Chestnut Lodge. We compiled, discussed, and repeatedly revised lists of aspects which would meet these criteria. Ultimately we arrived at a conceptual framework emphasizing the following aspects: approach-avoidance, activity content, control and influence, form and content of communication, and feelings expressed. We then used this framework to design questionnaire items and scales which would adequately report these aspects of relationships. In this task, however, we discovered distinct limitations in the ability of many ward staff members to discriminate subtle aspects of their relationships with patients, such as nuances and combinations of feelings expressed. In a number of ways we were forced to relinquish hopes of obtaining from questionnaire reports certain types of finely discriminative data.

In designing the questionnaire we chose to emphasize aspects of relationships which were "external," that is, observable and verifiable by a third person. We omitted questions concerning "internal" aspects of relationships, such as the unexpressed thoughts and feelings

---

[2] The ICL was originally designed to assess the relationships of neurotic outpatients being treated in group psychotherapy.

the participants had about each other, including their assumptions about their own and the other's goals and intentions in the relationship. The questionnaire would tell us, hopefully with reasonable accuracy, how frequently certain types of interactional behavior occurred. To determine the context and interactional sequence in which these behaviors occurred, we had to rely upon other methods, such as interviews, recordings of staff conferences, and direct observations of staff-patient interaction. Many types of interview were employed, including variations of the Critical Incident Technique (Flanagan, 1949), end-of-shift summaries, and focused exploration of specific problems within particular relationships.

In essentially its final form, the questionnaire was administered to the Third Floor staff at intervals of three to nine months for a period of two years. Over the same period at approximately the same intervals, the therapists of Third Floor patients completed a slightly modified version of the questionnaire. Our use of other data-collecting methods began before and continued beyond the two-year period of questionnaire use. The total period of data collection was five years.

In our earliest plans for reporting our study, we assigned high priority to data obtained by the questionnaire. We envisioned presenting a full description of each Third Floor patient's relationship patterns and comparing them with each other's patterns, and perhaps with those of other groups of patients. In addition, we had in mind a detailed comparison of changes in the psychotherapeutic relationship with changes in the patient's relationships with ward staff members. We wished to determine whether patients' relationships assumed stereotyped or varied and differentiated forms. A further question was whether staff-patient relationships differed regularly according to different roles occupied by the staff member; for instance, whether patients' relationships with the administrator differed consistently from the same patients' relationships with student nurses.

As our study proceeded, however, our plans for presentation changed. Our goal became less a comprehensive overview of the patients' relationships and more a focusing upon specific patterns which had emerged as salient in their relationships. We believe that these patterns form at least the rudiments of a theory of schizophrenia. They emerged from a confluence of multiple sources and methods of data collection, and are not preponderantly tied to any one source or method.[3]

The data which eventually coalesced into our final formulations included not only those from formal collection methods but those from innumerable informal contacts with Third Floor patients and staff members. The importance of what we learned in the course of living together in the same hospital community should not be minimized. The same is true of countless hours of discussion, both formal and informal, among the research and clinical staffs.

In planning the organization of this book, we sought the most meaningful integration and synthesis of our diverse types of information. We decided that the central unifying focus should be our theoretical formulations. These constitute Chapter II. The chapters which follow are designed to illustrate and document these formulations. We have relied heavily on case studies, since we believe they are especially suitable for illustration of the patterns of disturbed relationships we find characteristic of schizophrenia, particularly patterns of inconstancy, diffusion, and fragmentation. The case studies attempt not only to depict these forms of incoherence but also, in a sense, to contain them and bring into contiguous and simultaneous focus those parts of the patient's object world which in actuality had been split apart. This effort required selective synthesis of an enormous quantity of information gathered from a variety of vantage points and aimed at both depth and breadth, an approach which distinguishes these case studies from those based upon more limited information obtained from a few sources. For example, the full meaning of a therapist-patient interaction occurring in the morning might not be apparent until connected with something the patient told an aide in the evening or the next day.

In this manner, we chose for presentation those patients about whom we had both extensive and intensive reports and who, in addition, most clearly manifested the major varieties of disturbed relationship patterns typical of chronic schizophrenia. We have termed

[3] One result of our de-emphasis of the separate results of particular methods of data collection was a decision to place in an Appendix most of our report on the use of the questionnaire. There we present not only the findings from various applications of the questionnaire but also extensive methodological discussion concerning the design and testing of this instrument. These methodological considerations will be of interest primarily to researchers engaged in or contemplating similar studies.

these patterns *object clinging, object avoidance,* and *object redefinition.* They will be explained in the context of our overall theory in Chapter II.

In seeking to document our thesis as fully as possible, we have not limited ourselves to data from our own study, but in several chapters have drawn upon the studies of others. This is particularly true of Chapters III and IV which deal with predisposing and precipitating conditions in schizophrenia.

Several chapters are devoted to special problems manifest in the schizophrenic patient's relationships with staff members and in his overall adaptation to the hospital. Although at first glance several of these topics may appear disconnected from each other, they actually are linked by a key element of our theoretical system. This is the proposition that the schizophrenic person, because he lacks stable internal structure, is exceedingly dependent upon and vulnerable to the influence of external structure. This idea is fundamental to our discussion of such seemingly diverse topics as separation anxiety, time as a structuring factor in personality and social organization, problems of clinical administration in the mental hospital, and identity-role conflicts. We hope that our efforts to pull together divergent topics will serve the integrative purpose intended.

BIBLIOGRAPHY

Bullard, D. M. (1939), The Application of Psychoanalytic Psychiatry to the Psychoses. *Psychoanal. Rev., 26*:526-534.
—— (1940), Experiences in the Psychoanalytic Treatment of Psychotics. *Psychoanal. Quart., 9*:493-504.
—— (1940), The Organization of Psychoanalytic Procedure in the Hospital. *J. Nerv. and Ment. Dis., 91*:697-703.
Burnham, D. L. (1957), Concepts of Chestnut Lodge Therapists Regarding Schizophrenia and Psychotherapy. Presented at Third Annual Chestnut Lodge Symposium.
Cohen, R. A. (1957), Some Relations Between Staff Tensions and the Psychotherapeutic Process. In: *The Patient and the Mental Hospital,* ed. M. Greenblatt, D. J. Levinson, and R. H. Williams. Glencoe, Ill.: Free Press.
Flanagan, J. C. (1949), Job Requirements. In: *Current Trends in Industrial Psychology,* ed. W. Dennis. Pittsburgh: University of Pittsburgh Press.
Fromm-Reichmann, F. (1939), Transference Problems in Schizophrenics. *Psychoanal. Quart., 8*:412-426.

——— (1941), Recent Advances in Psychoanalytic Therapy. *Psychiat.,* *4*:161-164.

Leary, T. (1957), *Interpersonal Diagnosis of Personality.* New York: Ronald Press.

Searles, H. F. (1965), *Collected Papers on Schizophrenia and Related Subjects.* New York: International Universities Press.

Stanton, A. H. & Schwartz, M. S. (1954), *The Mental Hospital.* New York: Basic Books.

Sullivan, H. S. (1956), *Clinical Studies in Psychiatry.* New York: Norton.

Will, O. A. (1960), The Schizophrenic Reaction and the Interpersonal Field. In: *Chronic Schizophrenia,* ed. L. Appleby, J. M. Scher, and J. Cumming. Glencoe, Ill.: Free Press.

——— (1961), Process, Psychotherapy, and Schizophrenia. In: *Psychotherapy of the Psychoses,* ed. A. Burton. New York: Basic Books.

II

SCHIZOPHRENIA AND OBJECT RELATIONS

Donald L. Burnham

IT MAY BE WELL, before proceeding to our major thesis, to state our belief that as yet we possess no single, comprehensive, and adequate theory of schizophrenia. This is partly because schizophrenia is not a discrete nosological entity. It is sometimes necessary to remind ourselves that Bleuler (1911), in coining the term, referred to "the group of schizophrenias." The phenomena which are encompassed by the label schizophrenia are so diverse and far-reaching that construction of a unitary explanation is exceedingly difficult. It is still unclear as to whether conceiving of schizophrenia as a disease assists or hinders efforts to understand it. Some observers prefer to think of a syndrome, others of a faulty human reaction pattern, and still others of an evolutionary quirk. The point we wish to emphasize is that any sense of orderly classification associated with using the label schizophrenia may be partly spurious. Accordingly, when we speak of "the schizophrenic person" we should be aware that our capacity to generalize within a clearly established uniform class of persons is limited.

Now to the thesis which we propose as an explanation of many of the phenomena of schizophrenia. We believe that among the various types of schizophrenia there is at least one group of persons whose inborn psychic apparatus is normal but whose disordered early object relations interfered with normal development. It seems likely that another group has suffered compounding of genetically given weak-

15

nesses as a result of unfavorable early experiences. The existence of such groups is indicated by observations that in the course of treatment the psychological processes of these persons can be changed toward normality. We suggest that these are persons whose disordered object relations of infancy and childhood interfered with normal processes of psychological differentiation and integration. The resulting personality deficiencies are manifest in (1) a central system of control and personality organization (ego) which is so weak and easily disorganized as to limit the ability to aim and focus behavior purposefully, (2) a lack of autonomy, and (3) an incapacity to form reliable symbolic constructs or representations of reality. These deficiencies predispose the schizophrenic person to object relations characterized by a severe need-fear dilemma. Reactions to this dilemma consist of combinations of object avoidance, object clinging, and object redefinition. More precise definitions and detailed explanations of the terms we employ will be offered as we elaborate our basic thesis.

AUTONOMY

Autonomy means the capacity for self-regulation of behavior, as opposed to heteronomy, or regulation from without. The tendency toward increasing autonomy and decreasing heteronomy is a principle of normal growth (Angyal, 1958; Rapaport, 1958). To become relatively autonomous, a person must develop stable internal structure.[1] This development depends upon (1) maturation of genetically given ego apparatuses and functions (maturation may be facilitated or hindered by environmental influences); and (2) internalization of patterns of thought, affect, and action modeled after patterns used by the parents and other significant persons, either in regulating the child or in regulating themselves.

REALITY CONSTRUCTS

By the capacity to represent reality or to form a reality construct we refer in part to the ability to organize experience and selectively

[1] As Rapaport (1960) has pointed out, the concept of psychological structures refers to relatively enduring, quasipermanent patterns of function, not to anatomical structures.

to focus attention. Central in a person's reality construct are schemata comprising his definitions of self and others and their life situational contexts. In the course of normal development, a child progresses from the formlessness of William James' (1890) "blooming, buzzing confusion" to an extraordinarily complex structuring of his experience. From a myriad of inner and outer events he selects certain ones and articulates them into a reality construct. He develops the capacity to conceive of himself as a quasipermanent object among objects located in a universe with spatial and temporal coordinates and obedient to causal laws.

The organization of reality constructs is part of the capacity to symbolize; that is, to refer to objects and events and relationships between them by mental representations which stand for the actual objects and events. The capacity to symbolize perhaps most distinguishes man from other species. It enables a person to distance himself somewhat from the immediate press of internal and external events. It interposes between stimulus and response a capacity for delay or what has been termed "long circuiting." It also is the basis for the ability to anticipate events and to carry out experimental trial and error sequences with symbols rather than in concrete transactions with the actual objects.

Construction of an inner world that symbolically represents the objects in the outer world is an important part of the normal developmental process of internalization. When this ability to represent reality functions normally, it is man's most valuable tool. When it goes awry, it is his greatest handicap. Nowhere is this more evident than in schizophrenic, distorted symbolizations of reality. As Bleuler (1911) indicated, divorce from reality, or autism, is a fundamental symptom of schizophrenia.

The capacity to symbolize—and more particularly to organize a reality construct—is closely associated with a person's ability to function autonomously; this is precisely because he is not so caught up in and bound and driven by the immediate flux of events.

Figure 1 illustrates schematically the normal progression from a state of relative heteronomy to a state of relative autonomy (adapted from Angyal, 1958).

Now we shall consider which factors, in the course of development, may account for the structural weakness found in schizophrenia. We

THE TENDENCY TOWARD AUTONOMY IS A PRINCIPLE OF NORMAL GROWTH.

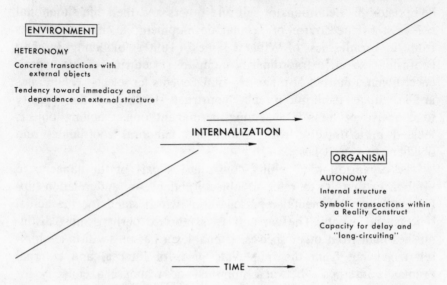

shall stress particularly the processes of differentiation and integration. These concepts have been widely employed as principles of growth and development in both biology and psychology (Allport, 1961; Angyal, 1958; Coghill, 1929; Searles, 1959; Sherrington, 1906; Werner, 1957; Witkin et al., 1962). As Werner stated, "Wherever development occurs it proceeds from a state of relative globality and lack of differentiation to a state of increasing differentiation, articulation, and hierarchic integration." Stated briefly, differentiation refers to the development of specialized parts, whereas integration refers to the bringing together of the parts into a harmonious whole.

DIFFERENTIATION

Witkin and his associates (1962) state, "Development toward greater differentiation involves progress from an initial relatively unstructured state, which has only limited segregation from the environment, to a more structured state, which has relatively definite boundaries, and which is capable of greater specificity of function."

For the purposes of our study of schizophrenia, two closely related aspects of differentiation are most important. One is differentiation of the person from his surroundings. This involves the development of a clear sense of separate identity and the capacity to distinguish inner from outer events in his symbolic structuring of reality. We refer to the consequence of this aspect of differentiation as separateness or individuality. The second relevant aspect is the development of a differentiated inner organization capable of specificity of function—that is, capable of discrete, specific reactions rather than indiscriminate, mass reactions. This requires the ability to perceive items as distinct from their backgrounds and to structure reality in a discrete, articulated, analytic manner rather than in a syncretic, diffuse, global manner. Normally, differentiation occurs in all personality subsystems. Basic drives and cravings differentiate into a hierarchy of derivative aims and interests. Affects differentiate from global pleasure and unpleasure into a spectrum of the fine nuances of feelings. Motor skills differentiate from uncoordinated mass movements to finely precise actions. These differentiated subsystems of personality, when adequately integrated, form the basis for relative autonomy.

INTEGRATION

Integration is the process by which differentiated parts or functions are brought together into a coherently articulated and harmoniously functioning whole. Differentiation and integration are correlated in that without differentiation into specialized parts there can be no integration of parts into a whole. However, differentiation does not guarantee integration. A person may be highly differentiated but poorly integrated. In other words, subsystems of personality may be highly developed but lacking in effective and harmonious articulation with each other.

Figure 2 schematically represents the processes of differentiation and integration which in normal development lead to a central organization capable of purposiveness and autonomy and the formation of reliable reality constructs.

CONSEQUENCES OF FAULTY DIFFERENTIATION AND INTEGRATION

The consequences of faulty differentiation and integration are precisely those deficiencies which constitute the major features of schizophrenia: (1) a weak, easily disorganized ego, (2) lack of au-

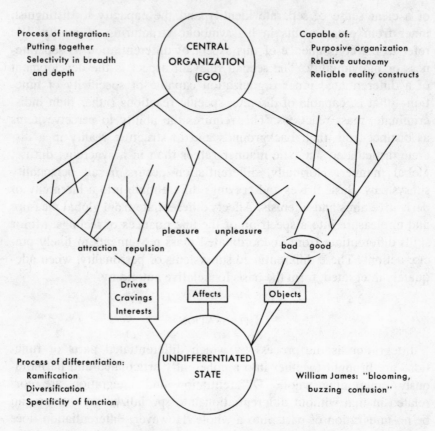

Process of integration:
    Putting together
    Selectivity in breadth
    and depth

CENTRAL
ORGANIZATION
(EGO)

Capable of:
    Purposive organization
    Relative autonomy
    Reliable reality constructs

pleasure   unpleasure

attraction repulsion   bad   good

Drives
Cravings
Interests

Affects

Objects

Process of differentiation:
    Ramification
    Diversification
    Specificity of function

UNDIFFERENTIATED
STATE

William James: "blooming,
    buzzing confusion"

tonomy, and (3) incapacity to form reliable reality constructs. Since differentiation and integration tend to occur together, it is impossible completely to separate the consequences of the one process from the consequences of the other. One can, however, make certain distinctions. For instance, using the classification of schizophrenic personalities which Wynne and Singer (1963) have devised, one could say that their amorphous type was the product of faulty differentiation, and their fragmented type the product of faulty integration.

Let us try to specify further the consequences of faulty differentiation, especially in the realm of separateness and autonomy. We should emphasize that by separateness we do not mean literal physical isolation or limitation of contact between self and environment. We refer rather to the capacity to maintain a clear symbolic distinction between self and environment or between inner and outer worlds.

This self-nonself discrimination is fundamental to psychological development in general and to structuring of reality in particular.

The primary self-nonself distinction occurs as the child becomes increasingly able to distinguish his self from his mother or mothering person. Presumably, if this basic discrimination proceeds favorably, further advances in differentiation will follow. If not, the entire process of differentiation may be impaired. Furthermore, the degree of constancy and reliability of his definitions and symbolic representations of self and others will depend, at least in part, upon the degree of consistency and reliability of his early object relations. Much has been written of overprotective and symbiotic mother-child relationships which impede a child's ability to differentiate a separate self and which may predispose him to schizophrenia. We shall discuss these and other differentiation-impeding factors in a subsequent chapter.

Relative autonomy, or the capacity for self-regulation, correlates with the sense of separateness. The word "relative" is used to emphasize that independence is never complete, and that, as with separateness, literal isolation from the environment is not implied. As we indicated earlier, autonomy stems in part from processes of internalization, including imitation, identification, and assimilation. For internalization to be more than rote imitation, it must be accompanied by sufficient differentiation of the self from others so that the internalized patterns become truly the person's own structural equipment.

A person who fails to develop separateness and relative autonomy remains dependent upon direction and control by others. His need for external regulation also constitutes a vulnerability, for he is more easily influenced than is the autonomous person. One of the schizophrenic person's greatest problems is the ease with which others may influence or—to use the literal meaning of the word—flow into him and disrupt his tenuous internal equilibria. Of these tenuous equilibria we shall say more when we discuss the consequences of faulty integration.

INNER-OUTER UNCERTAINTY, VULNERABILITY TO INFLUENCE, AND SCHIZOPHRENIC SYMPTOMS

The inner-outer uncertainty associated with lack of separateness, and the need-vulnerability to external influence associated with lack

of autonomy, are prominently reflected in the symptoms of schizophrenia. Blurring or loss of self-nonself boundaries are conspicuous.[2]
This involves not only body image uncertainty but general inner-outer
uncertainty, and an even more general difficulty in selectively organizing experience by distinguishing figure from ground and relevant
from irrelevant items. The difficulty in determining whether particular items in the stream of consciousness have inner or outer sources
affects all personality subsystems, including those of thought, affect,
and action (Burnham, 1961).

In the realm of thought, the poorly differentiated schizophrenic
person has difficulty distinguishing his own thoughts from those of
others. Hallucinations are a classic example of attributing an inner
event to an outer source. Inner-outer confusion is especially apparent
in hallucinations which derive from decomposition of the superego.
Forbidding, commanding, and threatening voices are perceived as
coming from outside, as did the voices of original rule-givers which,
in the interim, had been internalized into the superego's voice of con-
science (Jacobson, 1954; Modell, 1958; Schilder, 1953). This phenomenon is an excellent example of the tendency in schizophrenia for
poorly integrated internalized patterns to break down and become
reexternalized.

The schizophrenic person is uncertain not only of the origin of
the internal and external cues in his constructions of reality and meaning, but also of the proportionate weights he should assign to these
cues. He wavers unsurely between autonomy and heteronomy and is
unable to follow the normal tendency to locate inside himself what
he feels able to control, and outside himself what he feels unable to
control. Weakening or loss of the sense of autonomous control accounts
for many of the phenomena of body image distortion and depersonalization in schizophrenia (Angyal, 1958).

The schizophrenic person's thoughts are also excessively prey to
external influence. With his thoughts being pulled this way and that,
he is so distractible and suggestible that he becomes a slave to the
stimulus of the moment.

Inner-outer uncertainty and vulnerability to external influence also
pervade the realm of affects. Unmodulated wishes and fears exert un-

[2] We prefer to speak of self rather than ego boundaries (Federn, 1952), since by
ego we refer to the central cohesive organization of mental processes.

due influence on his reality construct. The slightest external cue may trigger intense affects. His percepts of others are determined more by his own feelings than by their actual behavior. If he is fearful in approaching another person, he is likely to perceive threat and hostility in the other and to ignore evidence of friendliness. The slightest gesture by the other may be taken as proof of malicious intent. Eissler (1953) described and labeled as "social animism" the schizophrenic person's selective interpretation of outer reality to fit the emotion which possesses him at the moment.

Similarly, he is inordinately vulnerable to external influence in the realm of action. He may take the most insignificant and unintentional motion of another person as a suggestion or command for action. Hallucinated voices directing actions are further evidence of uncertainty of self-direction and control.

Inadequacy of inner control systems is manifest variously. Poorly controlled impulses are likely to spill out into primitive forms of behavior, rendering him incapable of aiming or focusing his action upon chosen goals. He lacks purposiveness or what Hartmann (1953) termed "intentionality." He may display extreme indecision and a hunger for reliable external direction. Difficulties in starting or stopping action also are present and may range from literal immobility at one extreme to perseverative actions at the other.

Dividedness as a Consequence of Faulty Integration

Dividedness is a pathognomonic feature of schizophrenia; witness the literal meaning of the word and the many similar terms which have been employed, including splitting, dissociation, segregation, segmentalization, and sejunction.

Normally the ego maintains a balanced interplay between personality subsystems—drives, affects, thoughts, and actions—and integrates them into a harmonious whole. Drives and affects prompt action aimed toward gratification of needs and avoidance of discomfort. Thought is interposed as a means of controlling and guiding behavior toward attainment of these goals in a real world. Thought has a dual master-servant relationship to the motivational forces comprising drives and affects. On the one hand, it is driven by and serves these forces; on the other hand, it regulates them by delay and control of their discharge into action. In schizophrenia this normal interplay between thought and motivational forces is disrupted. Thought, instead of controlling drives and affects, may be rendered their virtual slave. As Eissler (1953) described, an emotion may take "full possession of the ego's whole area, attach itself to all ego functions, color the motives of action. . . ." Eissler added that the emotion accumulates new energy by activation of all memories related to it. In addition, current perception and cognition are distorted and selectively focused to form an interpretation of outer reality which fits and substantiates the inner emotional state.

In similar fashion, a drive impulse may dominate the entire psychic apparatus in schizophrenia. A person in the grip of sexual impulses may perceive sexual meaning in every aspect of the environment and simultaneously be flooded by memories of sexual experiences. As Sullivan (1956) put it, meaning is extravasated; it spills all over the landscape.

When the normal balance of thought, drives, and affects is upset, behavior is likely to change into primitive, relatively untamed patterns. Fenichel (1945) stated, "Some schizophrenic symptoms are direct expressions of a regressive breakdown of the ego and an undoing of differentiations acquired through mental development (a primitivization)." Werner (1957) referred to a process of "de-differentiation." In this process, which also involves disintegration, affects assume the form of engulfing, uncontrollable, intense floods of feeling, instead of their normal form as modulated signals which alert and guide the person to adaptive action. As primary process thinking becomes dominant, the logical forms of the secondary process are, so to speak, shoved aside. Action loses the qualities of purposive control, coordination, and continuity, and becomes instead impulsive, seemingly aimless, uncoordinated, and discontinuous.

FAULTY INTEGRATION, DEFECTIVE REALITY CONSTRUCTS, AND VULNERABILITY TO DISORGANIZATION

Dividedness and faulty integration go hand in hand with defective reality constructs that fail to assimilate significant areas of experience. The range of experience which a person can assimilate into his reality construct depends, in considerable part, upon what he has been taught is and is not acceptable for inclusion in his definitions of self and others. A child learns, primarily from his family, frames of acceptance and of rejection, to use the terms of Kenneth Burke (1959). These frames serve as molds for shaping his raw experience. He may learn, for example, that his self-definition should include no anger or rebellious impulses and that his definitions of his parents should include no imperfections. Experiences contrary to these definitions must be excluded from conscious representation.

Exposure to contradictory, inconsistent, and amorphously vague definitions also will limit a child's capacity to structure his experience clearly and coherently. These are problems of personality development and vulnerability to schizophrenia of which Wynne and Singer (1963) have written cogently.

A child developing in a family in which major areas of experience are, in one way or another, excluded from assimilation will form reality constructs which are rigid and prematurely closed. He is likely to make excessive use of exclusion mechanisms such as repression and denial.[3] His definitions of self and others will be rigidly constructed— the opposite of genuine object constancy. The overall result is a tenuous state of organization, vulnerable to disruption.

These defects are all the greater if, as is likely, the child has been taught to accept unquestioningly his family's versions of reality rather than to construct his own. In addition, if his family is poorly integrated into the community at large, he will have few opportunities for significant relationships with persons outside his family from whom to learn varying versions of reality. It is likely instead that his family-learned constructs will handicap his attempts to form satisfactory extrafamilial relationships. His inability to assimilate new experience prevents him from seeing the other person's point of view or the possibility of a range of alternative constructs. He is unable to explore and resolve discrepancies between his and others' versions of reality. Unresolved discrepancies lead in turn to his further alienation and social disarticulation. If his reality constructs differ too drastically from those of others, he finds himself literally dwelling in another world.

[3] We refer to repression which is excessive rather than to repression per se, a modicum of which appears essential to the normal selective organization of consciousness.

When confronted by experience which he cannot fit into his reality construct, he tries either to ignore or to distort it. This, of course, further weakens his reality construct and is likely to upset his tenuously balanced interplay of thought, affect, and action. He is ill-prepared for major social role transitions and is peculiarly vulnerable to cultural shock when confronted with an unfamiliar environment.

He is similarly incapable of handling new experiences from within, as happens when his rigid barriers of repression and denial are breached or circumvented by feelings, ideas, and impulses customarily excluded from his conscious self. If, for example, his reality construct has centered on a definition of himself as always kind and loving, he will be troubled by anger-arousing situations. His ability to repress and deny anger has a limit, which, when exceeded, is likely to imperil his entire reality construct.[4] When usually excluded feelings and ideas gain consciousness, he may experience relatively mild, transient feelings of depersonalization or derealization, or he may experience deep panic and disorganization. Once breached, the repressive barriers may give way to a flood of primitive unassimilated affects and impulses.[5] Psychotic reorganization and restructuring of reality may follow, with an attempt to explain away the incompatible feelings and impulses as the workings of an agent outside himself.

Psychotic restructuring of reality provides only a temporary and spurious sense of relief, however, because unshared by others it is an inadequate basis for relationships. A vicious cycle is likely to ensue, with unsuccessful relationships leading to further reality distortion, which in turn makes successful relationships even less likely, and so on.

This is similar to Norman Cameron's (1951) description of the reciprocal relationship between desocialization and disorganization. He emphasized that failure to communicate with others deprives a person of opportunities to check his thoughts against others'. His autistic distortions then go uncorrected and he becomes all the more fearful to communicate, thus establishing a vicious cycle. Sullivan (1953) had similar phenomena in mind when referring to failures to establish consensual validation of percepts and thoughts.

---

[4] Cf. McReynolds' (1960) theory of schizophrenia linking anxiety to the amount of nonassimilated experience which the preschizophrenic person carries. McReynolds suggests that when nonassimilation exceeds certain levels, gross personality disorganization will result.

[5] This is an extreme variant of the "return of the repressed."

In this section we have stressed the correlation of faulty integration, defective reality constructs, and vulnerability to disorganization. We turn now to consider another aspect of this structural weakness.

Primitive Systems of Control and Organization

The weakness of the internal structure of the schizophrenia-vulnerable person is further manifest in the unstable nature of his control systems. These systems are poorly differentiated and marked by archaic superego qualities; they are arbitrary, peremptory, automatic, and involuntary. They follow inflexible rules applied indiscriminately and without regard for their fitness in the particular situation. Impulses trigger automatic, abrupt controls, not allowing the interposition of thoughtful delay.

The primitive nature of his control systems reflects the schizophrenia-vulnerable person's desperate struggle to quell internal disorder which, since he lacks adequate flexible controls, threatens constantly. His strict controls account for various severe behavioral restrictions such as immobility, mutism, and refusal to eat, as well as such perceptual-cognitive restrictions as blocking and impoverishment of thought.

The archaic superego control system reflects the person's incomplete differentiation from early heteronomous controls and sources of authority. He is likely to show blind, unquestioning obedience or equally blind negativism toward the dictates which he has internalized from early authorities. He is unable to subject these dictates to critical evaluation or to distinguish between an authoritarian source of an opinion and the merit of the opinion itself. Obviously, this rigidity seriously limits his capacity to adapt flexibly to new life situations.

Object Need-Fear Dilemma

We turn now to discuss the schizophrenic person's disordered object relations, particularly his intense need-fear dilemma. Because he is poorly differentiated and integrated, he lacks reliable internal structure and autonomous control systems. Accordingly he has an inordinate need for external structure and control. He requires others to provide the organization and regulation which he is unable to provide for himself. It involves no stretch of the imagination to say that his very psychological existence depends upon his maintaining contact with objects, whether as individuals or as part of a social structure. As Fenichel (1945) graphically said, the schizophrenic person is an "object addict."

The very excessiveness of his need for objects also makes them inordinately dangerous and fearsome since they can destroy him through abandonment. Hence he fears and distrusts them. He may attempt to alleviate the threat of abandonment by repeated pleas or demands for proof of the object's constancy. Such pleas are insatiable because much of the inconstancy of his percepts of objects stems from his inner instability. Another defensive tactic, also of limited value, is the attempt to deny his need and his fear of separation.

The schizophrenic person's fear of objects stems not only from their power to frustrate his need for them but also from their enormous power to influence him. They can make or break him. Because he is so lacking in separateness and autonomy, he is particularly fearful of domination, enslavement, or engulfment. In addition, the influence of objects threatens to dissolve his tenuous self-nonself boundaries and even to collapse his entire structure of self.

This threat may be further understood if we consider that his precariously balanced inner structure is extraordinarily vulnerable to external influence in its most literal sense, "flowing into." He lacks adequate insulation from others. This is due not so much to a hyperpermeable stimulus barrier or "thin skin"[6] as to his lack of reliable internal structure. Like a ship at sea without adequate navigational equipment, he requires directions from external sources.

One may ask why dependence upon and vulnerability to external influence should be so threatening. Degree of threat varies according to the meaning of the object to the person. This meaning is determined by the person's inner structural balance and need disposition of the moment. At different times, different sectors of his inner structure are most open to influence. At one time the open sector may be his ego, at another his superego, and at still another his id. Furthermore, the openness may shift unpredictably from one sector to

[6] The hypothesis of perceptual hypersensitivity has been suggested as a pathogenic factor in at least one study of seriously disturbed children. (Cf. Bergman and Escalona, 1949.)

another, and the meaning of the object shifts correspondingly. These shifts contribute much to the instability of the schizophrenic person's relationships.

Influence in Ego Sector

Influence in the ego sector may not be threatening at all, at least for a time. The object may be experienced as a friendly, reliable mentor and regulator. Dramatic clinical improvement of a schizophrenic patient may attend an object's functioning as an auxiliary ego. However, such an arrangement has distinct limitations. For one thing, it may lead to excessive dependence and severe anxiety whenever the patient is separated from the object. In addition, the continuous presence of the auxiliary ego is difficult, if not impossible, to maintain. Eventually a heavy backlog of mutual anger may accrue from the patient's resentment of the dependent position and the auxiliary ego's resentment of continuous 24-hour duty. Accordingly, such relationships are basically unstable and liable to eventual disruption.

Distinctly more stable are situations in which the auxiliary ego is not one person but a social group, such as a highly structured military, religious, or business organization.

Influence in Superego Sector

We noted earlier that the schizophrenic person's control system consists of a primitive superego based on rigid arbitrary rules, closely derived from external authorities rather than from his autonomous judgment. Consequently, objects easily influence his superego system, usually in one of two ways, through severity or leniency. Each type of influence may evoke object fear and inner instability.

When its influence on the superego is severe, the object is experienced as a dreaded purveyor of threat, condemnation, restriction, and punishment. Primitive flight or fight defenses are employed to ward off the intrusive authority of the object. Obviously any relationship in which the object attains this meaning becomes strained and liable to disruption.

However, the person with unreliable inner controls may also welcome harsh influence, since it affords him relief from guilt and minimizes his fear of losing control of his impulses. Schizophrenic patients often seek punishment and may beg to be sent to a judge in the hope of receiving a sentence of imprisonment or execution. Offhand one might assume that the schizophrenic person would welcome a lenient influence on his typically harsh, restrictive, and arbitrary control system, but this assumption fails to take into account the fact that his superego, though harsh, constitutes his major means of self-control. Hence a lenient influence, especially if sudden or massive, may threaten him with total loss of control. Removal of old controls without opportunity for adequate development of new, flexible controls is likely to result in chaotic impulse discharge, as when a dictator is overthrown without adequate preparation of governmental machinery to replace him.

Another source of ambivalence toward lenient superego influence is the schizophrenic person's deep-rooted belief that loosening of superego strictures, though yearned for, constitutes traitorous disloyalty and usurpation of authority. In fact, he may regard moves toward modifying his superego as tantamount to destroying the original external authority.[7] Accordingly, any move toward replacing the internalized original authority by a more reasonable and flexible authority is likely to trigger reparation measures such as severe self-condemnation and self-mortification. A state of panic with fears of imminent world collapse may be precipitated. Reparation to the original authority frequently takes the form of hostile withdrawal from the new object which offers lenient superego influence, as if thereby to deny any wish to modify the original authority's dictates.

Influence in Id Sector

The schizophrenic person's id system is also highly susceptible to influence. Approaches toward interpersonal intimacy mobilize frightening and potentially unmanageable impulses, while upsetting tenuous internal balances. When this occurs, the object is viewed as dangerous. Part of the danger is the mobilization of primitive urges to obtain unlimited, unconditional, and magical oral supplies from the object. In their extreme form, these urges are felt as literal cravings to devour or merge with the object.[8]

[7] Cf. Hill (1955) for the hypothesis that the schizophrenic patient may regard defiance of his superego dictates as equivalent to defiance and murder of his mother.

[8] Numerous authors, including Klein (1946), Fairbairn (1954), and Guntrip (1952), have emphasized that the urge to incorporate or devour the object is a fundamental feature of schizophrenia.

The arousal of these and other primitive id impulses causes great discomfort in both the schizophrenic person and his objects. The usual result is mutual withdrawal and disruption of relationships.

Forms of Fear of Object Influence

The fear of object influence takes various forms. The patient may directly voice fears that the object will dominate, control, or enslave him and thereby deprive him of his separateness, independence, and identity. He may dread being literally swallowed up and devoured, or may refer to concerns that proximity to the object will contaminate, poison, or otherwise infect him with "bad stuff." Complaints of non-personified influencing agents such as electricity, mysterious rays, or machines are frequent. In whatever form, his fear of influence reflects his sensed lack of autonomy and corresponding need-fear of heteronomy.

As we have indicated, the patient not only dreads what the object may do to him, but also what he may do to the object. He especially fears that the primitive, incorporative form and intensity of his object-need will destroy the vital object.

Résumé

Before proceeding to discussion of how the schizophrenic person attempts to escape his need-fear dilemma, let us briefly recapitulate. We postulate that the nature of the schizophrenic person's early object relations interferes with normal processes of differentiation and integration. Interference with differentiation results in a lack of separateness and relative autonomy or the capacity for self-regulation. Interference with integration causes inability to assimilate major areas of experience into a reality construct, and inability to articulate subsystems of personality into a coherent and harmonious whole. The nonautonomous, nonintegrated personality structure is highly vulnerable to disorganization, to upsetting of the normal balanced interplay between thought and motivational forces.

These deficiencies contribute, in turn, to what we have termed the need-fear dilemma of the schizophrenic person. He has both an inordinate need and an inordinate fear of objects. His lack of separateness and self-regulatory structure renders him dependent upon external structure and extraordinarily susceptible to the influence of objects. This influence may affect various sectors of his poorly differentiated and integrated psychic structure, sometimes affording the temporary strength of an auxiliary ego, but usually causing disorganization by upsetting tenuous inner balances. Furthermore, inordinate need generates fear by raising the threat of loss or unavailability of the object. A major effect of the need-fear dilemma is marked instability of object relations.

REACTIONS TO THE NEED-FEAR DILEMMA

The schizophrenic person's relationships are pervasively shaped by efforts to avert or alleviate the pain of his need-fear dilemma and to avoid the disaster of complete disorganization. These efforts fall into three general patterns, usually in various combinations rather than in pure form: *object clinging, object avoidance,* and *object redefinition.* In discussing them, we shall give special attention to the manner in which each pattern affects the problems of unreliability of reality constructs and incongruence with the constructs of others.

Object Clinging

In this attempted solution of the need-fear dilemma, the patient, in effect, gives himself over to the need side of his conflict. He abandons efforts at differentiation and independence and attempts to fuse inseparably with others. A bewildering variety of terms has been employed to describe this type of relationship: symbiotic, narcissistic, orally fixated, object-addicted, anaclitic, self-centered, unilateral, possessive, overdependent, receptive, demanding, devouring, hunger-fulfilling, and others. These terms share common reference to the excessive need for supplies from the object, with little regard for the reciprocal needs of the object; in other words, a wish to receive but not give. However, this formulation does not convey the primitive quality of the object need, which comprises not only wishes to receive supplies (love, support, approval, help, praise), but, even more pertinently, wishes to fuse with, literally partake of, and become part of the structure of the object. The schizophrenic person wishes the object to provide the inner balance and integration he has been unable to achieve for himself. He seeks absolutely to possess and to be possessed by the object and is extremely intolerant of any frustration of this wish. In effect, he asks that the object live for him.

Fenichel's (1945) description of "object addicts" is pertinent:

> They do not need love especially but, rather, more general proof of connections with the objective world. Persons of this kind cling to everybody and everything. They are glued to their objects, directed by an extreme fear of losing them, always discontented, and extremely wearing on the persons around them . . . attempting to gain contact with the objective world but can do so only in abrupt attacks and for short periods. The remarkable violence of their efforts is due to their fear of again losing the objects.

Object clinging has serious limitations as an attempted solution to the need-fear dilemma. First, the patient seeks from others more than they can provide without completely sacrificing themselves. Second, the patient's wish for fusion is matched by his fear that it will utterly destroy both himself and the object. Third, clinging leaves undone the developmental tasks of differentiation and integration. Whatever structure it affords is borrowed and contingent upon the patient's maintaining contact with the object.

Nonetheless, clinging may partially succeed. Certain relationships established in this manner may be quite stable and enduring, even for a lifetime. Some children never leave home for this reason. Some leave home only when they have found a replacement to which they can cling, such as a spouse, employer, teacher-mentor, or social organization. If these are persons who enjoy, and perhaps need to be clung to, the clinging reaction may forestall overt or gross disorganization for an entire lifetime.

Object Clinging and Reality Construction. The clinging pattern involves passive, dependent deference to the object's reality construct and to his frames of acceptance and rejection. The object's definitions of persons and events are accepted without question; disagreement is unthinkable. Such blind acceptance means sacrificing one's own definition-creating capacities. At best, definitions contrary to the object's attain only an underground secret-self existence, split off from the public-self which is molded to fit the object's reality construct. For the most part, however, the clinging person is like a character in a book whose existence is totally determined by the author's definition of him. Obviously this gives him little opportunity for differentiation, integration, and autonomy.

Another problem associated with the clinging, definition-accepting reaction is that the reality construct offered by primary intrafamilial objects is often discrepant with the constructs of extrafamilial persons. If gross, these discrepancies interfere seriously with establishing relationships in the outside world. Furthermore, dependence upon the original source of reality definition becomes compounded. In venturing into the world, the clinging person is like a traveler in a strange land who is totally dependent upon his guide to tell him where he is and to interpret his surroundings for him. Accordingly, he fears separation from his reality interpreter and clings all the more.

Object Avoidance

Avoidance takes various forms. In one form the person becomes quietly withdrawn and seemingly detached, unresponsive, and disinterested in others. A less desocialized form of avoidance is fighting off by verbal or physical assaults all who approach.

It would be inaccurate to assume that the quiet, preoccupied patient dwells in a comfortable inner world of remembered or imagined relationships. On the contrary, his reality construct and his definitions of self and others are likely to be in a chaotic state of flux. This is in contradistinction to a nonschizophrenic person—for example, a lighthouse keeper—who, though isolated from objects, maintains a stable inner world.

Withdrawal may be the patient's way of trying to maintain extremely tenuous internal equilibria by limiting potentially disruptive object contacts and by restricting his behavioral repertoire to a few stereotyped patterns repeated with endless monotony. Attempts by others to engage him in interaction are regarded as intrusions which carry the threat of disorganization. His usual reaction is either a deepening of the gulf of unresponsiveness or an abrupt outburst of rage. Since to him disorganization is equivalent to destruction, he is literally saying: "Get away. You are destroying me."[9]

The patient may alternately cling and avoid, at times virtually oscil-

---

[9] This explanation of the schizophrenic patient's potential for unbridled aggression seems equally if not more plausible than the idea that he has abnormally strong innate aggressive drives or innate inability to neutralize these drives.

lating between the extremes of intense interaction and isolation. In describing this pattern, Bellak (1958) cited Schopenhauer's proverb of porcupines on a cold night who huddled together for warmth but hurt each other with their quills; pulling back to avoid this pain, they again suffered from the cold. Inability to achieve satisfactory distance-closeness balance is a conspicuous manifestation of the schizophrenic person's need-fear dilemma.

Object Avoidance and Reality Construction. Discrepancies between the reality construct of the avoiding person and the constructs of other persons remain largely unexposed because his interaction with them is so limited. This, as we indicated earlier, may establish a vicious cycle by allowing autistic distortions to go uncorrected and to proliferate further. And, of course, the avoiding person deprives his reality constructs of the richness and variety to be obtained from varied interaction with other persons.

Substitute Objects as a Form of Clinging-Avoidance

Substitute objects are very important to the schizophrenic person. They afford a compromise between his need and his fear. He avoids persons but clings to substitutes for them. Thereby he maintains or regains a semblance of object contact. All sorts of substitutes may be used, among them pets, books, television, phonograph records, treasured personal effects, and seemingly trivial trinkets. Substitutes also are found in the realm of abstractions. For example, political causes and social or religious ideologies may serve as substitutive preoccupations, sometimes to the point of monomanias, and frequently in the form of a plan for world reconstruction. The wish to bring peace and order to the outer world clearly reflects the intensity of the urge for inner world peace.

The substitute objects of the schizophrenic person are similar to the transitional objects of the developing child who may cling to a cuddly toy or a blanket in making the transition from his mother to a more dispersed set of human objects. This transition also involves a shift from primary identification and fusion to a more mature type of relationship. As these changes occur, the transitional objects are substitutes for the child's mother (Winnicott, 1953).

Among the various substitute objects to which the schizophrenic patient may cling are stereotyped words and phrases. Often these phrases represent remnants of his identity—name, address, social security number, and car license number—which he may repeat endlessly as if hoping thereby to keep alive a few constant identity fragments. He also may collect all manner of sticks, rags, and pebbles, and be intensely upset if any of them are discarded. Collecting photographs or magazine illustrations to represent needed persons is a somewhat more realistic effort to preserve an intact object world and deny loss and separation. Less realistic is the patient's attempt to deny the loss of early loved objects, as by misperceiving others, or even non-human objects (trees, furniture, animals), as the familiar persons of his past. The patient may also deny loss by believing himself to be the lost object, following the pattern of introjection of the lost object which Freud (1917) first described in *Mourning and Melancholia*. Such patients commonly utilize mechanisms of oral and respiratory incorporation and introjection.

Schizophrenic persons may avoid as well as cling to their substitute objects, since these, like human objects, may become sources of both fear and security. He also may be driven to deny his dependence on the substitute objects by discarding or destroying them, thus temporarily affording himself a sense of mastery and permanent possession which counters his fear of abandonment. Just as with human objects, he may alternately cling to, avoid, and destroy the substitutes.

Often the patient treats his body as a substitute object. This is the gist of Freud's (1911) idea that the schizophrenic patient withdraws his interest in external objects and replaces it by secondary narcissistic interest in his body, which results in phenomena such as hypochondriacal preoccupations and somatic delusions. A sense of loss of body parts and functions is frequent. Szasz (1957) has suggested that in schizophrenia the threat of object loss is so pervasive that the patient fears losing his body as well as his outer objects. Angyal (1958) has stated that a patient's experiencing parts of his body as dead or not belonging to himself derives from his losing his sense of autonomous control of his body.

Object Redefinition

Redefinition is a defense against the object inconstancy which characterizes the faulty reality constructs of schizophrenic persons. Constancy of objects develops in the course of normal differentiation and integration, and requires the capacity to conceive of objects which have a quasipermanent existence outside of one's self and independent of one's actions. This is in contrast to an infant's global perceptions in which self, objects, and the actions of each are not discriminated from each other (Piaget, 1954). Constancy further refers to the ability to maintain object representations that remain relatively constant regardless of the person's wishes, fears, and drive tension level, and regardless of the actual presence or absence of the object.

In schizophrenia this ability is deficient, and object representations are relatively undifferentiated from drive impulses and affects (Hartmann, 1953). This is partly due to the schizophrenic person's faulty integration of his feelings toward significant objects. Instead of a stable blend of feelings toward an object, he is likely to be flooded by first one, then another, contradictory feeling, especially need, then fear. His perception of the object changes according to the feeling of the moment. If love and need predominate, the object appears good, desirable, and approachable; if fear and hate, the object appears noxious and only to be avoided or destroyed. He may even perceive the object's entire identity as having changed from one time to another, and tends to attribute these changes to unreliability of the object rather than to instability within himself. Obviously this renders his relationships tenuous and unstable.

Only by integrating conflicting affects, particularly need and fear and related personality subsystems, can he achieve genuine object constancy. By object redefinition he can contrive a temporary pseudo-constancy. This involves his restructuring reality and stage-managing his objects. This defensive strategy is exemplified by a particular type of paranoid patient who imposes his definitions on objects, casting them in roles in a drama of his creation, often with Procrustean disregard for whether they fit the role or wish to play it. He may go so far as to insist that their claimed identities are false and assign them identities of his choosing. All that matters to the patient is that the drama and the cast of characters fit his needs, relieve his conflicts, and, in particular, afford him a sense of object constancy and inner stability.

The underlying goal of redefinition is to create a reliable good object. Idealization is frequent, and even rather unlikely candidates are seen as personifications of goodness, trustworthiness, and helpful-

ness, and are cast in the roles of magic helper and constant companion. To sustain the idealization, the patient must ignore, deny, or
otherwise exclude from consciousness any evidence which would contradict or contaminate his percept of the object as purely benevolent.
Such perceptual distortions can be maintained only so long. Eventually the idealization disintegrates, often with abrupt replacement of
adoration by disillusion-spawned hatred, to the astonishment of the
object who had been unaware of the role assigned him by the patient.
Or the patient may act upon his idealized percept and expect the
object to reciprocate in kind. The startled object, unaware of the
patient's assumptions, is likely to consider the patient's behavior highly
inappropriate. The relationship is then disrupted. The unfortunate
denouement of an autistic love affair is a case in point.

Idealization may be maintained longer when the patient chooses
as his good object someone with whom he has little or no actual contact and who in turn may not even know of the patient's existence.
This is often the situation when, for instance, a celebrity is cast in the
magic-helper role. Such an autistic, totally unilateral relationship may
persist for years and serve as a source of great comfort and pseudostability for the patient, as long as it is not put to the test of actual
encounter.

A more complex form of redefinition is the splitting of the object
field into good and bad actors containing principal hero and principal
villain roles. The patient may divide his entire object world into all-
good and all-bad groups. He then attributes all pleasurable experience
to the good group, and all unpleasurable experience to the bad.

The difficulty with this arrangement is that it does not agree with
shared reality. Further, the schizophrenic person's inner equilibria are
so precarious that encounters with even the most benevolent object
may precipitate disorganization and a sudden shift in the percept and
valuation of the object. Hence the split object world is an unstable one,
and each object encounter is fraught with deep uncertainty and unpredictability. This problem is compounded by the patient's tendency to
project the unreliability of his inner structure onto the outer world.

Characteristically, the object stage-manager defends against inconstancy by the apparent opposite—extreme cognitive certainty and
intolerance of ambiguity. He quickly and arbitrarily categorizes objects
according to the dictates of his inner needs, while ignoring whatever

does not fit his assumptive set and preconceptions. In the process he often ignores or denies major aspects of the object's being, hence depriving the object of self-confirmation. The object is expected to fit the patient's image of him regardless of the disparity between this image and his own experienced self (Brodey, 1961). The reverse situation exists in normal relationships where the tendency is for each person to modify his image of the other to accord with the other's actual behavior.

The degree of pseudostability provided by redefinition depends upon several factors. One is the extent to which the stage-manager attempts to carry his definitions into actual encounters with the redefined objects. Some patients limit their object redefining to a sort of remote mental control of the object, who may remain quite unaware of the role the patient has assigned him. Other patients, however, carry the process to the level of action. Here they meet with varying degrees of success, depending upon the relative plausibility of their definitions and the particular sector of reality which they seek to redefine. If their definitions are not too implausible and not too incongruent with the object's definitions of himself and reality, schizophrenic persons may obtain a rather surprising degree of cooperation in the redefinition process. Their sense of the absolute certainty of their reality constructs gives them certain powers for emotional leadership and persuasiveness. They sometimes succeed in establishing social movements and in recruiting followers who afford reinforcement of their convictions. History contains examples of persons, such as Hitler, who have succeeded to an appalling degree in restructuring reality to fit their psychotic image.

Less drastic reality restructuring and object redefinition often may attain partial success. For instance, not infrequently the schizophrenic person will find someone willing to serve in the role of magic helper and constant companion, especially if someone else is concurrently cast in the role of villain. It may happen that the object's own needs fit the expected role quite well. Certainly many persons need to play helping, controlling roles. To them the need side of the schizophrenic person's conflict has great appeal and role complementarity.

Despite these possibilities for partial, temporary success of the redefinition reaction, the more likely result is relationships that are strained, uncomfortable, unstable, and transient rather than enduring.

This is partly because the object stage-manager attempts increasingly to obtain, from those he defines as friends, confirmation and agreement for his versions of reality. Although temporarily he may recruit one or more persons who agree with him, in the long run these efforts usually fail. Frequently his attempts to assemble a cast for the staging of the personal drama collapse, and a fresh cast of characters must be recruited for a restaging of the drama.

BIBLIOGRAPHY

Allport, G. W. (1961), *Pattern and Growth in Personality*. New York: Holt, Rinehart and Winston.

Angyal, A. (1958), *Foundations for a Science of Personality*. Cambridge: Harvard University Press.

Bellak, L. (1958), The Schizophrenic Syndrome. In: *Schizophrenia: A Review of the Syndrome*, ed. L. Bellak. New York: Logos Press.

Bergman, P. & Escalona, S. K. (1949), Unusual Sensitivities in Very Young Children. *The Psychoanalytic Study of the Child, 3/4*:333-352. New York: International Universities Press.

Burnham, D. L. (1956), Misperception of Other Persons in Schizophrenia. *Psychiat.*, 19:283-303.

——— (1961), Autonomy and Activity-Passivity as Central Issues in the Psychotherapy of a Schizophrenic Man. In: *Psychotherapy of the Psychoses*, ed. Arthur Burton. New York: Basic Books.

Bleuler, E. (1911), *Dementia Praecox or the Group of Schizophrenias*. New York: International Universities Press, 1950.

Brodey, W. M. (1961), The Family as the Unit of Study and Treatment: 3. Image, Object and Narcissistic Relationships. *Amer. J. Orthopsychiat., 31*:69-73.

Burke, K. (1959), *Attitudes Toward History*. Boston: Beacon Press.

Cameron, N. & Magaret, A. (1951), *Behavior Pathology*. Boston: Houghton Mifflin.

Coghill, G. E. (1929), *Anatomy and the Problem of Behavior*. New York: Macmillan.

Eissler, K. R. (1953), Notes Upon the Emotionality of a Schizophrenic Patient and Its Relation to Problems of Technique. *The Psychoanalytic Study of the Child, 8*:199-251. New York: International Universities Press.

Fairbairn, W. R. D. (1954), *An Object-Relations Theory of the Personality*. New York: Basic Books.

Federn, P. (1952), *Ego Psychology and the Psychoses*. New York: Basic Books.

Fenichel, O. (1945), *The Psychoanalytic Theory of Neurosis*, p. 436. New York: Norton.

Freud, S. (1911), Psycho-analytic Notes Upon an Autobiographical Account of a Case of Paranoia (Dementia Paranoides). *Standard Edition, 12*:9-82. London: Hogarth Press, 1958.

———— (1917), Mourning and Melancholia. *Standard Edition*, *14*:243-258. London: Hogarth Press, 1957.

Guntrip, H. (1952), A Study of Fairbairn's Theory of Schizoid Reactions. *Brit. J. Med. Psychol.*, *25*:86-103.

Hartmann, H. (1953), Contribution to the Metapsychology of Schizophrenia. *The Psychoanalytic Study of the Child*, *8*:177-198. New York: International Universities Press.

Hill, L. B. (1955), *Psychotherapeutic Intervention in Schizophrenia*. Chicago: University of Chicago Press.

Jacobson, E. (1954), Contributions to the Metapsychology of Psychotic Identifications. *J. Amer. Psychoanal. Assn.*, *2*:239-262.

James, W. (1890), *The Principles of Psychology*. New York: Dover, 1950.

Klein, M. (1946), Notes on Some Schizoid Mechanisms. *Internat. J. Psycho-Anal.*, *27*:99-110.

McReynolds, P. (1960), Anxiety, Perception, and Schizophrenia. In: *The Etiology of Schizophrenia*, ed. D. D. Jackson. New York: Basic Books.

Modell, A. H. (1958), The Theoretical Implications of Hallucinatory Experiences in Schizophrenia. *J. Amer. Psychoanal. Assn.*, *6*:442-480.

Piaget, J. (1954), *The Construction of Reality in the Child*. New York: Basic Books.

Rapaport, D. (1958), The Theory of Ego Autonomy. *Bull. Menninger Clin.*, *22*:13-35.

———— (1960), The Structure of Psychoanalytic Theory: A Systematizing Attempt. *Psychol. Issues*, Monograph 6. New York: International Universities Press.

Schilder, P. (1953), *Medical Psychology*. New York: International Universities Press.

Searles, H. F. (1959), Integration and Differentiation in Schizophrenia: An Over-All View. *Brit. J. Med. Psychol.*, *32*:261-281.

Sherrington, C. S. (1906), *The Integrative Action of the Nervous System*. London: Constable.

Sullivan, H. S. (1953), *The Interpersonal Theory of Psychiatry*. New York: Norton.

———— (1956), *Clinical Studies in Psychiatry*. New York: Norton.

Szasz, T. (1957), The Psychology of Bodily Feelings in Schizophrenia. *Psychosom. Med.*, *19*:11-16.

Werner, H. (1957), *Comparative Psychology of Mental Development*. New York: International Universities Press.

Winnicott, D. W. (1953), Transitional Objects and Transitional Phenomena: A Study of the First Not-Me Possession. *Internat. J. Psycho-Anal.*, *34*:89-97.

Witkin, H. A. et al. (1962), *Psychological Differentiation*. New York: Wiley.

Wynne, L. C. & Singer, M. T. (1963), Thought Disorder and Family Relations of Schizophrenics: II. A Classification of Forms of Thinking. *Arch. Gen. Psychiat.*, *9*:199-206.

III

CHILD-PARENT RELATIONSHIPS WHICH IMPEDE DIFFERENTIATION AND INTEGRATION

Donald L. Burnham

In the preceding chapter we presented the thesis that inadequate psychological differentiation and integration produce a weak personality structure lacking in autonomy and vulnerable to schizophrenic disorganization. These deficiencies are accompanied by an inordinate need and fear of the influence of other persons. We maintain that this need-fear dilemma not only predisposes a person toward schizophrenic disorganization, but also determines the form of that disorganization.

The degrees of differentiation and integration attained by the developing child depend in great measure upon the quality of his early relationships. In this chapter we shall consider various ways that these relationships may impede or prevent normal differentiation and integration. Many of our formulations of child-parent relationships are constructed from retrospective reports of young adult schizophrenic patients in psychotherapy and from the quality of the patient-doctor relationships which they formed. We also draw extensively upon other investigators' studies of child-parent relationships and family interaction. Though many of these studies were not specifically designed as inquiries into differentiation and integration, they bear much relevance to our thesis. We shall first discuss factors impeding differentiation and then factors impeding integration, though in actuality, of course, these sets of factors are usually intertwined.

INTERFERENCES WITH DIFFERENTIATION

In this section we shall consider in turn interferences with each of the three major interrelated aspects of differentiation: (1) the capacity to distinguish self from others and to function with relative autonomy—that is, to regulate one's self rather than to be regulated by others; (2) the capacity for a diversity of specialized behavioral responses in contrast to automatic mass reactions; and (3) the capacity to form differentiated rather than limited and stereotyped constructs of reality and of objects.

Interferences with Separateness and Autonomy

The attainment of separateness and relative autonomy requires opportunities for self-initiated and self-guided behavior. These encourage the child to choose his own goals and to aim his behavior toward them—in other words, to behave purposefully. To develop this ability, the child must discover and gain confidence in the reliability of adaptive resources which are his own and not those supplied him by his parents.

Numerous investigators have described relationships which impede the child's development of separateness and autonomy. The mother-child relationship has been particularly emphasized, but recently the importance of the total family matrix in the child's development has become increasingly apparent. In much of the discussion which follows we shall, as a descriptive convenience, refer to the mother-child relationship; this, of course, oversimplifies the enormous complexity of the total configuration of family relationships in which the child is enmeshed.

In describing differentiation-impeding mother-child relationships, a variety of terms have been employed: overprotective, infantilizing, domineering, overpowering, and symbiotic (Jenkins, 1952; Hill, 1955; Levy, 1943; Limentani, 1956; Lu, 1961; Mahler, 1952; Searles, 1958, 1959; Kasanin, Knight and Sage, 1934; Gerard and Siegel, 1950; Tietze, 1949; Mark, 1953; Foudraine, 1961; Sanua, 1961). These descriptions share the fundamental idea that the child is prevented from emerging as a person in his own right, with thoughts, feelings, and impulses of his own. He is kept in a passive, dependent position; moreover, he is treated as part of the mother's personality or at best as an appendage of her. A mother who herself is poorly differentiated will impede her child's differentiation. Similarly detrimental to differentiation is a mother who overprotects her child in a compromise between her aggression toward him and her possessive need for him (Alanen, 1958).

The differentiation-impeding mother imposes her definition of the child upon him rather than ratifying his emergent definition of himself. Her definition treats him as an instrument of her personality, designed to serve her needs, and all aspects of his behavior which are incongruent with her needs are systematically overlooked or interdicted.

The imposition of definitions by the mother, or by the entire family, usually involves typecasting. The child is expected to conform to type, and little or no positive recognition is given to his individual variations from this image. One patient said, "My mother told me I was a certain type, and I was supposed to behave according to my type. If I said or did anything else, she would say, 'I don't know where you learned that. . . . You do get outlandish notions. . . . I hope you never behave that way in public.' "

The child may be forced into predetermined roles according to the particular needs and limitations of the mother and the entire family. A frequent role is that of scapegoat, with the child serving as a vehicle or receptacle for those attributes which the mother and other family members repudiate within themselves. By perceiving their denied "badness" in him, they preserve "good" self-images. A mother who is very doubtful of her competence may deny these feelings, while defining her child as helpless, sick, and incompetent.[1] Acceptance of this definition is the price he pays for closeness to his mother. To oppose her by trying to define himself otherwise—as competent and independent—would cost him her approval. Thus he is doubly damned. He is "bad" if he tries to separate from her, but to remain close to her he must accept her "bad" definition of him.

---

[1] In a series of identical twin pairs discordant for schizophrenia, it was noted that the schizophrenic twin had from an early age been defined by the parents as the weaker, more dependent, and less competent of the two (Pollin, Stabenau and Tupin, 1965). The reasons for these definitions were, it should be noted, exceedingly complex, and not simply a matter of "scapegoating."

Further, he is likely to live in fear that his behavior will bring disgrace not only to himself but to his entire family as well. For instance, a child whose mother denies her own dread of social ineptitude is likely to be haunted by the ever-present question, "What will others think of me and my family if I am not careful to behave exactly as my mother has instructed me?"

In addition to the scapegoat role, a variety of other differentiation-impeding definitions may be imposed upon the child. He may be expected to be his mother's compensation for all her deprivations at the hands of her parents, husband, and other children. Or he may be assigned the role of her ego ideal and be expected to accomplish all that she aspired to but never attained. Still another role-assignment may be that of replacement for an object lost by his mother—one of her parents, a former lover, or a previous child. Or he may be assigned the role of the duplicate of an odd or mentally ill relative: "You are just like your Uncle John, and you know what a time we had with him." Paradoxically, despite his being defined as incompetent, he may also be assigned the role of savior of his mother or of the entire family. The child may attempt to fill this role by assuming the burden of being "the crazy one" in his mother's stead (Searles, 1958, 1959). Leaving aside the moot question of volition in such role-acceptance, the differentiation-impeding effect of such a process seems clear.

It may be objected that some such role assignments are inevitable in any mother-child relationship in any family, normal or disordered. This is true, but our concern in this chapter is with definitions and roles which are so absolutely and peremptorily imposed that the child is precluded from all other lines of self-definition.

The process of role assignment which blocks individuation may occur not only in relationship to a particular parent but also in relationship to the total family matrix. Wynne and his associates (1958) have studied families in which collective family needs for "pseudomutuality" have prevented processes of differentiation and individuation. It appears that the child who is most blocked from individuation may eventually become schizophrenic. "Pseudomutuality" is maintained within such families by interdiction of any open disagreement between family members. The family ethos is, "We are one; there are no differences between us." Accordingly, they interdict any divergence from the role structure which they have created to sustain their homeostatic needs. To be acceptable, the child must limit his behavior to fit the assigned role. Any other behavior is ignored, denied, and excluded from open recognition.

The assigned role may be that of family scapegoat, "the stupid one," "the helpless one," or "the peculiar or crazy one" (Wynne, Ryckoff, Day, and Hirsch, 1958; Bowen, 1960; Brodey, 1961; Vogel and Bell, 1960). Other family roles include those of "splitter" or "reconciler" of the parents (Lidz, Cornelison, Fleck, and Terry, 1957).

Dependency fosters the child's acceptance of imposed definitions. The more dependent he is, the more he accepts others' judgments of him. As Wahl (1956) wrote, "The child has little capacity to comfort himself by hope, reason, language, or decisive changes in his environment, as can an adult. . . . He is dependent upon . . . others, not only for his bread and butter, but for any sustained conception of himself, his worth, and his adequacy." A characteristic of differentiation-impeding relationships is that they reinforce and perpetuate this dependence upon others for a self-definition. This may occur in a variety of ways.

One is the inculcation and perpetuation in the child of the belief that without his parent or family he is lost, helpless, and virtually nothing. Repeatedly he is told in one form or another, "Whatever would happen to you if I were not here to tell you what to do?" This message may be conveyed by close, overprotective supervision of the child, coupled with quick disapproval of any moves he might make toward self-regulation. The net result is fixation of the child's belief that he needs his mother, or a substitute, to guide and control not only his overt actions but his feelings and thoughts as well.

Inculcation of this belief frequently is associated with overt and covert threats of separation from and loss of the mother, or of excommunication from the family. Also implied but unacknowledged is that the mother desperately needs the child to remain a child in order to reassure herself of her own adequacy and competence. She usually goes to great lengths to try to prove to herself and to everyone else that she is truly a competent adult and not the frightened, helpless child she fears herself to be. Despite her denials, however, the child may sense a powerful threat that separation from his mother would destroy not only himself but his mother as well.

The child's belief in his basic and unalterable dependence is further encouraged by a lack of confirmation and a devaluation of internal processes which might serve as cues for self-regulation. The differentiation-impeding mother characteristically overlooks or ignores what arises from within the child. If she does notice, she tends to label the child's internal processes as inaccurate and untrustworthy. Bruch (1962) suggests that the mother of the preschizophrenic child often gives

> . . . contradictory and inappropriate responses to signs and signals originating within the child. If failure of confirmation of child-initiated behavior is severe and extends to many areas, to bodily sensations as well as to higher mental functions, the outcome will be an individual who lives chiefly by responding to stimuli coming from others, without awareness of and reliance upon his inner processes. Bodily sensations, thoughts, and feelings are experienced as originating in the outside. Such an individual will have a defective sense of self-effectiveness and will be lacking in initiative and spontaneity. This deficit is a prerequisite for later schizophrenic development.

A striking example of failure to confirm the significance of the child's inner processes was afforded by a mother who, when her young son complained of head pain, said, "That can't be; you don't have headaches."

A child treated in this manner will very likely grow up believing that the only reliable guides to thought and action come from outside himself; to wit, a patient who complained that without a thermometer on the wall of his room he had no way of knowing when to wear a sweater. With limited awareness of, and virtually no trust in, inner cues, he looked continually to others for directions.

White (1965), in emphasizing the importance of action in development, suggests that the ultimately schizophrenic person fails to achieve a solid sense of effectiveness as an active agent who can successfully influence his environment. As a result he is weak in assertiveness, initiative, and active testing of reality.

This accords with other studies of children destined to become schizophrenic. Descriptions of these children frequently feature terms indicating lack of initiative and autonomy, such as conforming, passive, apathetic, shut-in, and submissive (Birren, 1944; Bower, Shellhamer, and Daily, 1960; Bowman, 1934; O'Neal and Robins, 1958; Wittman and Steinberg, 1944).

This brings us to consideration of factors interfering with another aspect of differentiation.

Interferences with Differentiation of a Diversity of Specialized Responses

In order to develop a diversity of specialized responses the child must receive recognition and respect for a variety of behavior patterns, rather than respect only for behavior conforming to a single pattern (Foote and Cottrell, 1955). This entails an interpersonal climate in which there is respect for individually different skills, values, interests, and solutions to problems, in contrast to a system embracing only one set of values. Typically the differentiation-impeding parent enforces a one-value system by responding favorably only to those aspects of the child's behavior that fit this system. Anything novel about the child's behavior is discouraged.

Value imposition occurs as the mother attaches explicit labels to the child's actions. She is likely to apply labels which define and value his actions in terms of their effect on her rather than in terms of events in him which precede and accompany his actions. What he is feeling and what he intends with his actions may be totally ignored in the process. If, for instance, he innocently rustles the pages of a newspaper, he may be stunned to have his mother shout, "Stop it! Must you always do things to annoy me? You did it on purpose. Have you no consideration for how hard I work?" Here the entire definition of his action is in terms of its effect on his mother. On top of that, he is expected not to have a differing definition but to adopt her definition as his own.

All forms of opposition to the parents are interdicted, thus binding the child in the dependent position. He is especially discouraged from active or angry opposition, and is enjoined by the powerful threat that the parents will collapse if made the target of his anger. Thus he fears that if he manifests anger, he will destroy the very sources of supply upon which his existence depends. Subsequently, as he internalizes and organizes his parents' prohibitions and values into a superego system, the same parenticidal meaning attaches to any defiance of his superego (Hill, 1955).

The prohibition against anger extends to any defiance or deviance from the imposed value system, or any expression of dissent and curiosity. The child is expected to accept unquestioningly as gospel his parents' definitions and rules. This inclines him toward a passive, receptive approach to learning rather than toward active inquiry and independent pursuit of knowledge. Truth is what he has been told, not what he has tested for himself. Clearly, this limits his differentiation of a diverse, flexible repertoire of behavior and prevents his discovering and developing inner resources for independence from his parents and their omnipresent regulation. Thus his dependence is propelled into a vicious spiral.

His differentiation is further hampered by proscriptions against privacy and secrecy. With private thoughts not permitted, the child has less opportunity to discover and gain confidence in a mind of his own. Thus a major avenue to separation and individuation is blocked. Parents who demand this kind of response want their child to be one with them. To insure that he is not contaminated by divergent opinions and definitions, they may insist that he tell them everything about his day—where he has been, what he did, and with whom he did it (Mark, 1953). This, of course, interferes with the child's discovering values, opinions, and definitions that differ from those of his parents. Should he later disorganize into schizophrenia, his symptoms very possibly will include beliefs that others are reading his mind or that his thoughts are being broadcast to the world.

In carrying out their imposition of definitions, the parents are highly unreceptive to criticism, and especially intolerant of the child's comparison of them with other parents. These restrictions are part of a general interference with his developing a differentiated structure of reality and of the object world.

Interferences with the Formation of Differentiated Reality and Object-World Constructs

Differentiation-impeding parents tend to convince the child that he needs them constantly to interpret social reality for him (Stierlin, 1959). He is placed in the position of a traveler in a strange country who must depend upon an interpreter to evaluate his encounters with others as well as his performance in these encounters. At best he can venture away from his parents only if he carries with him a mental guidebook filled with their definitions and rules. The guidebook of social reality imposed by the parents usually is poorly differentiated, rigid, and stereotyped, lumping persons into large classes or types rather than distinguishing among varied and different individuals with multiple personality facets. As previously mentioned, the phrase, "He is the type who . . ." is frequent. The child comes to believe that he and others are expected to behave and to be judged according to type, with little room for variation within the type or within the same person from one time to another. According to the parents' definitions, social interaction is governed by rigid rather than flexible rules and by fixed conceptions of what is acceptable and what is unacceptable.

Cameron and Magaret (1951) describe the preschizophrenic child as deficient in role-taking skills, the normal basis for flexible adaptation to varied social situations. The child who is unable to imagine himself in the social roles of others will have limited awareness of their thoughts, feelings, and motivations. Cameron and Magaret suggest that this lack of role-taking skill may result from limited experience in varied social contexts, limited either because the family has been geographically isolated from others, or because it has moved so frequently that the child has had insufficient opportunity for sustained extrafamilial relationships. It would seem that a more important pathogenic factor than geographic insularity would be a lack of functional integration of the family into the surrounding community. In addition, parents who themselves are limited to a narrow stereotyped view of social reality are ill-equipped to assist their children in establishing a differentiated view. Witkin (1962), for example, has found that poorly differentiated mothers are likely to have poorly differentiated children.

Devereux (1939) offers a similar social theory of schizophrenia that emphasizes the problem of a poorly differentiated map of reality. He postulates an inflexibility of adaptation to new life situations, due to excessive reliance upon the assumption that rules learned in earlier situations can be applied without modification to the new. A person whose reality construct and repertoire of adaptive skills are limited is likely to disorganize if suddenly thrust into a new and drastically different cultural and social setting. Devereux (1939) and Faris (1934) suggest that a child reared in too close a family circle would be ill-prepared for new situations. This would seem especially likely if the family impedes his differentiation.

Another interference with reliable reality constructs is a family atmosphere pervaded by an excessive "double-bind" communication pattern (Bateson et al., 1956). Double-binds consist of contradictory messages at different metacommunicative levels, continued exposure to which renders the child both perplexed as to how to interpret the message and liable to censure however he interprets it. Under these circumstances he comes to doubt the reliability of his own perceptual equipment. He can be certain of very little about his interactions with others except that they are confusing, contradictory, and unreliable. As a consequence he develops modes of symbolizing his experience which are adaptive to intrafamilial communication but maladaptive to the extrafamilial world. He has particular difficulty in asserting his definition of relationships with others, but is vulnerable to and defensive against their definitions.

A person's constructs of social reality and his object relations are naturally reciprocal. Faulty development in either sphere inevitably leads to deficiencies in the other, particularly when the child of a poorly differentiated family is blocked from establishing offsetting healthy relationships outside the family.

INTERFERENCES WITH EXTRAFAMILIAL OBJECT RELATIONS

In the course of normal development the range and variety of a child's object relations expand beyond his primary intrafamilial objects. In various ways this facilitates differentiation. Establishment of auxiliary sources of emotional support lessens his exclusive dependence on primary sources, thereby giving him a base from which he can expand his range of permissible behavior. It also provides opportunities for discovering new aspects and forming new definitions of his self on the basis of recognition and appraisals accorded him by others. To cite a simple example, a child whose family has taught him that his appearance and behavior are shameful and unlikable may be very pleasantly surprised to discover that outside the family he is held in high esteem. In particular he may find that qualities such as curiosity or self-assertiveness which were negatively valued by his family are positively valued by others. A differentiated set of object relations offers him a richer variety of appraisals as well as opportunity for learning that there are different versions of reality—different ways of viewing the world and people. The availability of a greater range of identification models is still another important aspect of extrafamilial object relations.

Opportunity for communication outside the family also is important. Communication with others is essential to the development and maintenance of reasonably accurate and socially adaptive thought patterns. This has been well demonstrated by natural and contrived experiments in social isolation and sensory deprivation. It has been suggested that the preschizophrenic person's lack of communication with others contributes to ultimate disorganization of his thinking. By not sharing his thoughts with others, he deprives himself of opportunities to validate or correct them through comparison (Cameron and Magaret, 1951; Sullivan, 1953). Without this corrective checking process or consensual validation, thoughts and percepts may become increasingly autistic. A vicious cycle of withdrawal and autism ensues. As the socially withdrawn person communicates his ideas less, his thoughts become increasingly autistic, he hesitates even more to express them, and so on. The child of a differentiation-impeding family with limited extrafamilial contacts is especially vulnerable to such a cycle.

The family may directly inculcate xenophobia in the child. Particularly if the family members are poorly articulated into their social context, they will teach him to distrust the extrafamilial world and to shun strangers and their different ways of behavior and thought. A differentiation-impeding mother is likely to indicate to her child that he is safe only with her, and that "the others" of the outside world, or even others within the family, are not to be trusted. Further, he is imbued with the belief that he himself is not to be trusted alone in the outside world, and that without his parents' immediate supervision he will be unacceptable and incompetent. This is reinforced by his being told repeatedly, "I can accept you because you are my child, but others will not be so indulgent. You are not safe away from me."

Perhaps even more pernicious is the warning, "You may be able to fool others for a while, but if you are not careful they'll really get to know you and then won't want anything to do with you. We in the family can put up with you because you belong to us." To the degree that the exact nature of his badness and unacceptability is never specified but kept ominously vague, he is unable to modify or eliminate specific features of his behavior. Instead he carries with him a menacing sense of ineradicable, fundamental badness.

This combination of expectations is hardly likely to encourage the child to expand his set of object relations. On the contrary, it predisposes him to automatic anxiety in interactions with strangers in unfamiliar social contexts, thus seriously impeding his development of stable extrafamilial relationships. His ventures into relationships will be cautious, guarded, and inhibited. Chances are that he will have been told that sexual and aggressive impulses are especially bad, dangerous, and unacceptable. To the extent that he has accepted these definitions and has repressed and suppressed such impulses he will shy away from children who express these impulses more freely. Further, insofar as his peers are likely to regard his excessive "properness" as "queer" and "sissyish," they will be given either to painful teasing or to outright rejection and isolation of him. He is thereby deprived of opportunities to acquire new definitions of himself and the object world, and more differentiated identification models.

We turn now to discuss factors which impede integration.

INTERFERENCES WITH INTEGRATION

Integration refers to the attainment of coherence, harmony, and unity of personality organization. It is the basis for consistency and continuity of self-definition. We noted in the preceding chapter that disunity and disharmony may occur both among and within systems of thought, affect, and action. We also noted that a major factor contributing to personality dividedness is a reality construct which excessively uses nonintegrative exclusion mechanisms such as repression and denial and thereby precludes assimilation of significant areas of experience.

What types of child-parent relationships foster nonintegrative reality constructs? One type is a relationship or family context that imposes limited, narrow, and rigid definitions upon the child. Lacking the autonomous resources to leave his parents, and feeling acceptable to them only on condition that he fit their definitions of acceptability, he must try somehow to exclude from his self any feelings, thoughts, or actions which do not fit. Generally this leaves him with recourse to two attempted solutions. One is to develop a "secret self" in which are hidden all ideas, feelings, and impulses contrary to his parents' definitions of the real and the acceptable. In some ways this solution is less ominous for the child's future psychological health than is the second method, which consists of excluding from his consciousness anything that might bring him into opposition with his parents. This exclusion process is cumulative and gives rise to powerful unconscious personality subsystems split off in repression from his conscious ego. His heavy reliance on denial and repression in order to conform to rigid parental definitions also seriously impairs his ability to test reality independently.

Another type of integration-impeding relationship subjects the child to definitions which are contradictory, inconsistent, or amorphously vague and which he lacks the ability to clarify or resolve. This inability is part of a general family incapacity to recognize, confront, and cope with inconsistencies and contradictions, whether within or among individual family members.

What we are saying is that the child will be unable to register, let alone comment upon and deal with, parental definitions that are vague, labile, and contradictory, if the parents themselves are unable to recognize or acknowledge these qualities in their definitions. A prerequisite of the ability to integrate contradictions is the ability to acknowledge their presence, and this is difficult in a family situation where contradictions seldom become a sustained focus of shared attention.

The child's integrative capacities are further hindered if the parents adopt a defensive denial of ambiguity, uncertainty, and inconsistency, and act as if they were unwaveringly certain and constant in their definitions. This makes it extremely difficult for the child to question or dispute the parents' versions of reality. Their definitions are presented as embodiments of universal, unquestionable truth. Distinctions between opinion, belief, and truth are blurred. The child is discouraged from discriminating between the intrinsic merit of a definition and the source of the definition, especially when he has been taught to regard the source as his indispensable emotional support and guide to reality. Insofar as he is discouraged even from noticing the existence of alternative versions and interpretations of reality, the possibility of presenting these alternatives in open opposition to his parents is completely ruled out.

Faced either with narrow and rigid definitions or with amorphous, labile, and contradictory definitions, the child's only recourse may be to nonintegrative mechanisms by which he ignores, dismisses as irrelevant or erroneous, or somehow excludes from consciousness all aspects of himself or others which might contradict his parents' reality constructs. This seriously limits the range of new experiences which he can assimilate in reasonably congruent fashion. The range of social situations to which he can adapt with reasonable comfort is correspondingly narrow. The disintegrative effect of his nonassimilation of incongruent data is cumulative as more new experiences are encountered. This places his entire personality structure under strain and in danger of ultimate collapse into chaotic disorganization, especially if he encounters inescapable life circumstances so much at variance with his parents' definitions as to undo the repression he has employed in following them.

Types of Unassimilable Contradiction

Let us turn now to consider some of the contradictions which the child may be forced to try to handle by nonintegrative means. Contradiction may be intraparental, interparental, or between a parent and persons in the extrafamilial world.

The schematic prototype of intraparental contradiction is the good mother-bad mother split. It is postulated that the child's experience of any mother-child relationship will be inconsistent. At times it will be good or pleasurable; at other times bad or unpleasurable. How the child perceives and represents to himself this inconsistency will depend upon the stage of development of his reality construct, including his definitions of himself and his object world. At a very undifferentiated stage he may not even conceive of himself and his mother as separate entities. Goodness and badness at this stage would be perceived as global senses of pleasure or unpleasure. At a later stage, if he has learned to distinguish his mother and himself as separate, he may perceive goodness and badness in terms of changes in his mother. Sometimes she is a good, satisfying mother; on other occasions she is a bad, frustrating mother. Various personality theorists have suggested that the young child may initially form separate images of good mother and bad mother. Only subsequently, if his development is normal, does he fuse these into a single, integrated representation of his mother. This is a major basis for object constancy which is in turn fundamental to normal personality organization. A significant feature of schizo-phrenia-vulnerable personalities is their tenuousness of object constancy and corresponding proclivity for regression to more primitive developmental stages of object representation.

The mother plays a vital role in facilitating or hindering her child's formation of an integrated definition of herself. He requires her assistance and encouragement to perceive her inconsistencies and changeability, rather than her insistence that he unrealistically perceive her as unfailingly and completely good. Her ability to assist her child toward an integrated percept of her depends upon her own capacity for integration. If poorly integrated, she will have little capacity to tolerate criticism. She will refuse to acknowledge any but her own favorable definition of herself. For instance, if the child perceives her as bad—angry, unfair, cruel, or anything unpleasant—the mother is likely to insist that the child must be mistaken. Instead of confirming, she invalidates the child's percept, saying, "You are wrong—I have only love and concern for you." This confronts the child with the necessity for revising or repudiating his own percept, as well as introducing doubt and distrust of his basic perceptual equipment.

The child frequently is encouraged to revise his percept by transferring blame and criticism elsewhere—to himself, to a third person, or to some impersonal extraneous agent. His poorly integrated mother may be only too ready to assist him in transferring blame to himself, especially if she already has cast him in the role of repository for repudiated aspects of herself. She will be quick to tell him that his entertaining a bad thought about her is sure evidence of his own ingratitude, selfishness, excessive sensitivity, or morbid imagination.

The mother also may be quick to encourage him to purify his percept of her by transferring the blame to a third person, either within or outside the family. This may be coupled with implications that the outside world is dangerous, untrustworthy, and contaminating, while she is the only source of security and the only reliable interpreter of reality. It is understandable how such implications will impede his establishing satisfactory extrafamilial relationships; for example, her repeated warning of the bad influence of potential playmates will not facilitate his having comfortable peer relationships.

Nonintegrative exoneration of the mother also may be carried out by blaming an impersonal agent such as the weather, food, or sickness.

Frequent are statements such as, "What has gotten into you? Are you sick?" The disintegrating effect of such maneuvers is readily apparent in the depersonalizing statement, "You are not yourself today." The attribution of badness to the influence of an evil spirit or to the devil is common in some cultures and subcultures.

These various techniques of handling adverse percepts of his mother by making a scapegoat of himself or of third parties have serious ultimate consequences to the child. As we have pointed out, they tend to keep him dependent upon a single source of emotional support. Labeling himself bad forestalls a developing sense of confidence in the validity of his own perceptual processes and in his capacity for independent reality testing. Labeling third persons as bad hinders development of auxiliary sources of emotional support. Further, his repression of unfavorable percepts of his mother necessitates his denying hurt and anger within himself. The overall effect is a serious lack of integration of major sectors of feeling and thought.

The failure to integrate good and bad mother configurations of experience occupies a prominent position in several theories of predisposition to schizophrenia. Sullivan (1953) postulates that unfused images of good and bad mother and of good and bad self, accompanied by dissociation (repression) of major areas of experience, result in an unintegrated self highly vulnerable to schizophrenic disorganization when dissociative barriers break down and previously excluded ideas and affects erupt into awareness.

Hill (1955) offers a similar but more complex formulation that vulnerability to schizophrenia is partly determined by persisting divided infantile configurations of experience, organized around a split good-bad personification of the mother. In a somewhat idiosyncratic use of the terms, Hill designates these split configurations as id and superego: id refers to a good experience configuration comprising "good mother-breast-mouth-magic protection and supplies"; superego refers to a bad experience configuration comprising "bad mother-devastating punishment-abandonment-destruction." Hill postulates that the schizophrenia-susceptible personality is under constant threat of domination or engulfment by one or the other of these persistent divided configurations. The person is driven to such intense efforts either to reconstitute the "good mother" pattern or to avoid the "bad mother" pattern that he is unable to establish more realistic, less extreme forms of object relations. This is the same pattern we have designated as the schizophrenic person's need-fear dilemma, to which he reacts with extremes of clinging and avoidance.

Hill further postulates that this dividedness results from maternal instability and inconsistency so extreme as to deprive the child of a reliable, unconditional supply of good experience which he can internalize and from which he may draw support.

This problem may be compounded by the mother's paradoxical expectation that the child provide strength, support, and good experience for her. Thus the child is confronted with a severe contradiction: he is expected to remain helplessly dependent upon his mother, but at the same time to function as an emotional supplier to her.

Parental contradiction regarding dependence-independence may expose the child to the expectations on the one hand that he be dependent, and on the other hand that he strive toward upward mobility and social recognition, goals for which his dependency equips him poorly. This contradiction may be further reinforced if the parents treat his occasional assertive success as unacceptable rivalry with themselves. Lu (1961) observed this pattern in comparing the child-parent relationships of lower-class patients and their nonschizophrenic siblings. She also noted that the onset of schizophrenia frequently occurred under two sets of circumstances: (1) when the patient-to-be was suddenly faced with a concrete demand that he assume independent adult responsibility, and (2) the loss of certain relationships supportive of his dependence.

Parental contradiction in the dependence-independence and compliance-assertiveness dimensions may occur as a sharp discontinuity of expectations between intra- and extrafamilial settings. The parents expect the child to be passively compliant at home, but aggressively assertive in the outside world. This discontinuity is further sharpened if his extrafamilial peers place high value on assertiveness and the ability to stand up for one's personal rights. Such inconsistencies make it difficult for the child to negotiate the developmental transition to extrafamilial object relations.

The child may be exposed to many other serious contradictions in addition to those we have especially emphasized. His parents may inculcate values and ideals which are incongruent with actual life circumstances. For instance, by unrealistic praise and expectations they may set achievement ideals which are grossly discrepant with their child's actual abilities. The preachment that all parents and all children have only pure love for each other makes it very difficult for the child to integrate much contrary experience in the actual relationship. The contradiction between what the parent says and what he does may appear in many forms.

An especially pernicious contradiction may be presented by the mother who defines herself as a self-sacrificing martyr whose only concern is for her child; in actuality, however, her major, if not her only concern is herself, and the child is merely an instrument serving her needs (Wolman, 1957). Her claimed selfless devotion is contradicted by her actual selfish exploitation. However, it is very difficult for the child to perceive clearly this contradiction, let alone comment upon it or have his percept confirmed by others.

Interparental Contradictions. A child's integration may be seriously impeded by contradictions between his parents, as when they confront him with incongruent sets of expectations. His mother expects him to be one person, his father another. To please one parent is to risk alienation from the other. Lidz and his co-workers (1957) have demonstrated the prevalence of this pattern in so-called schismatic families. Frequently the child is employed by each parent as an instrument in parent-parent conflicts. For instance, father's criticism of the child's dress and grooming may be designed primarily as an attack on mother. The disintegrative as well as the depersonalizing effect of such instrumental use of the child seems clear.

Family vs. Outside World Contradictions. When the child of a differentiation- and integration-impeding family encounters the extrafamilial world, he is likely to be confronted by further contradictions. He has been taught an undifferentiated reality construct comprising rigid cognitive schemata for organizing his experiences and fixed rules for social interaction. Having also been taught that he should not form his own reality constructs by thinking independently, he is ill-equipped to adapt flexibly when confronted by situations and events which do not fit the rigid schemata he was forced to develop in order to coexist with poorly integrated parents whose own schemata were based on excessive repression, denial, and projection.

Contradiction between intra- and extrafamilial values is especially likely along lines of submissiveness vs. assertiveness, self-expression vs. reticence, and competition vs. obedience.

After gearing himself to one set of values within his family, he is then confronted by an opposite set in the outside world. In the face of this switch he will be all the more disconcerted if his parents reverse their previous attitudes. For instance, his mother, who earlier discouraged him from speaking his mind, now may say, "Why don't you speak up to people? How do you ever expect to make friends if you are so quiet? You have no personality." Previously he may have been discouraged from establishing extrafamilial friendships and may even have been made to feel that to do so would be traitorously disloyal to his family. Now he must put up with such incriminations as "What's the matter with you? You have no friends. You must be one of the least popular children in your school."

Another likely contradiction as the child ventures to the outside world concerns his thinking for himself. Having in the past been encouraged to rely exclusively upon his parents' guidance, he may suddenly find himself blamed for not making his own decisions or plans, and for not knowing his own mind.

These and other contradictions are very disturbing to the undifferentiated and unintegrated youth. He lacks the means of recognizing and partially accepting or resolving contradictions. As a result he may be forced either to withdraw from the social scene or to become confused.

INTEGRATION AND PROCESSES OF IDENTIFICATION

Consideration of the disintegrative effects of parental contradictions leads naturally to discussion of the place of identification in the task of personality integration. Identification refers to the process of internalizing patterns of behavior manifest by other persons. It assists the child in bridging the transition from regulation by the environment to self-regulation.

In normal development a child acquires patterns of organizing his thoughts, affects, and actions by internalizing patterns provided by models in his environment. His primary models usually are his parents. Internalization includes processes of imitation, identification, and assimilation. Normal identification should be distinguished from mechanical, rigid imitation. It requires synthesis and integration of the internalized patterns into a coherent whole. Failing this, identifications remain split off from the reach of conscious self-definition and control. Also required is sufficient differentiation of the developing self from others so that the internalized patterns become truly the person's own equipment. Further important features of normal identification are diversity, flexibility, and selectivity, which permit the child to select this aspect of one person and that aspect of another as qualities to assimilate into himself. This is in contrast to rigid total identification with a single model.

Normal integrative identification may be impeded in various ways. One obvious hindrance occurs if the primary model is extremely unstable, inconsistent, and poorly differentiated and integrated. As Hill (1955) indicates, if a mother's "goodness" is precariously conditional, the child is unable to internalize a reliable source of goodness. To the degree that the child identifies with an unstable primary model and its inconsistencies of thought, feeling, and action, he is ill-equipped for future adaptation to the extrafamilial world.

Wynne and his co-workers (1958) suggest that in addition to each of the parents, the models for internalization may include patterns of total family interaction. For instance, a pattern of fragmented, incoherent family interaction may be internalized and subsequently become manifest as a fragmented patterning of thought.

Integrated identification will also be impeded if one parent interdicts the child's identifying with the other parent. For example, a mother may in various ways depict her husband as an unsuitable model for her son. Thus she prohibits the son from closeness and identification with his father; the penalty for resembling his father is loss of his mother's acceptance. Of course, the father may apply the same sanction against the child's identifying with the mother.

Interference with successful paternal identification appears as a significant feature in the childhood of many young male schizophrenic patients. This may relate to a family role structure which contradicts the cultural norm. In a series of male schizophrenic patients studied by Kohn and Clausen (1956), it was found that such patients were more likely to have come from a family in which the mother was relatively dominant and the father relatively weak and passive than was the case in a series of matched controls.[2]

The prohibition against identification may stem from the parent himself because of certain personal attributes which he has been unable to integrate in himself. For instance, a father at great pains to deny any vestige of his own passivity may ruthlessly castigate his son for identifying with passive traits which he himself manifests, his denial notwithstanding.

Still another interference with identification is the parents' interdiction of identification with extrafamilial persons. This may seriously limit the number and variety of identification models available to the child. A diversity of models is desirable provided the child is able to synthesize the resulting identifications into a single, stable identity. If not, the result of multiple unintegrated identifications may be manifest as grossly contradictory character traits or as multiple personality subsystems which may come alternately to the fore in Jekyll-Hyde fashion. A paucity of identifications is likely to be accompanied by narrow limitation and rigidity of the child's behavioral patterns and to be featured by mechanical imitation rather than by more flexible identification.

Identifications poorly integrated with one another and with the central personality organization are disruptive to harmonious purposive behavior. Like underground enemy agents they are a lurking source of potential disorder and give rise to serious conflict as well as incoordination and erratic changeability of behavior. There is always the danger of their unpredictably overthrowing the central ego organization and subjecting the person's behavior to the domination of this or that identificatory splinter force.

Poorly integrated identifications are a major source of breakdown of inner-outer, self-other mental boundaries. They are susceptible to easy projection. Freud points to this as a source of delusions of reference (1914). Decomposition of the superego is an important source of delusions. A superego composed of poorly integrated identifications is easily projected and reallocated to the external world (Fenichel,

---

[2] This finding must be interpreted with caution, since the same authors also found a similar family role pattern in families lower on the socioeconomic scale who did not have schizophrenic children. It appears that this role pattern may be deviant in middle-class families but the norm in lower-class families.

1953; Schilder, 1953; Jacobson, 1954). Failure to achieve integrated identifications also contributes to inability to carry on "internal communication" with internalized parents. This, in turn, impairs the person's capacity for internal deliberation, self-consideration, and reality testing, which are the basis for self-regulated purposeful behavior and relative independence. Accordingly, the person remains dependent upon external sources of direction, emotional support, and fear-reduction (Wahl, 1956).

SUMMARY

In this chapter we have discussed child-parent relationships and family contexts which may impede a child's differentiation and integration.

Differentiation-impeding relationships prevent his attaining self-other separation and autonomy, the capacity for diverse specialized responses, and the ability to form differentiated reality and object-world constructs. These relationships tend overprotectively to bind the child in dependency upon one or both of his parents or upon the total family matrix. They impose upon him others' definitions of himself and the object world rather than encourage and ratify his own emergent definitions. They prevent him from realizing and gaining confidence in internal resources and capacities for self-direction. Inadequate, restricted, and distorted maps of social reality also are imposed upon him, and he is discouraged from developing extra-familial sources of emotional support and definition of his self. As a consequence he remains dependent upon his primary objects for support, direction, and definition. Not only is he taught that he is incapable of separateness, but also that it is bad and undesirable and that his acceptability rests upon his remaining dependent upon his primary objects.

Integration-impeding relationships lead to nonassimilation of significant areas of experience by encouraging or requiring exclusion mechanisms such as excessive repression and denial. One interference with integration consists of imposing narrow, rigid definitions upon the child. Another consists of vague, inconsistent, or contradictory definitions, coupled with hindrance of the child's capacity for realizing and integrating contradictions. Important types of contradiction are intraparental, interparental, and parental vs. extrafamilial. The good mother-bad mother split is a schematic prototype of intraparental contradiction. Especially important contradictions occur in the dimensions of dependence-independence and compliance-assertiveness. Failure to integrate contradictions results in the accumulation of split-off subsystems and increasing strain on total personality organization.

Identification processes are vital to the developmental task of integration and may be impeded in various ways. To the degree that identifications are narrowly limited, tenuous, or split and unsynthesized into a coherent identity, the total personality organization is seriously weakened and vulnerable to disorganization.

BIBLIOGRAPHY

Alanen, Y. O. (1958), Academic Dissertation from the Psychiatric Clinic of the University of Helsinki, 208-213.

Bateson, G., Jackson, D. D., Haley, J., & Weakland, J. (1956), Toward a Theory of Schizophrenia. *Behavior. Sci., 1*:251-264.

Birren, J. E. (1944), Psychological Examinations of Children Who Later Became Psychotic. *J. Abnorm. Soc. Psych., 39*:84-95.

Bowen, M. (1960), A Family Concept of Schizophrenia. In: *The Etiology of Schizophrenia,* ed. D. D. Jackson. New York: Basic Books.

Bower, E. M., Shellhamer, T. A., & Daily, J. M. (1960), School Characteristics of Male Adolescents Who Later Became Schizophrenic. *Amer. J. Orthopsychiat., 30*:712-729.

Bowman, K. M. (1934), A Study of the Pre-psychotic Personality in Certain Psychoses. In: *The Biology of the Individual,* Vol. 14, Proceedings of a Conference of the Association for Research in Nervous and Mental Diseases. Baltimore: Williams and Wilkins.

Brodey, W. M. (1961), The Family as the Unit of Study and Treatment. 3. Image, Object and Narcissistic Relationships. *Amer. J. Orthopsychiat., 31*:69-73.

Bruch, H. (1962), The Constructive Use of Ignorance: Effectiveness in Psychotherapy. *Bull. Assn. Psychoanal. Med.,* A Report of the May 1, 1962, Scientific Meeting of the Association, *2*:19-23.

Cameron, N. & Magaret, A. (1951), *Behavior Pathology.* Boston: Houghton Mifflin.

Devereux, G. (1939), A Sociological Theory of Schizophrenia. *Psychoanal. Rev., 26*:315-342.

Faris, R. E. L. (1934), Cultural Isolation and the Schizophrenic Personality. *Amer. J. Sociol., 40*:155-164.

Fenichel, O. (1953), Identification. In: *The Collected Papers of Otto Fenichel: First Series,* ed. H. Fenichel and D. Rapaport. New York: Norton.

Foote, N. N. & Cottrell, L. S., Jr. (1955), *Identity and Interpersonal Competence*. Chicago: University of Chicago Press.

Foudraine, J. (1961), Schizophrenia and the Family: A Survey of the Literature 1956-1960 on the Etiology of Schizophrenia. *Acta Psychotherapeutica, 9*:82-110.

Freud, S. (1914), On Narcissism: An Introduction. *Standard Edition, 14*:73-102. London: Hogarth Press, 1957.

Gerard, D. L. & Siegel, J. (1950), The Family Background of Schizophrenia. *Psychiat. Quart., 24*:47-73.

Hill, L. B. (1955), *Psychotherapeutic Intervention in Schizophrenia*. Chicago: University of Chicago Press.

Jacobson, E. (1954), Contributions to the Metapsychology of Psychotic Identifications. *J. Amer. Psychoanal. Assn., 2*:239-262.

Jenkins, R. L. (1952), The Schizophrenic Sequence: Withdrawal, Disorganization, Psychotic Reorganization. *Amer. J. Orthopsychiat., 22*:738-748.

Kasanin, J., Knight, E., & Sage, P. (1934), The Parent-Child Relationship in Schizophrenia. I. Over-Protection-Rejection. *J. Nerv. and Ment. Dis., 79*:249-263.

Kohn, M. L. & Clausen, J. (1956), Parental Authority Behavior and Schizophrenia. *Amer. J. Orthopsychiat., 26*:297-312.

Levy, D. M. (1943), *Maternal Overprotection*. New York: Columbia University Press.

Lidz, T., Cornelison, A., Fleck, S., & Terry, D. (1957), The Intrafamilial Environment of Schizophrenic Patients. II. Marital Schism and Marital Skew. *Amer. J. Psychiat., 114*:241-248.

Limentani, D. (1956), Symbiotic Identification in Schizophrenia. *Psychiat., 19*:231-236.

Lu, Y. (1961), Mother-Child Role Relations in Schizophrenia: A Comparison of Schizophrenic Patients with Nonschizophrenic Siblings. *Psychiat., 24*:133-142.

Mahler, M. S. (1952), On Child Psychosis and Schizophrenia—Autistic and Symbiotic Infantile Psychoses. *The Psychoanalytic Study of the Child, 7*:286-305. New York: International Universities Press.

Mark, J. C. (1953), Attitudes of Mothers of Male Schizophrenics Toward Child Behavior. *J. Abnorm. and Soc. Psychol., 48*:185-189.

O'Neal, P. & Robins, L. N. (1958), Childhood Patterns Predictive of Adult Schizophrenia: A 30-Year Follow-up Study. *Amer. J. Psychiat., 115*:385-391.

Pollin, W., Stabenau, J. R., & Tupin, J. (1965), Family Studies with Identical Twins Discordant for Schizophrenia. *Psychiat., 28*:60-78.

Sanua, V. D. (1961), Sociocultural Factors in Families of Schizophrenics: A Review of the Literature. *Psychiat., 24*:246-265.

Schilder, P. (1953), *Medical Psychology*, ed. D. Rapaport. New York: International Universities Press.

Searles, H. F. (1958), Positive Feelings in the Relationship Between the Schizophrenic and His Mother. *Internat. J. Psycho-Anal., 39*:1-18.

——— (1959), Integration and Differentiation in Schizophrenia: An Over-all View. *Brit. J. Med. Psychol., 32*:261-281.

Stierlin, H. (1959), The Adaptation to the "Stronger" Person's Reality. *Psychiat., 22*:143-152.

Sullivan, H. S. (1953), *The Interpersonal Theory of Psychiatry.* New York: Norton.

Tietze, T. (1949), A Study of Mothers of Schizophrenic Patients. *Psychiat., 12*:55-65.

Vogel, E. F. & Bell, N. W. (1960), The Emotionally Disturbed Child as a Family Scapegoat. *Psychoanal. Rev., 47*:21-43.

Wahl, C. W. (1956), Some Antecedent Factors in the Family Histories of 568 Male Schizophrenics of the U. S. Navy. *Amer. J. Psychiat., 113*:201-210.

White, R. W. (1965), The Experience of Efficacy in Schizophrenia. *Psychiat., 28*:199-211.

Witkin, H. A. et al. (1962), *Psychological Differentiation.* New York: Wiley.

Wittman, M. P. & Steinberg, D. L. (1944), A Study of Prodromal Factors in Mental Illness with Special Reference to Schizophrenia. *Amer. J. Psychiat., 100*:811-816.

Wolman, B. B. (1957), Explorations in Latent Schizophrenia. *Amer. J. Psychother., 11*:560-588.

Wynne, L. C., Ryckoff, I. M., Day, J., & Hirsch, S. I. (1958), Pseudo-mutuality in the Family Relations of Schizophrenics. *Psychiat., 21*:205-220.

IV

CIRCUMSTANCES OF ONSET OF SCHIZOPHRENIA: RELEVANCE TO FAULTY DIFFERENTIATION AND INTEGRATION

DONALD L. BURNHAM

THIS CHAPTER CONCERNS the circumstances contributing to the onset of schizophrenia. We seek to define as precisely as possible various types of precipitating stresses, and personality structural defects unable to withstand these stresses. We shall be concerned with why a particular stress may disorganize one personality but not another, and why a particular personality may be vulnerable to some stresses but not to others. We shall advance evidence of the salience of faulty differentiation and integration in determining vulnerability to schizophrenia. We suggest, for instance, that a personality poorly differentiated in the sector of self-other separation will be especially vulnerable to disorganization if removed from familiar social contexts. A poorly integrated personality will encounter special stress in situations which threaten to mobilize unintegrated impulses and affects.

Before proceeding to more detailed discussion, however, let us comment briefly on some of the difficulties and limitations particular to the study of onset of schizophrenia. One is the difficulty in accurately dating onset. Often it is insidious, and covert psychosis may long antedate public recognition of it. Further, in trying to determine the date and circumstances of onset, one usually must depend upon the uncertain retrospective reports of the patient, his family, and his associates. The criteria used by the patient or others to define and label him as "mentally ill" are highly variable according to the individual, his family, and their sociocultural milieu. The cultural relativity of social deviance as a criterion for the diagnosis of mental illness is well established. The borderlines between the categories "peculiar," "nonconforming," "sick," and "crazy" are understandably blurred and subject to individual interpretation. In addition, the tolerance of various forms of deviance varies greatly among different families and different subcultures.

To define and to measure accurately acute and chronic psychological stress is equally problematic. What constitutes stress for one person may not be so for another. The stressfulness of events and situations depends upon their personal meaning to an individual. Furthermore, the availability of emotional support and external structure may considerably mitigate and mask the impact of stress. This is particularly true for the poorly differentiated person.

With these reservations in mind let us turn to consider what we can learn from the circumstances of onset of schizophrenia. These conditions are especially relevant to differentiation and integration insofar as they enable us to see more specifically *how* failure of these developmental processes may lead to schizophrenia. Although faults in differentiation and integration are likely to occur together, for purposes of exposition we shall discuss them separately. First we shall consider vulnerability to disorganization associated with faulty differentiation.

Onset and Faulty Differentiation

We have described the poorly differentiated person as lacking (1) clear, stable, self-other separation; (2) specialized, discrete adaptive skills and inner resources which provide the basis for the transition from heteronomy to autonomy; and (3) a differentiated construct of reality and the object world. These deficits render him peculiarly dependent upon and vulnerable to the influence of his environment. He is imbedded in his environmental matrix in a special way. If he loses supportive external structure he is likely to disorganize.

Furthermore, his disorganization is likely to take the form of de-differentiation, or breakdown, of whatever characteristics of differentiation he has tenuously acquired and maintained. He loses his sense of separateness. His self-other boundaries blur, and he loses his sense of possession of his thoughts, feelings, and body processes—of himself. He feels fused with others or even with the entire cosmos. This fusion tendency reflects strong urges to regain lost external support by uniting with some strong object, whether a parent, a politically or economically powerful personage, God, or some nonpersonified spiritual power.

A second major line of dedifferentiation is his loss of discrete specialized responses. He regresses into global, indiscriminate, mass reactions and loses his ability to distinguish relevant from irrelevant events. He can no longer exercise selectivity of thought, feeling, and action. As his object world construct dedifferentiates, he lumps objects indiscriminately into procrustean, stereotyped categories, and his object definitions become kaleidoscopically inconstant.

The poorly differentiated person's susceptibility to dedifferentiation when confronted with the loss of customary external structure is due to the relative weakness of his inner structure and his lack of autonomous adaptive skills. He is unprepared to adapt to unfamiliar environmental conditions. We shall present evidence that these two factors—loss of customary support, and confrontation by unfamiliar adaptational demands—are prominent in the circumstances of onset of schizophrenia. In our discussion we emphasize role-transition crises, a topic to which we now turn.

Role-Transition Crises

Social role is a key concept in viewing the individual's relationship to the social structure of which he is a part. Role refers to the behavior expected of a person by virtue of a particular position he occupies within a social structure. At each stage of life development there are differences both in the range of roles a person is capable of filling and in the range of roles the social structure provides for and demands of him. In addition, the fit between the person's capabilities and the roles open to him will vary at different life stages and from person to person. In the usual life course, role capabilities and opportunities expand and differentiate progressively until middle age and then gradually contract. In normal psychosocial development the person progresses through a series of role transitions, among others, from child to adult, from student to wage earner, and from single to married to parent.

Smoothness of role transitions depends upon many factors. One is the definiteness of culturally prescribed schedules and rites of passage for major role transitions. Another is the degree of smooth continuity between what is expected of the child and what is expected of the adult. Discontinuity occurs when behavior interdicted in the child role is expected in the adult role, or when there has been inadequate preparation and training for the shift to a new role.

Important types of discontinuity occur in the dimensions of responsibility vs. nonresponsibility, dominance vs. submission, and sexuality (Benedict, 1938). The problem of role discontinuities is further compounded in stratified societies where transition from one class status to another may be particularly difficult. In this regard, proclaimed values and social reality may conflict. Negroes in the United States, for example, are often confronted by an official moral code emphasizing equal opportunity for all, contradicted by actual conditions which deny them such opportunity (Davis, 1938).

Even more important to our present topic, however, than the role contradictions presented by a particular society and culture are the limitations which the poorly differentiated person brings to the task of role transition. He is singularly ill-equipped to make role transitions that require separation from his family or shifts from dependent heteronomy to independent autonomy. Situations which demand these changes constitute major life crises for him and may plunge him into schizophrenic disorganization.[1] We turn now to present evidence in support of this thesis.

The undifferentiated person's predominant role is a dependent one in relation to supportive primary objects. He may function with seeming adequacy as long as he can remain in this role. His typical mode of adaptation is passivity and compliance. Frequently, though by no means universally, children who later become schizophrenic are described as obedient, compliant "model children" and "model students." It is only when circumstances force a transition from this conforming role that their limitations become apparent.

The poorly differentiated person may even manage partial separa-

[1] This sequence is similar, though not identical, to what has been described as the "Social Breakdown Syndrome" (Gruenberg, 1967).

tion from his primary objects without disorganizing, provided that he avoids a full or genuine transition from the dependent role. This involves finding a substitute source of support and guidance. Such a replacement may be in the person of another relative, a teacher, an employer, or a spouse. Or it may be a social organization which provides detailed regulation of his life; religious orders and military organizations are notable examples. The words "order" and "organization" connote the structure which they provide for the individual. For some undifferentiated persons strict obsessional routines provide supportive structure. With the help of one or another of these forms of supportive structure, the poorly differentiated person may continue his entire life without disorganization—that is, so long as he does not encounter an inescapable demand that he make a transition to a more autonomous role.

However, he remains vulnerable to disorganization if events force him out of a dependent, heteronomous role. These include events which deprive him of supportive structure. Death, serious illness, or incapacitation of supportive objects obviously are extraordinarily threatening events for the undifferentiated, dependent person. An event which reveals the previously supportive object as weak and itself needful of support and protection may be especially threatening. The dependent person is ill-prepared to change roles and become a helper and protector to his former supporter.

The normal timetable of psychosocial development specifies points at which separation from primary objects and transition to less dependent roles are socially expected. Leaving the parental home for school, a job, or the military service are typical instances of such role transition points, as are marriage and parenthood. For the poorly differentiated person these events present severe challenges and deserve the term "role-transition crises."

Characteristically, the differentiation-impeding family tries to prevent, delay, or avoid role transitions entailing separation. There is strong emphasis on pathological types of closeness and loyalty. Occasionally a member of such a family will comment with candor, "We are just a bunch of babies who can't stand being separated from each other." Even such common and relatively minor separations as those occasioned by brief trips, visits away from home, summer camp, or beginning school constitute major crises. The poorly differentiated person may also experience the threat of losing external support in less direct forms, such as phobias of height, water, school, or strange places.

One schizophrenic girl recalled that her initial episode of disorganizing panic occurred during her first overnight stay away from her mother. Some years later, when she enrolled in school courses designed to prepare her for a job away from home, she suffered temporary panic. Then, as she approached graduation, she disorganized into a full-blown schizophrenic psychosis.

We turn now to consider various other role-transition crises which may cause the poorly differentiated person to undergo schizophrenic disorganization.

Role-Transition Crises of College Students. The college student faces multiple role-transition challenges, especially if going to college represents his first sustained geographical and emotional separation from his family. Among them are greater opportunity and demand that he organize his own activities and study efforts; transition from familial object relationships to enduring extrafamilial relationships; establishment of sexual attachments; possible choice of a mate; and occupational career decisions. Salient in each of these challenges is the task of achieving greater independence and autonomy. The degree of stress contained in a particular challenge will depend upon the degree to which the individual student's personality has differentiated in the sector relevant to meeting this challenge. Accordingly, studies of disturbed college students afford much evidence for our thesis.

The kind of student most vulnerable to disorganization has been described as having been bound in an extraordinarily dependent parental relationship. At college these students were able, with support and gratification of dependency, to achieve a conforming type of adjustment. However, when they attempted to become more independent and to find their own identities, through choice of heterosexual partner and choice of career, their previous adjustment became inadequate (Carlson, 1958).[2]

---

[2] Although Carlson diagnosed the students in her series as "acute confusional state," they appear to have been sufficiently similar to acute schizophrenic patients to bear distinct relevance to our study of circumstances of onset of schizophrenia.

Another description of students who broke down revealed that their adaptation to the role of student had been handicapped by rigid compliance with adult norms of scholarly excellence, moral perfection, and submissiveness, to the neglect of the norms characterizing the intimate, informal life of the peer group. "Their eagerness to conform to the official adult norms no doubt earned for them the rebuffs, ridicule and social rejection of their peers" (Demerath, 1943). These students were poorly prepared to make a transition from "model child" to member of a student peer group.

Immediate "last straw" precipitating events are very likely to include sex role conflict and heterosexual sex role rejection (Langsley, Kammerer, and Pope, 1963). This is especially likely if the student is attempting to shift from a family environment in which sex was taboo to a peer situation in which it is expected and even flaunted. Overt conflicts with parents over this change intensifies the student's anxiety.

Worry over academic performance frequently is entangled with conformity-rebellion conflicts. Failure is not the only threat. Paradoxically, academic success may be equally threatening because it means a step toward independence for which the student feels unready. Similarly, graduation may be intensely feared by the poorly differentiated student, and he may procrastinate by means of indecision and changes of major courses. Making a choice of occupational career may be exceedingly difficult, especially if it involves disagreeing with parental wishes. Sometimes acute disorganization is precipitated by a letter or phone call from the parents criticizing the student (Carlson, 1958).

Students who begin to disorganize under the challenge of transitions to independence and autonomy frequently seek to reestablish parental lines of external direction. By such means as daily letters or phone calls from home they may regain a measure of stability and security.

The issue of independence vs. dependence also shapes the form that schizophrenic disorganization is likely to take in the disturbed student. For instance, the intense wish for external support may be expressed in hallucinations of voices of family members breathing words of comfort and encouragement (Coon, 1961). Also conspicuous are ideas representing extremes of passive victimization and active assertion. On the one hand, the student may feel extremely vulnerable to external influences which accuse, persecute, and threaten to expose him. On the other hand, he may become convinced that he has great personal power and mastery, not only of his personal destiny but of others' lives as well. The prominence of these themes seems clearly to derive from the struggle with role transition from heteronomy to autonomy.

Still further evidence is contained in observations that many of these students are likely to reorganize very quickly when they find a psychotherapist who offers them external support. Of course, in order for this improvement to become durable, considerable headway must be made toward differentiation and autonomy. Otherwise these students remain vulnerable to the need-fear dilemma and to possible disorganization whenever threatened by loss of or separation from their supportive objects.

Military Role Transitions. A move to military service may prove the undoing of the poorly differentiated person. His fundamental lack of autonomous resources and his need-fear of external regulation render him unprepared for this new role which combines removal from his family with the challenge of a very different social situation and role structure. The transition will be especially sharp if he has not previously experienced mass group living, to say nothing of the newness of military rules, discipline, and hazing practices (Bourne, 1967). He may be bewildered by the diverse range of opinions, values, and customs which recruits bring from their widely disparate backgrounds.

Several studies of onset of schizophrenia in military service are relevant to our thesis of role-transition crises. The crisis may occur at any one of the various stages of a military career—recruit, overseas transfer, combat, or discharge.

Study of recruits who became or were first diagnosed as schizophrenic during basic training revealed certain distinctive features of their pre-Army lives. Many had been regarded by their families as simple and naïve, and in need of protection from the outside world. Often they had been noticeably dependent upon their older siblings for establishment of social relationships; that is to say, they had not made friends of their own but had moved into the circle of their siblings' friends (Rowe, 1959). Here we have a clear description of poorly differentiated young men who became disorganized when removed from a supportive external structure and confronted by a situation literally and figuratively unfamiliar.

The behavior of these recruits during basic training was pertinent also to the issue of faulty differentiation. They had difficulty in assuming responsibility for carrying out assigned duties and such routine tasks as care of their gear, and they seemed to wish to be ratified as exceptions to general rules and responsibilities. This was particularly manifest in their complete helplessness when it came to learning new skills, even those as rudimentary as making a bed the "Army way." Their ability to think for themselves was limited; rather, they showed a mechanical, unquestioning reliance upon external directions. For example, several became upset because they were unable to do the number of push-ups reputed to be the minimum required of each recruit. They managed somehow not to notice that none of their squad-mates could meet this reputed requirement either (Erikson and Marlowe, 1959).

A study of psychosis in Navy inductees disclosed a high frequency of homesickness and difficulties in achieving emancipation from home. The investigator observed, "The boy who has never learned to make his own decisions, who is still emotionally dependent on his home and parents, may make a satisfactory military adjustment, but he will suffer in so doing, and his chances of failure are greater than those of the boy who has achieved some degree of freedom from familial bonds" (Will, 1944).

Transfer, especially overseas, may precipitate a role-transition crisis and disorganization later in the military career. One study of the breakdown of soldiers overseas found that a high proportion of these men had been transferred from one duty station to another a few months prior to onset of their psychosis. It appeared that transfer had meant the loss of established supportive relationships; this had, in turn, contributed to poor adaptation to the new duty station. In some instances, however, transfer had been prompted by an already deteriorating work performance. In their new duty posts these men, by their helpless attitudes, evoked responses from their officers that varied in effectiveness according to different combinations of emotional support, control, and limit-setting (Aronson and Polgar, 1962).

These men seem to fit our definition of poorly differentiated persons dependent upon external structure.

Combat is still another phase of the military career in which schizophrenic disorganization may occur. It has been pointed out that the solidarity of the primary group, such as the squad, is an important determinant of the individual soldier's capacity to withstand combat stress. Consequently, the soldier who feels that in one way or another he has lost the support of his primary group is more vulnerable to breakdown (Kardiner and Spiegel, 1947). Studies with similar findings are cited by Retterstøl (1966), who writes, "Eitinger (1955) found that nervous breakdown is more frequent in soldiers who join their units separately than in soldiers who join in a group. Studies on Korean War soldiers seem to indicate that transfer to new and unknown units may precipitate psychosis, 'probably as a result of nonintegration into the unit' (Harris et al. 1955)." The poorly differentiated, nonautonomous soldier would appear to be especially vulnerable to the stress of losing the support derived from primary group membership.

Further evidence of the vulnerability of the poorly differentiated person is contained in the finding that a group of soldiers who broke down during combat had significantly fewer inner resources than a comparison group who did not break down. As a group, those who disorganized were more rigidly controlled and less equipped with inner convictions and morale-strengthening cognitive processes. They were more repressed and conforming, and less likely to gripe and be aware of antagonism toward troops who had it easier than they. They were also relatively unable to comfort themselves or to strengthen their resolve by such thoughts as, "It's important to finish the job so I can get home; I can't let the other men down; we are fighting for something important; I hate the enemy" (Rose, 1956). Clearly, these men were more dependent upon external sources than were their more autonomous fellow-soldiers who better withstood combat stress.

Paradoxically, still another military role-transition crisis for the poorly differentiated person may occur when he is discharged to civilian life. If he has found a modicum of security and direction in the Army, he may feel lost upon leaving it, and schizophrenic disorganization may ensue (Sutherland and Barnes, 1946).

Transition to Marriage Roles. Conspicuous among the adult roles which the poorly differentiated person has difficulty filling successfully is that of marital partner. It is both tempting and fearsomely challenging to him—tempting because it offers a possible substitutive escape from his child role, challenging because he is unprepared to make this a genuine transition.

The mere intention to marry may suffice to upset the poorly differentiated person and to trigger schizophrenic disorganization. He may be unable to choose between his family and his fiancée, fearing that whichever way he chooses he may lose everything. Since he lacks internal resources, the threatened loss of external support is tantamount to the threat of total destruction, especially if his family has overtly or covertly threatened to disown him if he leaves them for another person. For some, breakdown may occur only after marriage has made separation from the parental family an actuality. On the other hand, there are poorly differentiated persons who find in marriage a fairly successful replacement for dependency upon primary objects. This involves a spouse who is willing to permit such a person to continue functioning in a more or less childlike role rather than insisting that he fulfill a more adult role.

Genuine role transition also may be avoided by failing to actually separate from the parental family. Living with the parents, daily visits, frequent phone calls, and the like serve to forestall true movement toward separateness and autonomy or toward genuine integration of a marriage apart from his parents. Vacillation between his parents and his spouse may occur for years, often with literal moves back and forth between parental and marital homes. Should the spouse insist that a final choice be made between parental and marital affiliation, a severe crisis may be precipitated. In their study of a series of married women who became schizophrenic, Sampson and co-workers (1964) described this type of crisis as one of two major precipitating patterns. They termed it "crisis of separation" and observed that it occurred with women to whom marriage had initially appealed as a possible means of breaking away from a symbiotic maternal attachment.

In a study of mother-daughter symbiotic relationships, Lyketsos (1959) found that in each case schizophrenic breakdown occurred when the daughter attempted to separate herself from her mother, whether by establishing a heterosexual relationship, by attempting an independent occupational career, or by being forced by circumstances to live apart from her mother.

A very similar pattern in a man is described with remarkable clarity in a case reported by Weakland and Jackson (1958). This patient experienced enormous difficulty in making choices and decisions which might place him in opposition to persons on whom he depended. Psychosis occurred in a setting of mounting pressure to decide between his wife and his mother. As he began to disintegrate, his inability to make a choice spread even to the simple task of discriminating between different-sized envelopes in his post-office job. His difficulty in choosing between two supportive objects appeared to be associated with desperate fear of abandonment, presumably deriving much of its force from his lack of autonomous resources.

Role Transition to Parenthood. The transition to parenthood is likely to be particularly difficult for the poorly differentiated person because it entails becoming a provider, instead of a recipient, of support, guidance, and protection. It requires relinquishing the primary dependent role in the family to the baby, who now has first claim on that role. This and the confrontation by new role demands may precipitate schizophrenia.

Postpartum psychoses afford excellent examples of this sequence of events. In one study of puerperal breakdown, the typical husband-wife relationship was a pathological, mutually dependent, two-person equilibrium which had been upset by the intrusive birth of a child. The wife had derived a subtle form of support from having a relatively weak, passive, dependent husband who leaned upon her, doubtless thereby partly denying her own dependency. However, this role pattern collapsed when she was faced with her newborn infant's needs for nurturance. She then looked to her husband for help. When he failed to fill the supportive role, the wife disorganized into psychosis (Lomas, 1959).

Similarly, husbands who are poorly differentiated may be plunged into schizophrenic disorganization by the birth of a child or even by the decision to conceive a child, which threatens to deprive the husband of his dependent role. A typical example of this pattern was a marriage in which the weakly autonomous husband depended upon his wife for all manner of counsel and advice, which she offered in nightly talks extending into early morning hours. For several years she enjoyed the role of counselor, which provided her with a sense of competence and denied much of her own insecurity. Gradually, however, she became increasingly frustrated, burdened, and disillusioned with this role. She decided that becoming an actual mother might be a solution. She hoped that a real baby would buffer her from her husband's dependent demands and would encourage, if not force, him to assume a more adult role. After repeated failures to conceive and at least one miscarriage, a boy child was adopted.[3] When the wife channeled the bulk of her attention and energy to caring for the child, the husband's general life adaptation deteriorated markedly and schizophrenic disorganization ensued.

In another marriage of mutually dependent persons, the wife at first enjoyed her husband's dependence. She thought, "I'm all he has —his only source of warmth. He brings out the mother in me; I like to be needed." Gradually this pleasure palled, and she thought, "I'm getting frightened. He is so possessive. He wants me to be responsible for all decisions. I feel trapped." She had day and night dreams of escape and freedom. Therewith she decided that having a child might solve the problem and make her husband more of a man. Reluctantly he agreed to attempt pregnancy. Within days thereafter he became acutely schizophrenic, with a pronounced delusional fear that his air supply was about to be shut off.

Loss of Parent Role. Just as the attempted transition to the parent role can precipitate schizophrenia, the threatened or actual loss of this role may provoke disorganization of the undifferentiated person. This danger is greatest in persons for whom the parental role has provided covert fulfillment of a need to be needed, or perhaps even nurtured by the child—a need that the parents have concurrently denied by emphasizing the child's dependence. These persons also are likely to have clung to the role of parent in order to mask fears of inability to fill other adult roles.

Witness, for example, the mother whose only adult role is that of mother, and who desperately needs confirmatory validation in that role. As long as the child is small, dependent, and dutifully accepting

---

[3] Repeated miscarriages, as well as deferral of pregnancy with multiform rationalizations, are frequent in this type of marriage.

of the reciprocal role, he buttresses his mother's defensive system, confirms her self-definition as a good mother, and counterbalances her sense of failure to achieve other roles.

However, as the child's developmental timetable opens up new roles to him in school and peer relationships, he no longer is so confirming of his mother. On the contrary, instead of providing proof of her worth and goodness, he may actively and defiantly challenge her. The mother, threatened by possible loss of her one, though only half-way, successful role, may disorganize into schizophrenia.

Later life developments such as children marrying and moving away, loss of occupational role, and death of spouse and friends may serve greatly to restrict a person's role opportunities and to precipitate schizophrenic disorganization.

Loss of role and subsequent disorganization may also occur in association with conditions of social isolation or disarticulation.

Role Loss and Social Disarticulation

Social structure is important not only to the development of individual psychic structure but also to its maintenance, as natural and contrived isolation experiences have demonstrated. Removal from familiar surroundings or drastic change of one's place in the social structure can be exceedingly stressful.

In this regard the thoughts of William James (1890) are very cogent:

> Sudden alterations in outward fortune often produce such a change in the empirical *me* as almost to amount to a pathological disturbance of self-consciousness. When a poor man draws the big prize in a lottery, or unexpectedly inherits an estate; when a man high in fame is publicly disgraced, a millionaire becomes a pauper, or a loving husband and father sees his family perish at one fell swoop, there is temporarily such a rupture between all past habits, whether of an active or a passive kind, and the exigencies and possibilities of the new situation, that the individual may find no medium of continuity or association to carry him over from the one phase to the other of his life. Under these conditions mental derangement is no unfrequent result.

The effects of removal from customary social contexts may become suddenly and dramatically apparent, as in the onset of acute psychosis during prolonged train or air travel (Singh, 1961; Flinn,

Gaarder, and Smith, 1959). Fundamentally similar is the onset of acute schizophrenia in the setting of a convention in a strange city. Clinical observations of such cases have emphasized the disorganizing effect of the loss of customary social reinforcement of superego and ego controls in the carnival atmosphere away from home (Lefever, 1962).

Several other lines of evidence concerning the effects of isolation or changed surroundings are pertinent to our thesis. Epidemiological studies suggest links between incidence of schizophrenia and social isolation, as do studies of schizophrenia in emigrants, refugees, and prisoners of war.

Concerning social isolation and schizophrenia, one finding is that the incidence of schizophrenia tends to be highest in the center of a city and to diminish progressively in more peripheral and suburban zones (Faris and Dunham, 1939). Alternative explanations of these findings have been advanced. The "stress" explanation argues that the social disorganization in the center of the city causes a higher incidence of schizophrenia. The "drift" explanation argues that already disturbed individuals, by drifting toward the slum and flophouse districts, account for the higher incidence in the center of the city.

Other studies have shown positive correlation of the incidence of schizophrenia with the proportion of persons living alone in a geographic zone (Jaco, 1954; Hare, 1956; Gerard and Houston, 1953).

It is still a moot question whether social isolation is a cause or effect of schizophrenic disorganization. Perhaps the most that can definitely be said is that at the time of his hospitalization the schizophrenic person is likely to be suffering a lack of social structural support. Whether this association is causal, concomitant, or incidental is uncertain (Kohn and Clausen, 1955; Kohn, 1967).

Studies of the incidence of schizophrenia among emigrants and refugees are similarly difficult to evaluate, but contain findings distinctly relevant to the difficulties encountered by the undifferentiated person when he is deprived of customary social structure and confronted by new social expectations and demands, along with the isolating barrier of an unfamiliar language (Krystal and Petty, 1963; Retterstøl, 1966; Tyhurst, 1951).

Ødegaard's classic study (1932) revealed a substantially higher incidence of schizophrenia among a group of emigrants from Norway to Minnesota than among the stay-at-home Norwegian population or among the American population in Minnesota for the same time period. An unanswered question is the degree to which a tendency for misfits to emigrate affected these findings.

There also is evidence of a connection between serious mental disorder and geographic mobility within the same country (Tietze, Lemkau, and Cooper, 1942; Leacock, 1957).

In another study of migrants in New York State in 1940, a higher incidence of schizophrenia was found among both out-of-state born and foreign-born migrants than among New York-born residents. In addition, the incidence among recent migrants was higher than among earlier migrants (Malzburg and Lee, 1956). An earlier study found that out-of-state migrants to California had much higher rates of mental hospital admission than did long-established residents of the state (Rosanoff, Handy, and Plesset, 1915).

To be a minority group member living apart from one's subculture appears especially stressful. In Chicago, Faris and Dunham (1939) found the highest incidence of mental disorder among the foreign-born persons living in areas not inhabited predominantly by persons of their own ethnic background. Similarly, Schwartz and Mintz (1963) discovered in Boston that Italian-Americans living in predominantly non-Italian neighborhoods had distinctly higher rates of schizophrenia than those living in predominantly Italian neighborhoods. Lemert (1948) found in rural Michigan that the first admission rate to mental hospitals of the native-born children of foreign-born or mixed foreign-native-born parentage was higher than the admission rates for either the native-born or foreign-born groups in the same region. It appeared that the children were attempting more of a shift to new cultural ways than had their parents.

Refugees face problems closely resembling those with which emigrants must contend, and there is evidence that these problems may precipitate schizophrenia. Kino (1951) studied Poles evacuated to England during World War II. Several of these refugees adapted satisfactorily only so long as they lived in groups with fellow Poles, but became acutely psychotic when moved to jobs which isolated them from compatriots. Those who became schizophrenic had limited ability to communicate in English. In addition, they were hypersensitive and low in self-reliance, both qualities typical of poorly differentiated persons. In the initial phases of psychosis several of them sought a protective woman, one in an actual affair with an older woman, and another delusionally with the Virgin Mary. Koranyi et al. (1963) made similar observations in their studies of Hungarian refugees, as did Eitinger (1960) in Norway and Pedersen (1946) in Sweden.

Cumulatively, these studies of the effects of social dislocation and disarticulation appear to lend considerable weight to our thesis that role transitions and drastic changes of environment often contribute to the onset of schizophrenia, particularly in poorly differentiated persons who are excessively dependent on and vulnerable to the influence of their social contexts.

Role Transitions and Attempted Growth

Much of the preceding discussion has perhaps suggested that role transitions are imposed upon a person from without. Frequently this may be the case, especially since each society expects its members to follow culturally prescribed developmental schedules that specify the ages at which particular role transitions should occur. At the same time, however, role transitions often involve the individual's active, assertive attempts at change and growth. Efforts to change from old to new roles and behavior patterns—from dependence to independence, from heteronomy to autonomy, from accommodation to self-assertion, and from intra- to extrafamilial relationships—all require individual choice and initiative. The success or failure of such attempted growth depends not only on how well equipped the person is to make the transition but also on whether his environment facilitates or hinders his efforts. Since the poorly differentiated person is not adequately prepared for genuine transitions and usually is imbedded in a social context which discourages them, his growth attempts may founder and lead to his disorganization. In addition, severe inner conflict about attempted change may contribute to his becoming deeply upset. Still further, growth under these stringent circumstances may necessitate a phase of disorganization as part of the process of breaking down old patterns and assembling new ones (Dabrowski, 1964).

This view of positive thrusts toward growth and change occasioning turmoil is inherent in Erikson's delineation of "identity crises" (1959).

Others have advanced similar formulations of schizophrenic phenomena. French and Kasanin (1941) presented two case histories to illustrate their belief that acute schizophrenia may be a transitional and constructive episode in the course of a person's changing from old to new methods of adjustment. Their patients' psychotic thoughts reflected intense struggles to free themselves from their families and to achieve heterosexual relationships. Similar observations have been reported by still others (Jackson and Watzlawick, 1963; Anonymous, 1955).

Boisen (1947) described a series of patients for whom the onset of schizophrenia was integrally associated with desperate attempts to change major life roles and to take developmental steps in a forward direction. The typical sequence reported by these patients was a deep sense of personal failure and guilt over not having achieved a satisfactory life role, followed by a sudden conception of a new social role, and then by schizophrenic disorganization. Frequently the patient was convinced that his new social role had been given him by an outside agency and that he was directed by superhuman cosmic authority with which he identified and had close contact. The wish for such supplies from a powerful outside source is, of course, characteristic of poorly differentiated persons.

Another description of role-transition struggle and acute schizophrenia is that of a Guatemalan girl who protested and tried to evade the traditional feminine role in a society which afforded few, if any, alternative roles (Paul, 1953).

The breakdown of pseudotransitions may precipitate schizophrenia. An example of this was the case of a young woman who, though she married and bore children, achieved only a pseudoseparation from her father. Her husband was a disappointing replacement, and her efforts to move to a role in a higher social class were frustrated. When her father, to whom she was still deeply attached, fell ill, this woman broke down in schizophrenic disorganization, with a central delusion that she was married to a doctor who had been a previous autistic love object. Apparently he symbolized her yearned-for father-replacement and the fulfillment of her ambitions for social role change (Myers and Roberts, 1954).

Social mobility aspirations are especially likely to lead to role-transition crises for the poorly differentiated person if he has been subjected to parental contradictions, such as the expectation on the one hand that he remain dependent, but on the other that he better his and the family's social status (Lu, 1961).

Similar contradictory role pressures were found to confront the eldest sons of Japanese families dependent upon small family businesses for their livelihood (Caudill, 1964). Closely attached to and relatively undifferentiated from their mothers, these sons were at the same time expected to step into the traditional role of family leader in the event of their fathers' incapacitation or death. These eldest sons suffered a higher incidence of schizophrenia than the eldest sons of salaried and wage-earning families, who exterted distinctly less pressure upon the eldest son to assume the traditional role of family leadership.

ONSET OF SCHIZOPHRENIA AND FAULTY INTEGRATION

The poorly integrated person lacks cohesion and harmony within and among his subsystems of personality. He employs excessive all-or-none denial and repression to exclude from consciousness those areas of experience and those feelings, thoughts, and impulses that do not fit his preferred construct of reality. His rigid control of cognition and action cramps his behavioral repertoire and restricts the range of social situations to which he can adapt.

Departure from fixed behavioral routines and familiar social contexts is likely to confront him with events that he cannot readily assimilate because they do not fit his schemata for organizing his experience. This threatens to disrupt his tenuous inner balances by arousing unintegrated, split-off subsystems of thought, feeling, and action.

A spiraling chain reaction of derepression, disequilibrium, and disorganization is likely to ensue. Failure of integration involves failure to develop flexible, compromise means of expression and control of impulses and affects. Hence when the poorly integrated person's rigid controls are abrogated, he is flooded by unmanageable impulses and feelings in raw, unattenuated form. These include all manner of aggressive and sexual impulses for which he has inadequate controls. Overwhelming panic and gross disorganization may follow.

The situations most likely to precipitate this sequence of derepression, disequilibrium, abrogation of controls, and disorganization are those which threaten to arouse previously dissociated personality subsystems or to weaken old control systems, or which require change to new control systems.

Change or Loss of External Structure

Moves away from the family matrix and major role transitions are stressful and potentially disruptive for the poorly integrated person. They confront him with new and difficult-to-integrate experiences. Feelings and impulses that were taboo in the family setting are *de rigueur* in the new social settings. This is especially likely in connection with expressions of intimacy, sexuality, self-assertion, and aggression.

For example, a youth from a family in which sex is proscribed may be greatly disconcerted to discover in college or military service that sexual talk and activity are the rule, and that not to engage in them risks social ostracism.

The same applies to shifts in the valuation of other forms of self-expression and self-assertion. Often the poorly integrated person is the product of a family that discouraged him from thinking for himself, expressing his opinions, choosing his interests and companions, and making important life career decisions, especially if such choices were in opposition to parental dictates. Outside the family he discovers that these forbidden traits are expected of him if he is to gain approval. His previously acceptable dependence and passivity are now scorned, and in their stead bold assertiveness is positively valued.

Any attempt to integrate these new values will require drastic changes of control systems, for which the poorly integrated person is ill-prepared. Not only are his controls rigid but they have depended upon continuous external reinforcement for their maintenance. Removal from familiar contexts means loss of this reinforcement and the danger that his controls will collapse. This is in contrast to a person with more autonomous controls. Further, the all-or-none principle has permitted him little room for experimenting with partial or compromise expression of basic impulses. Moreover, if he suddenly attempts to behave differently, he violates not only parental dictates but his own too-rigid superego. The feared loss of approval of supportive objects may become actuality if his changed behavior is distressing and unacceptable to those objects. The resultant anxiety, guilt, and uncertainty can very easily spiral into confusion and panic.

Gradual Overburdening of Defense Systems

The disruption of inner balance and control is not necessarily always precipitated by a major social transition or a singular life event. It may be the result of a gradual accumulation of events which overburden and finally collapse a defense system. For example, a person who has employed a masochistic life-style to buttress denial of sadistic aggression in himself may eventually accumulate such a burden of suffering and injustice at the hands of others that uncontrollable rage and murderous impulses erupt in him. This untoward development threatens the core of his defensive system—denial of his aggressive urges—and may plunge him into disintegration and panic. The following case excerpt illustrates such a sequence:

A young wife and mother had been inculcated with extremely rigid definitions of what was proper for her to think, feel, and do. Anger was strictly excluded from these definitions. It became increasingly difficult for her to maintain this exclusion when she was burdened with the care of several small children. To her great dismay, they evoked in her not pure benevolence, but mounting frustration and annoyance. This was compounded by her husband's failure to give her practical assistance and emotional support. Moreover, her children failed to abide by her definitions of properness; in their interaction with her and with each other outbursts of anger were frequent. Under this cumulative pressure her long-repressed rage finally erupted and she threw one of the children down the stairway. Thereupon she abruptly disintegrated into schizophrenic panic. Her psychotic restitutional efforts took the form of a delusion that she and the local minister were soon to be married. This belief, accompanied by a sense of being totally infused with love, served to deny and rerepress much of her bitterness and rage.

A similar cumulative overburdening of a defense system may occur in a person devoted to a career of good deeds and reparative actions. If his good deeds come to be resented and rejected by the intended recipients, or if a good deed inadvertently results in serious harm to another person, his whole personality structure may come crashing down. A typical instance of this was a nurse whose choice of career

had been heavily determined by defensive denial of feelings of deprivation and envy. Upon the unexpected death of one of her patients,
with the very remote possibility that she had not correctly carried out
all treatment orders, the nurse developed a fear of poisoning all the
patients under her care and disorganized into acute psychosis.

Intimacy as Precipitant of Disintegration

Moves toward intimacy frequently precipitate disorganization in
the poorly integrated person who has habitually maintained defensive
distance between himself and others. For one thing, lessening of this
distance is likely to trigger sudden derepression of unintegrated
sexual impulses.

Since Freud's formulation of the Schreber case (1911), the association of certain types of schizophrenia with derepressed homosexual
urges has been well established. The phenomenon of "homosexual
panic" ushering in certain types of schizophrenia is also well known.

Heterosexual urges may have an equally disorganizing effect. Onset
of schizophrenia in a young man sometimes is preceded by dreams
of sexual relations with women, initially unidentified but subsequently
emerging clearly as his mother. A frankly incestuous dream may
drive him to attempt suicide and then to disorganize into schizophrenia
(Sullivan, 1962).

In addition to its emergence in the form of forbidden sexual impulses, the urge for greater intimacy may gain less direct expression
in the form of strange oral cravings, compulsions to acquire substitute
objects, and unaccountable impulses to join some social organization.
The emergence of these unfamiliar behavior patterns is likely to be
accompanied by a sense of depersonalization. The thoughts, "I am
not myself; I am possessed by some alien power; I am losing control
of myself," are frequent, and disorganization may follow if the person
is unable to integrate these new aspects of himself.

The person may try to account for and ward off the unacceptable
ideas, feelings, and impulses by delusionally attributing them to some
external source, in the fashion classically described by Tausk (1919)
in his paper "On the Origin of the Influencing Machine." The accompanying terrible sense of vulnerability to external influence is testi-
mony that the breakdown of tenuous integration and internal control
gives rise to a wish-fear of powerful external control. This wish-fear

is further accentuated by dedifferentiation and loss of self-other boundaries.

Situations Mobilizing Unintegrated Identifications

Another threat to the poorly integrated person is the arousal of unacceptable feelings and thoughts associated with identifications that he has been unable to integrate. Intense ambivalence toward early objects may have prevented his identifying with them, or identification may have been blocked by the person's fear that it would entail loss of self. Poorly differentiated persons, in particular, see frighteningly little distinction between resembling another person and becoming that person (Greenson, 1954).

Situations that tend to mobilize unintegrated identifications are threatening to the poorly integrated person. Important role transitions, like marriage, occupational career decisions, and parenthood, may have this effect. Stepping into a role previously associated with a parent may force sudden awareness of long-denied part-similarities to that parent. This was the case in a series of women who became schizophrenic in connection with crises of identification with their mothers. They had attempted to quell extreme ambivalence toward their mothers by denying any similarities to them and by repressing memories of traumatic experiences with them (Sampson, Messinger, and Towne, 1964). A similar pattern of disorganization following derepression of an unintegrated maternal identification also has been observed in at least one study of postpartum psychoses (Zilboorg, 1929).

The phenomenon of "anniversary reactions" which usher in schizophrenia also appears related to mobilization of warded-off identifications as well as to the painful reliving of old object losses. An "anniversary reaction" may occur as a patient reaches the age a parent was at death or when his child reaches the age he was when the parent died (Hilgard and Newman, 1959, 1963). In either event the disorganizing effect seems to stem from the arousal of poorly integrated constellations of feelings.

"Last Straw" Precipitants of Disorganization

Integration may be so tenuous that a seemingly insignificant event may precipitate derepression and disorganization. In a study of psychogenic precipitation of schizophrenia, Kant (1942) described a young woman, severely sexually repressed, who became overtly psychotic after being enlightened about the actual meaning of some vulgar jokes she had heard without initial understanding.

The attribution of great significance to a seemingly minor event is the result of weak control and faulty integration of dangerous feelings and impulses. This precarious combination enables the feelings and impulses, in effect, to seize upon otherwise irrelevant events in the environment, in the manner termed by Sullivan "extravasation of meaning" (Sullivan, 1956). A general collapse of the capacity to select relevant from irrelevant stimuli may result. Thus, a person struggling to repress and otherwise control sexual urges may quite suddenly begin to perceive sexual meaning in even the most adventitious gestures of other persons, in the arrangement of the furniture, or in the food he is served.

Seemingly trivial events often derive much disintegrative impact from their symbolic meaning to the poorly integrated person. Only at the superficial, conventional symbolic level are they trivial. A youth suffering serious masturbation conflict was thrown into a psychotic panic when informed that he needed a minor abdominal operation (Kant, 1942). After his temperature had been taken rectally, a man hospitalized for a physical illness developed an acute paranoid psychosis with delusions of homosexual assault. Desperately homesick for the old country, an immigrant woman, while listening to a hymn, took the words, "Come, let us go," as a divine command to leave her marital home and return to the home of her childhood; thereupon she became acutely disorganized (MacCurdy, 1915). In these examples a seemingly incidental event, by dint of linkage to underlying preoccupations, forced a breach in barriers of repression and denial. This, in turn, released a flood of hitherto unconscious impulses, an ever-present danger for persons who have failed to integrate major sectors of experience.

SUMMARY

In this discussion of the circumstances of onset of schizophrenia our aim has been to further clarify how faults in differentiation and integration render a person vulnerable to schizophrenic disorganization under specific conditions.

The poorly differentiated person lacks stable, relatively autonomous inner structure and is peculiarly dependent upon and easily influenced by external structure. Accordingly, if he loses customary supportive structure or is confronted by unfamiliar adaptational demands, he is liable to disorganize. Normal social role transitions are likely to constitute crises for him and may lead to schizophrenic disorganization. To illustrate this phenomenon, we presented evidence of the disorganizing potential of transitions to the roles of college student, soldier, spouse, and parent.

We also discussed precipitation of disorganization by loss of familiar external structure and role opportunities. The apparent linkage between social isolation and incidence of schizophrenia was noted, and studies of the effects of social dislocation among migrants, refugees, and prisoners were reviewed.

The onset of certain types of schizophrenia may involve struggles toward personal growth and attempts to change from old to new behavior patterns and roles. Conflict about such attempts may be accentuated by contradictory role pressures exerted by family and social milieu.

The poorly integrated person tends to exclude from consciousness major areas of experience and to rely upon rigid systems of behavioral and cognitive control. This renders him vulnerable to disorganization in situations that inescapably confront him with experience that he cannot readily assimilate or that abrogate his rigid, brittle control systems. A spiral of derepression, disequilibrium, and disorganization may be triggered by role transitions, loss of external structure, and overburdening of defense systems. Situations of increased intimacy are particularly threatening if he has relied heavily upon defensive interpersonal distance. The arousal of sexual impulses and other forbidden urges can be very threatening to him, and may be accompanied by depersonalization and derealization experiences en route to further disintegration. The mobilization of unintegrated partial identifications is another precipitant of disorganization in the poorly integrated person.

When integration is extremely tenuous, disorganization may be triggered by seemingly trivial events that take on special symbolic meanings linking them to underlying, previously dissociated preoccupations.

BIBLIOGRAPHY

Anonymous (1955), An Autobiography of a Schizophrenic Experience. *J. Abnorm. and Soc. Psychol., 51*:677-689.

Aronson, J. & Polgar, S. (1962), Pathogenic Relationships in Schizophrenia. *Amer. J. Psychiat., 119*:222-227.

Benedict, R. (1938), Continuities and Discontinuities in Cultural Conditioning. *Psychiat., 1*:161-167.

Boisen, A. T. (1947), Onset in Acute Schizophrenia. *Psychiat., 10*:159-166.

Bourne, P. G. (1967), Some Observations on the Psychosocial Phenomena Seen in Basic Training. *Psychiat., 30*:187-196.

Carlson, H. B. (1958), Characteristics of an Acute Confusional State in College Students. *Amer. J. Psychiat., 114*:900-909.

Caudill, W. (1964), Sibling Rank and Style of Life Among Japanese Psychiatric Patients. Supplement to May issue of *Psychiatrica et Neurologia Japonica.*

Coon, G. P. (1961), Acute Psychosis, Depression, and Elation. In: *Emotional Problems of the Student,* ed. G. B. Blaine, Jr. and C. C. McArthur. New York: Appleton-Century-Crofts.

Dabrowski, K. (1964), *Positive Disintegration.* Boston: Little Brown.

Davis, K. (1938), Mental Hygiene and the Class Structure. *Psychiat., 1*:55-65.

Demerath, N. J. (1943), Adolescent Status Demands and the Student Experiences of Twenty Schizophrenics. *Amer. Sociolog. Rev., 8*:513-518.

Eitinger, L. (1955), Militaerlivets Innflytelse pa unge norske Menns psykiske Liv. En klinisk og socialpsykiatrisk Undersokelse, Oslo.

———— (1960), The Symptomatology of Mental Disease Among Refugees in Norway. *J. Ment. Sci., 106*:947-966.

Erikson, E. H. (1959), Identity and the Life Cycle. *Psycholog. Issues,* Monograph 1. New York: International Universities Press.

Erikson, K. T. & Marlowe, D. H. (1959), The Schizophrenic in Basic Training. In: *The Symptom as Communication in Schizophrenia,* ed. K. L. Artiss. New York: Grune & Stratton.

Faris, R. E. L. & Dunham, H. W. (1939), *Mental Disorders in Urban Areas.* Chicago: University of Chicago Press.

Flinn, D. E.; Gaarder, K. R.; & Smith, D. C. (1959), Acute Psychotic Reactions Occurring During Travel. *U. S. Armed Forces Med. J., 10*:524-531.

French, T. M. & Kasanin, J. (1941), A Psychodynamic Study of the Recovery of Two Schizophrenic Cases. *Psychoanal. Quart., 10*:1-22.

Freud, S. (1911), Psycho-analytic Notes on an Autobiographical Account of a Case of Paranoia. *Standard Edition, 12*:9-82. London: Hogarth Press, 1958.

Gerard, D. L. & Houston, L. G. (1953), Family Setting and the Social Ecology of Schizophrenia. *Psychiat. Quart., 27*:90-101.

Greenson, R. R. (1954), The Struggle Against Identification. *J. Amer. Psychoanal. Assn., 2*:200-217.

Gruenberg, E. M. (1967), The Social Breakdown Syndrome—Some Origins. *Amer. J. Psychiat., 123*:1481-1489.

Hare, E. H. (1956), Mental Illness and Social Conditions in Bristol. *J. Ment. Sci., 102*:349-357.

Harris, F. G., Meyer, J., & Becker, H. A. (1955), Experiences in the Study of

Combat in the Korean War. I. Report on Psychiatric and Psychological Data. Research report. Walter Reed Army Institute of Research. Walter Reed Army Medical Center, Washington, D. C.

Hilgard, J. R. & Newman, M. F. (1959), Anniversaries in Mental Illness. *Psychiat., 22*:113-121.

—— (1963), Parental Loss by Death in Childhood as an Etiological Factor Among Schizophrenic and Alcoholic Patients Compared with a Non-patient Community Sample. *J. of Nerv. and Ment. Dis., 137*:14-28.

Jackson, D. D. & Watzlawick, P. (1963), The Acute Psychosis as a Manifestation of Growth Experience. In: *Acute Psychotic Reaction,* ed. W. M. Mendel and L. J. Epstein. Psychiatric Research Reports of the American Psychiatric Association, No. 16.

Jaco, E. G. (1954), The Social Isolation Hypothesis and Schizophrenia. *Amer. Sociolog. Rev., 19*:567-577.

James, W. (1890), *The Principles of Psychology.* New York: Dover Publications, 1950.

Kant, O. (1942), The Problem of Psychogenic Precipitation in Schizophrenia. *Psychiat. Quart., 16*:341-350.

Kardiner, A. & Spiegel, H. (1947), *War Stress and Neurotic Illness.* New York: Hoeber.

Kino, F. F. (1951), Aliens' Paranoid Reaction. *J. Ment. Sci., 97*:589-594.

Kohn, M. L. (1967), Social Class and Schizophrenia: A Critical Review. Presented to the F. F. R. P. Conference on the Transmission of Schizophrenia, San Juan, Puerto Rico.

—— & Clausen, J. A. (1955), Social Isolation and Schizophrenia. *Amer. Sociolog. Rev., 20*:265-273.

Koranyi, E. K., Kerenyi, A. B., & Sarwer-Foner, G. J. (1963), Adaptive Difficulties of Some Hungarian Immigrants. IV. The Process of Adaptation and Acculturation. *Comprehen. Psychiat., 4*:47-57.

Krystal, H. & Petty, T. A. (1963), The Dynamics of the Adjustment to Migration. *Psychiat. Quart.,* Supplement *37*:119-133.

Langsley, P. R., Kammerer, B., & Pope, S. (1963), Acute Psychosis in a College Population. In: *Acute Psychotic Reaction,* ed. W. M. Mendel and L. J. Epstein. Psychiatric Research Reports of the American Psychiatric Association, No. 16.

Leacock, E. (1957), Three Social Variables and the Occurrence of Mental Disorder. In: *Explorations in Social Psychiatry,* ed. A. H. Leighton, J. A. Clausen, and R. N. Wilson. New York: Basic Books.

Lefever, H., Jr. (1962), personal communication.

Lemert, E. (1948), An Exploratory Study of Mental Disorders in a Rural Problem Area. *Rural Sociol., 13*:58.

Lomas, P. E. S. (1959), The Husband-Wife Relationship in Cases of Puerperal Breakdown. *Brit. J. Med. Psychol., 32*:117-123.

Lu, Y. (1961), Mother-Child Role Relations in Schizophrenia: A Comparison of Schizophrenic Patients with Nonschizophrenic Siblings. *Psychiat., 24*:133-142.

Lyketsos, G. (1959), On the Formation of Mother-Daughter Symbiotic Relationship Patterns in Schizophrenia. *Psychiat., 22*:161-166.

MacCurdy, J. T. (1915), A Psychological Feature of the Precipitating Causes in the Psychoses and Its Relation to Art. In: *Studies in Abnormal Psychology,* Series V, 297-320. Boston: Badger.

Malzburg, B. & Lee, E. S. (1956), *Migration and Mental Disease.* New York: Social Science Research Council.

Myers, J. G. & Roberts, B. H. (1954), A Sociological-Psychiatric Case Study of Schizophrenia. *Sociol. and Soc. Res., 39*:11-17.

Ødegaard, Ø. (1932), Emigration and Insanity: A Study of Mental Disease Among the Norwegian-born Population of Minnesota. *Acta Psychiatrica et Neurologica,* Supplement IV. Copenhagen: Levin and Munksgaard.

Paul, B. D. (1953), Mental Disorder and Self-regulating Processes in Culture —A Guatemalan Illustration. In: *Interrelations Between the Social Environment and Psychiatric Disorders.* New York: Milbank Memorial Fund.

Pedersen, S. (1946), Psychopathological Reactions to Extreme Social Displacements (Refugee Neuroses). *Psychoanal. Rev., 36*:344-354.

Retterstøl, N. (1966), *Paranoid and Paranoiac Psychoses.* Springfield, Ill.: Charles C Thomas.

Rosanoff, A. J., Handy, L. M., & Plesset, I. R. (1915), Some Neglected Phases of Immigration in Relation to Insanity. *Amer. J. Psychiat., 72*:45-48.

Rose, A. M. (1956), Neuropsychiatric Breakdown in Combat. *Psychiat., 19*:87-94.

Rowe, R. H. (1959), The Symptom in Past History. In: *The Symptom as Communication in Schizophrenia,* ed. K. L. Artiss. New York: Grune & Stratton.

Sampson, H., Messinger, S. L., & Towne, R. D. (1964), *Schizophrenic Women: Studies in Marital Crisis.* New York: Atherton Press.

Schwartz, D. T. & Mintz, N. L. (1963), Ecology and Psychosis Among Italians in 27 Boston Communities. *Soc. Probl., 10*:371-374.

Singh, H. (1961), A Case of Psychosis Precipitated by Confinement in Long Distance Travel by Train. *Amer. J. Psychiat., 117*:936-937.

Sullivan, H. S. (1956), *Clinical Studies in Psychiatry.* New York: Norton.

——— (1962), Cultural Stress and Adolescent Crisis. In: *Schizophrenia as a Human Process.* New York: Norton.

Sutherland, G. F. & Barnes, M. E. (1946), "Furlough" Psychosis. *Amer. J. Psychiat., 102*:670-673.

Tausk, V. (1919), On the Origin of the "Influencing Machine" in Schizophrenia. In: *The Psychoanalytic Reader,* ed. R. Fliess. New York: International Universities Press, 1948.

Tietze, C., Lemkau, P., & Cooper, M. (1942), Personality Disorder and Spatial Mobility. *Amer. J. Sociol., 48*:29-39.

Tyhurst, L. (1951), Displacement and Migration. A Study in Social Psychiatry. *Amer. J. Psychiat., 107*:561-568.

Weakland, J. H. & Jackson, D. D. (1958), Patient and Therapist Observations on the Circumstances of a Schizophrenic Episode. *A. M. A. Arch. Neurol. and Psychiat., 79*:554-574.

Will, O. A., Jr. (1944), Psychoses in Naval Inductees with Less than Fifteen Days' Active Duty. *U.S. Naval Med. Bull., 43*:909-921.

Zilboorg, G. (1929), The Dynamics of Schizophrenic Reactions Related to Pregnancy and Childbirth. *Amer. J. Psychiat., 8*:733.

V

CONDITIONS AFFECTING
THE DEVELOPMENT
OF RELATIONSHIPS

Arthur I. Gladstone

The purpose of this chapter is to describe some of the factors that affected the formation of patient-staff relationships on Third Floor. This will provide a background for the examination of specific relationships and particular features of relationships in later chapters. We shall begin by considering processes which occur in the formation of all relationships, then discuss briefly how the special characteristics of schizophrenic patients are likely to affect these processes, describe the social conditions on Third Floor which influenced the formation of relationships, and finally report on the findings of our questionnaire study which depicted the kinds of relationship that most commonly resulted under these conditions.

In common usage, "relationship" refers to a particular kind of inter-action between two people, one which goes on over a longer period of time or is more significant to the participants than other personal interactions. In this book we talk of "relationship" whenever two people interact repeatedly, even if the interactions are perfunctory and the partners hold little significance for one another. We decided on this inclusive approach because one of our purposes was to explore the effect and significance of various kinds of relationships and we did not want to prejudge this by excluding certain kinds of interaction at the beginning. Furthermore, the significance of a relationship is a matter of degree, not an either-or question, so that a distinction between "significant" and "nonsignificant" relationships requires an arbitrary boundary until some natural one can be found.

The primary requirement for the formation of a relationship is that there be some contact between two individuals, so that there is the opportunity for interaction. Contact is determined by two factors: *propinquity* and *approach-avoidance behavior*. Propinquity makes encounters between people likely or necessary. The person who lives in a mental hospital ward has the opportunity for repeated encounters with other patients and with staff members; some of these encounters will be forced on him. Approach-avoidance behavior determines how much use will be made of the opportunity for interaction. For contact to occur, one person must approach the other and the other must either approach also or, at least, not avoid effectively. In addition to locomotion, approach behavior includes orienting movements (addressing oneself to the other), and verbal and gestural expressions of interest in and readiness for interaction. Likewise, avoidance behavior includes, in addition to locomotion, movements of orienting away from the other (turning the head, etc.) and expressions of disinterest in and refusal of interaction.

When two people have come into contact, there is *communication* between them. Two fundamental questions that can be asked about any communication process are: What is it about? (In other words, what is the content of the messages?) How effective is it? (In other words, how well do the participants express themselves and how well do they understand each other?) The second question is, of course, particularly crucial when one of the partners is a schizophrenic patient who is likely to have difficulty both in expressing himself clearly in commonly accepted terms and in understanding the communications of others. However, both questions are important in all relationships. How satisfied the partners are with the content and effectiveness of their communications will help determine how interested they are in maintaining and extending their interaction.

An important aspect of content is communication about personal matters. This shows trust and interest in the partner and may be an invitation to further development of the relationship. The amount and kind of personal communication indicates the level of intimacy which a relationship has reached.

A related aspect of communication content concerns the *feelings expressed,* especially feelings about the partner. The expression of feelings may invite or discourage further interaction and may also encourage or discourage particular kinds of behavior by the partner. (This does not necessarily mean that feelings are expressed with the conscious intention of influencing the partner.)

Many techniques may be used in the deliberate attempt to *influence or control* the behavior of the partner (coaxing, reasoning, threats, physical force, etc.). The kinds of techniques used by each partner, their effectiveness, the extent to which one partner comes to dominate the other, and the extent to which there is friction or smoothness in making decisions and reaching agreement will certainly affect the satis-factoriness of the relationship for each partner and the course of its development.

The *kinds of activities* which the partners engage in provide another indicator of the character of the relationship and determinant of its satisfactoriness. In the mental hospital it is appropriate to distinguish between activities resulting from hospital routines and procedures, which are more-or-less imposed on a patient, and those activities which the patient himself initiates or actively engages in.

The foregoing commonsense analysis of the kinds of behavior which occur in the development of any relationship provided the basis for the Relationship Questionnaire which we devised to collect data on the relationships between patients and staff members. (A detailed account of the construction and contents of this questionnaire is provided in the Appendix.) For each aspect of relationship behavior mentioned above (approach-avoidance, communication effectiveness, personal communication, expression of feelings, influence and control attempts, and joint activities), there were several questions, each concerning a particular type or manifestation of the behavior. (We did not ask about propinquity on our questionnaire because this dimension applied to all the people studied, as will be described later in the present chapter.) This classification of the aspects of behavior found in interpersonal relationships was not intended to be either exhaustive or precise. However, we believe it includes the kinds of behavior which are essential in the development of all relationships and is specific enough for our purposes. Two of these aspects, expression of feelings and control attempts, seem to be generally recognized as significant in all interpersonal interaction. For example, Foa (1961) cites five sets of factor analytic studies of interpersonal behavior "by various investigators and dealing with different types of groups and ratings," in each of which two principal dimensions were found to be Dominance-Submission and Love-Hostility. Each of the other aspects of relationship behavior has been discussed by previous writers and most of them have been studied in various social settings.

The common patterns of schizophrenic interpersonal behavior have already been described in detail (in Chapter II). Here it may suffice to remind the reader of these patterns and mention briefly some of their effects on the formation of relationships.

The patient who engages in object-clinging behavior shows tremendous eagerness for attention from others and appears ready to form close relationships with them. However, when someone responds to this eagerness and attempts to form a relationship with such an object-clinging patient, it soon becomes apparent that only a very one-sided relationship is possible. The patient is intensely demanding and devouring. Nothing is ever enough. Any inattention, delay, refusal, or absence may be the grounds for bitter reproach and even for abrupt and stubborn withdrawal from the relationship. It is clear that only someone who is very giving and very persistent can engage in such a relationship and that the course of the relationship will be stormy, at best.

The patient who avoids objects through withdrawal may seem to eliminate any possibility of relationship, but it is rare for a patient to do this completely. Certainly none of the patients that we studied succeeded in avoiding social interaction altogether (although some reduced it drastically), nor did any of them seem to be attempting total withdrawal. The problem with the relatively withdrawn patient is to discover at what times and on what terms he will accept, or even welcome, the company of another human being.

Some patients alternate between object clinging and object avoidance, thus expressing both their need for others and fear of others. Such alternation is likely to be bewildering, or at least disconcerting, since it is more closely related to the inner state of the schizophrenic patient than to the actions of the other. Thus the possibility of relationship with such a patient depends to a large extent on the ability of the other to adapt to the fluctuating moods and take them in his stride.

The patient who engages in object redefinition presents a tricky problem to those who deal with him. Part of the problem is to discover the role in which one has been cast and the rest of the problem is how to deal with the departures of this role from reality. Popular thinking suggests that it may at times be necessary to "humor" such a patient. Other possibilities are to try to understand the reality distortion and then interpret it to the patient, to ignore it, or to contradict it. If the reality distortion is not too great or can be handled satisfactorily, relationships with object-redefining patients may be more like normal relationships, since these patients are generally better organized and more consistent in their behavior than other patients.

From the foregoing comments it can be seen that every aspect of relationship behavior is likely to be affected in a relationship with a schizophrenic patient. Clinging and withdrawal, and their alternation obviously refer to approach and avoidance behavior, which often is more extreme (both in amount and in variability) with schizophrenic patients than with most other people. The patient's conflict over need for and fear of others will also be shown in exaggerated and often ambivalent expressions of feeling and in exaggerated or especially variable reactions to influence and control attempts.

There is likely to be a communication problem, since every schizophrenic patient has a deviant style of communication (disorganized, highly concrete, using invented words or conventional words with idiosyncratic meanings, etc.). As Cameron and Magaret (1951) point out, schizophrenic patients are generally deficient in the ability to take the role of the other, which is so important in successful communication. On the other hand, sometimes the patient's skill at certain kinds of communication may be disconcerting and disrupting. For example, some schizophrenic patients are highly sensitive to body movements and other nonverbal indicators of feeling, and can detect feelings which the other person is trying to conceal or is unaware of.

The very fact of being a patient in a mental hospital provides a pitfall. The patient is always likely to be regarded as crazy unless proven otherwise. In popular thinking, and often in professional thinking, a mental patient is not to be taken too seriously, not to be trusted completely, not to be treated as other people are. This common attitude produces a great barrier. It is not a barrier to interaction itself except where fear is great, but it certainly interferes with the development of respect, trust, intimacy, and understanding. It may lead to a special kind of relationship, in which the patient is treated as incompetent and uncomprehending, often with kindness, sometimes with fear, but never with respect or human directness.

Less obvious but equally important is the way that patients regard staff members. Mental hospital patients very commonly see staff members as jailers and oppressors. (One Third Floor patient, the first time he saw me, came over to me and asked, "Are you a victim or a victor?") At Chestnut Lodge patients from wealthy families sometimes see staff members as servants and social inferiors. Viewing the staff as jailers encourages evading, resisting, and deceiving them, which some patients work at very actively. Viewing the staff as servants and inferiors encourages demanding, complaining, and disdaining behavior. Another common conflict of viewpoint concerns who the staff members are working for. Staff members generally regard themselves as employees of the hospital, responsible to the hospital administration, and perhaps as representing society. Patients generally think that staff members should be working for *them* and should be primarily concerned with patient needs and wishes. An additional disrupting and distancing effect on interaction comes about when a staff member fails to realize how a patient regards him or else takes the patient's view as another proof of craziness.

The preceding two paragraphs refer to the general conceptions or stereotypes which patients and staff members are likely to have about one another. In addition, the members of each group have some conceptions of what is desirable and proper behavior for the members of the other group. These conceptions vary a great deal from one individual to another but a few fairly common elements can be pointed out. The staff member's conception of desirable behavior includes the patient's recognition that he is mentally ill and his willingness to be treated. At Chestnut Lodge, treatment consists first and foremost of individual psychotherapy and all staff members convey to the patient that this is his most important task and the most hopeful route to his improvement and release from the hospital. Also, it is generally desired that the patient conform to hospital rules and routines and "cooperate" with staff members (which usually means being docile and passively accepting care and regulation). Staff members differ in the extent to which they expect conventional social behavior of patients. Some (especially psychotherapists) feel that patients should be free to express their craziness in the hospital; others (especially aides) may make great efforts to enforce conventional social customs and taboos with respect to dress, speech, manners, and the like.

Patient conceptions of desirable behavior for staff members are harder to discover and probably more diverse. One common theme is that staff members are *medical* personnel and should behave as such. This may be coupled with demands for medication, for operations, and for other traditional and tangible medical procedures. It may also be coupled with the patient's refusal of attentions by the staff on the grounds that he is not sick and does not need to be in a hospital. It can also fit in with all kinds of delusional ideas about one's body and what has been or might be done to it. Another common theme, related to the patient conception of staff members as servants, is that staff members should be more considerate, helpful, sympathetic, and responsive to patient requests than they are. This theme fits in very well with the demanding behavior of object-clinging patients.

From these brief comments about the conceptions and demands which staff and patients have of each other, it can be seen that there is much opportunity for misunderstanding and for action at cross-purposes. Such difficulties are common and often persistent, with poor communication impeding attempts to clear them up. (Examples of such difficulties will be found in the chapters presenting case studies of individual patients. Some data on patient and staff conceptions of one another will be found in the section of the Appendix on the questionnaire given to both patients and staff members.)

We come now to the specific conditions affecting patient-staff relationships at Chestnut Lodge. We will begin with the setting and formal structure. Inpatients are housed in seven living units, all of which have approximately the same formal organization. Third Floor, the unit which was studied intensively, usually houses about a dozen male patients. The administrator of the unit is a psychiatrist, who devotes about half his time to his responsibility for this group of patients. The nursing personnel on the unit are under the direction of a Head Nurse, who devotes her full time to this responsibility. During the day and evening there are usually three to five staff members on duty, mostly aides. Often one or two of these staff members are student nurses. During the period under study all the nurses (except one male nurse, present for about a month) and student nurses were females and all the aides were males. During any given week there are about a dozen different members of the nursing staff whom the patients may encounter on their living unit during the day and evening. (At various times the number of different aides on duty during a week has ranged from seven to 12, the number of nurses from zero to two, and the number of student nurses from zero to seven.) One or two members of the housekeeping staff will be there during the day, performing such tasks as cleaning, making beds, and collecting laundry.

In addition to the foregoing people who are regularly on Third Floor, other members of the hospital staff may come there from time to time. A social worker is assigned to each patient (usually the same social worker for all the patients on Third Floor) and she may spend some time with the patient, but this can vary from a considerable amount to very little time, depending on the needs of the patient and the inclinations of the social worker, as well as the competing demands on her time. Some psychotherapists come to Third Floor to see their patients, instead of seeing them in their offices. The nursing supervisor and the "doctor on call" (usually one of the younger psychiatrists on the staff, but sometimes an outside doctor) make regular visits in the course of their duties. A member of the Activities Department staff may come to Third Floor from time to time to arrange activities and trips for the patients. Other members of the hospital staff may also come to Third Floor to visit or in the course of errands. Other patients may also visit Third Floor, particularly on special occasions, such as parties. During some periods there have been specific times of day during which visiting was permitted between Third Floor and the two adjacent units for female patients. Relatives and friends visiting patients and occasionally professional people who are visiting the hospital may also come to Third Floor at times.

Each patient is assigned to a psychiatrist who is his psychotherapist. The amount of time therapist and patient spend together may vary somewhat, but most often it is four hours per week. This is the only relationship which is literally imposed on the patient. A patient is often able to avoid contacts with any or all other members of the hospital staff, or at least to keep such contacts to a bare and perfunctory minimum. However, the therapist is usually far more insistent and persistent in approaching and spending time with a reluctant patient than is anyone else. This works the other way too, of course. A patient may be found uninteresting or repulsive by most staff members, who may seek to limit their contacts with him (despite hospital policy to the contrary), but he can generally count on getting his four hours a week from his therapist even when everyone else is avoiding him. Many hospital practices and common attitudes of staff members support the primacy of the patient's relationship with his therapist. Only acute emergencies are allowed to interfere with the therapeutic sessions; all other activities and routines must give way to them. If the patient is reluctant to see his therapist he may be escorted to the therapist's office. If this does not seem advisable, the therapist will come to Third Floor to see his patient. Sometimes force or the threat of force is used to insure the contact; the patient may be put in a cold wet sheet pack or an aide may be present during the session to help control the patient. Changes of therapist are made with great reluctance; regardless of whether the request for a change is made by patient or therapist or even by both, the Director of Psychotherapy will usually urge them to try again. During the period of our study only four patients on Third Floor had their therapists changed, in contrast to the many other changes of personnel (reported below). The most common occasion for such changes is the resignation of the therapist from the hospital staff. Thus the patient and his therapist are usually committed to each other (or "stuck" with each other) until one of them leaves. Other pressures and processes also help to focus the patient's attention and communications on his therapist. The nursing notes (containing a report of the activities and behavior of the patient, written at the end of each eight-hour shift by one of the nursing personnel) are routinely sent to the therapist every day. (Therapists vary considerably in the value they put on these reports and how they make use of them, but most of them at least read the nursing notes regularly and patients are generally aware that their therapists get such reports.) Patients who talk about personal problems, anxieties, confusions, bizarre ideas, and the like to other members of the hospital staff will sometimes be told to "take that up with your therapist." Many staff members, especially therapists, feel that patients should not talk very much about such matters to other people for fear of "diluting the transference."

There is some encouragement for members of the nursing staff to form individual relationships with patients. An aide is usually assigned three or four patients, to whom he is expected to pay more attention than to the other patients and whose nursing notes he is expected to write. Preferences of both patients and staff members are taken into account in making these assignments and they often remain the same over considerable periods of time, thus facilitating the development of relationships. However, such relationships are far less favored or protected than those with therapists. One interfering factor is the turnover among staff members, which will be described below. Another is the common feeling that nursing staff members should not get "too involved" with patients, that such relationships should be "professional" rather than "personal." Another very important factor is lack of training and support. The therapists have all had considerable training and experience in psychotherapy and have frequent opportunities to discuss their work with their colleagues and to receive criticism, suggestions, and support. Nursing staff members have not had any comparable training and have less opportunity for supportive discussion. Their behavior with patients is therefore more dependent upon following the example of others, plus whatever may be suggested by their own backgrounds, personality, and ingenuity. Most of the aides are recent high school graduates from the local community who welcome a job that does not require special training or skills (and who usually have no intention of making a career of working in a mental hospital). Some aides are students (college, graduate school, seminary). Only a very small proportion of aides have worked at Chestnut Lodge or other institutions for a few years and regard such work as their more-or-less permanent occupation. The student nurses come from two southern nursing schools; most of them do not have any special interest in psychiatric nursing. The regular nurses are obviously older and more experienced than the student nurses and than most of the aides also. (Occasionally a patient who is upset or depressed is assigned a "special," a member of the nursing staff who stays with the patient constantly during a shift and whose only responsibility is the care of this particular patient. However, the "specials" are sometimes staff members from other units whom the patient may not know, and, since a great many different people are often used in succession to "special" a patient, the opportunities to form significant relationships may be limited unless the "specialing" continues for an unusually long time.)

Third Floor patients spend most of their time on Third Floor. The door is always locked, which means that patients cannot leave the unit unless a staff member opens the door for them. Many patients are not allowed to leave the unit unless they are accompanied by a staff member. Almost all patients do leave the unit three times a day to go down to the dining room for meals. In the dining room they encounter patients and personnel from other units as well as dining room personnel, but relatively little interaction occurs at mealtime and almost none of it is between people from different units. Most patients also leave the unit at other times during the day to go to their therapeutic hours, to attend activities at the Center Building and elsewhere, or to leave the hospital grounds (usually accompanied by a staff member unless the patient has "unaccompanied privileges"). Since it is not considered desirable for patients to spend all their time on the unit, activities and excursions are frequently planned, both for individuals and for groups of patients, which will take them elsewhere. In the course of these excursions the patient will encounter other patients, hospital personnel, and people who are not connected with the hospital, but he will have little opportunity for repeated and sustained interaction with particular people unless he has more freedom of movement than the average Third Floor patient. However, a few Third Floor patients do have a privilege status which enables them to remain off the unit all day, usually at the discretion of the charge nurse.

To summarize, the principal people with whom a Third Floor patient is able to interact repeatedly are his fellow-patients on Third Floor plus frequent visitors from the adjacent female units, the nurses and aides on Third Floor, the administrator of Third Floor, the social worker, the Activity Department worker assigned to Third Floor, and the patient's individual psychotherapist. These are the people with whom he has the most opportunity to form relationships. The interaction with the psychotherapist is so structured that a significant relationship almost invariably develops. The responsibility of the administrator for important decisions about a patient's life (privileges, medical care, transfers, trips, and visits, and many other aspects of daily life) plus his frequent presence on the ward make him an important figure for all patients. Interactions with other people are less structured (except for an occasional "special"), so that the development of other relationships depends to a greater extent on the activity of the people involved. For the purposes of our study we decided not to collect data on relationships in which both partners are patients (because of the difficulty of securing information from the participants). We also did not collect data on relationships with social workers and activity workers. Data were collected on interactions of patients with all other staff members mentioned.

The interpersonal environment on Third Floor was not highly stable for either patients or personnel. During the two and three-quarter year period (September 1, 1957, to June 30, 1960) when most of the data for this study were gathered, there was a total of 38 different nurses and aides who worked on Third Floor during the day and evening. Not one of these people was there for the entire period. The distribution of lengths of stay was as follows:

Length of Stay	Aides	Nurses	Totals
Less than 3 months	8	2	10
3 months up to 6 months	9	1	10
6 months up to 1 year	7	1	8
1 year up to 2 years	5	1	6
2 years or more	4	0	4
	33	5	38

During this time there was a total of 82 student nurses who worked on Third Floor for periods ranging from one to eight weeks each. However, Dr. Gibson served as administrative psychiatrist for Third Floor during the entire period (except for a one-month vacation each summer) and spent some time on the unit every day, so that he was a highly stable figure in this changing group.

During this same two and three-quarter year period there were 36 different patients who lived on Third Floor for varying lengths of time, including three patients who were there throughout. The distribution of the patients' lengths of stay was as follows:

Length of Stay	
Less than 3 months	11
3 months up to 6 months	4
6 months up to one year	9
1 year up to 2 years	4
2 years or more	8
	36

Each patient had an individual psychotherapist (except one patient who was on Third Floor for a very brief period); four of them were reassigned to new therapists in the course of this period.

The foregoing figures do not give the total lengths of stay of all patients and personnel, because those who were already on Third Floor at the beginning of the period and those who were still there at the end of it spent some time on Third Floor which is not included in the above figures. However, for present purposes it is sufficient to show the amount of change during the period of intensive data-gathering. Another way of describing the situation is in terms of arrivals and departures. During this 33-month period 29 new nurses and aides came to Third Floor, 82 new student nurses came, and 28 new patients came. This means an average of more than four new arrivals per month and about the same number of departures, in a group of about 20 people.

This turnover rate is not particularly high for a hospital setting, but it is high compared to those settings in which people usually form their significant relationships, such as family, neighborhood, school, and work settings. A high turnover does not prevent the formation of significant relationships, especially when there are opportunities for intensive contact, but it leads to frequent interruption of those that occur. Continued exposure to such a situation may well encourage caution or apathy about getting closely involved with others.

We have surveyed the processes involved in the formation of relationships, the ways in which these processes are affected when one of the participants is a schizophrenic patient, and particular conditions on Third Floor that may affect the development of relationships. Now we turn to a questionnaire study which gives an overview of what actually happens on Third Floor, the result of these processes and conditions.

We will start with interaction between patients and nursing personnel. Our principal data on this relationship come from a detailed questionnaire filled out for every patient by every nurse and aide at three-month intervals. (The questionnaire and the cluster analysis will be described in detail in the Appendix, so they are treated briefly here, without technicalities.) The questions on this questionnaire are grouped into the following scales, each referring to some segment of patient or staff behavior in social interaction:

Patient Behavior

Approach
Avoidance
Personal Communication
Clarity of Communication
Problem Behavior (Harmful to self or to others)
Expression of Positive Feelings
Expression of Negative Feelings
Compliance (with staff efforts at control)

Staff Member Behavior

Approach
Personal Communication
Expression of Positive Feelings
Expression of Negative Feelings
Use of Control Technique

Joint Behavior

Active Activities (patient active)
Passive Activities (patient passive)

Cluster analyses were made of the correlations among these scales, to see which kinds of behavior tend to go together. Such analyses were done twice with questionnaire data from Third Floor collected approximately a year apart. On the second occasion the questionnaire was administered throughout the hospital and cluster analyses made for all seven units. Two clusters appeared consistently throughout, that is, both times on Third Floor and in all seven units of the hospital on the second occasion. These clusters indicate some consistent features of patient-staff interaction, at least in this hospital.

One cluster includes the following five scales, all positively correlated with one another:

Patient Behavior	*Staff Behavior*
Approach	
Personal Communication	Personal Communication
Expression of Positive Feelings	

Joint Behavior
Active Activities

This cluster obviously refers to the patient's ability to make social overtures (approaching staff members, talking to them, and expressing positive feelings toward them). Staff members tend to talk more to patients who make such overtures and to engage more in joint activities with them. The staff members' response pattern seems like the common response to friendly social overtures. The patients' behavior pattern also sounds like the common way of initiating friendly social interaction. This is perhaps a more interesting finding than may appear at first. The staff members are presumably more-or-less normal so that a conventional social response is not surprising in them. But the patients are hospitalized mental patients, most of them schizophrenic persons noted for bizarre and unconventional behavior. It would be perfectly possible for them to approach in an unfriendly way, for example, and patients sometimes do. But there is surprisingly little deviation from the overall pattern. For example, out of 13 patients on Third Floor in December 1960, 11 showed consistency among the three scales (approaching, communicating, expressing positive feelings), the three scale scores never being more than half the possible range apart (in rank units) and usually much closer than that. What this cluster seems to represent is interest (or lack of interest) on the part of a patient in friendly interaction with nursing personnel, expressed in at least roughly the same way as social interest is conventionally expressed.

Because these are group data (the ratings of a patient by various nursing staff members have been averaged), they show the general attitude which patients have toward staff members, rather than specific attitudes toward individual staff members. They show that some patients are generally more able than other patients to express interest in social interaction with staff members. Staff members generally respond favorably to such indications of interest, just as most people would in most social situations. We have already mentioned that they tend to communicate and engage in joint activities more frequently with these friendly patients. The total amount of time that they spend with such patients is greater. Furthermore, when a patient increases or decreases in friendly approaching behavior the amount of time staff members spend with him also tends to go up or down correspondingly.

The other cluster which appeared consistently in the questionnaire analyses includes three scales plus two others, each of which is generally correlated with the first three but which have rather low correlations with each other. The interrelations of these scales may be represented as follows:

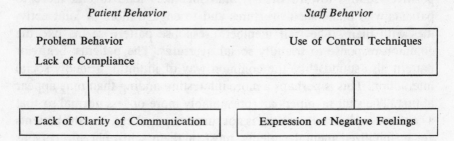

Patient Behavior   *Staff Behavior*

| Problem Behavior
Lack of Compliance | Use of Control Techniques |

| Lack of Clarity of Communication | Expression of Negative Feelings |

(The Compliance scale and the Clarity of Communication scale have negative correlations with the others, which has been expressed in the above diagram by prefixing each with the phrase "lack of.") The key scale in this cluster is obviouly the problem behavior of the patient. Patients who engage in problem behavior (harmful to themselves or antisocial) are likely to be more confused and disorganized than other patients, as shown by the poorer quality of their communication. The problem behavior leads to attempts by staff members to control it (by making suggestions to the patient, coaxing and reasoning with him, using force, etc.), attempts which are generally resisted by the patient. The problem behavior and the resistance to efforts to control it tend to annoy or anger the staff members, leading them to express negative feelings toward the patient. (Patients who are confused in their communications are not likely to receive such expressions of negative feeling unless they also engage in problem behavior.) As with friendliness, patients who show problem behavior are likely to have more time spent with them by staff members. When the amount of problem behavior a patient engages in goes up or down, the amount of time staff members spend with him similarly tends to go up or down. Thus problem behavior may be a way of producing interaction with staff members, and staff members sometimes describe such behavior as "attention-getting" (as do parents and teachers in talking about similar behavior in children). Whether this is the conscious intention or not, problem behavior certainly gets attention, at Chestnut Lodge as elsewhere. There are two important differences between this way of initiating interaction and making friendly overtures. One is that it bypasses the usual process of mutual choice. The problem patient does not have to admit any liking for or even interest in the people whose attention he gets. And they do not have to admit any liking for or interest in him. Someone who is convinced that he is uninteresting to other people, perhaps even violently repulsive, may therefore find it much easier to engage in problem behavior than to make friendly social overtures. However, such behavior and the angry attention it gets may further confirm the patient's belief in his unattractiveness. The second important difference between problem behavior and friendly overtures is that problem behavior brings the issue of dominance and submission very sharply to the fore. Problem behavior, by definition, is behavior which staff members will try to control or change. Since patients rarely submit immediately or completely to control attempts, there is usually some kind of a struggle. With rare exceptions, staff members do not give in either, and they are likely to be supported in control attempts by their colleagues, as well as by hospital procedures and other institutional pressures. Problem behavior therefore initiates influence and control attempts by staff members which are likely to continue until the patient submits or leaves the hospital.

Friendly overtures and problem behavior seem to be alternative patterns of behavior available to the patients. It is conceivable that a patient could do both, but probably not at the same time. And it is certainly conceivable that a patient could do neither. But on the whole we might expect a patient to do one or the other, and this seems to be what happens. For two administrations of the questionnaire (January 1960 and December 1960) the Third Floor patients were divided into high, medium, and low categories for each behavior pattern. Only one patient was high on both behavior patterns at the same time (January 1960). The same patient was the only one who was low on both patterns at the same time (December 1960). All the other patients were in the high or medium category on one pattern and in the medium or low category on the other pattern at the same time.

The foregoing two patterns are the only ones which we found, generally, on every administration of our questionnaire and with every group of patients and staff members. Additional kinds of behavior have been associated with these patterns at particular times. For example, approaching behavior by staff members was associated with the problem behavior pattern in January 1960, but it was associated with the friendly overtures pattern in December 1960. In other words, at one time the nursing personnel were making their most active efforts to interact with the problem patients and at the other time to interact with the friendly patients. At certain times additional clusters appear, indicating behavior patterns which are prevalent enough at those times to show up in the correlations. For example, in December 1960 there was a cluster consisting of four scales: personal communication by the patient and by the staff member, and the expression of negative feelings by the patient and by the staff member. This suggests a kind of negative involvement, an argumentative or angry kind of inter-action. The fact that this cluster did not appear in the January 1960 questionnaire analysis is presumably related to the fact that of the three patients who were most highly involved in this kind of inter-action, two had not been on Third Floor at the time of the January questionnaire.

There would be little point in further discussion here of the occa-sional clusters and variations in clusters that may be found in our data. These variations are due to the particular behavior of particular peo-ple and therefore can most appropriately be considered by examining the relationship patterns of individual patients, as we shall do in detail in later chapters.

We shall now briefly consider relationships with psychotherapists. The patient's relationship with his therapist is, of course, much nar-rower in time, place, and activities than his relationships with nursing personnel. The patient usually sees his therapist for four hours a week, according to a regular schedule. They usually meet in the patient's room or in the therapist's office. Sometimes they may go for walks or auto rides together, and occasionally engage in other activities to-gether, usually depending on whether the therapist considers such other activities to be worthwhile.

For an overall picture of these relationships we shall use the results from a questionnaire administered to therapists. This questionnaire was generally comparable to the questionnaire used with nursing per-sonnel, but there were some important differences. For example, there were no items referring to approach behavior by the therapist. This reflects an important difference in the expected (and actual) behavior of therapists and nursing personnel. The nursing staff member has many opportunities to approach or refrain from approaching each patient in the course of an eight-hour shift on Third Floor. The therapist may not have to approach the patient at all if the patient comes to see him in his office, or he may approach the patient once, by going to the patient's room at the time of the therapy hour. In other words, the therapist would usually have at most one occasion to approach his patient in the course of a day, so there did not seem to be much point in asking the therapist about his approach behavior on the questionnaire. (However, the therapist can show varying degrees of responsiveness to his patient's approaches. This will be discussed in the chapters presenting data on individual patients.)

Another difference between nursing and therapist questionnaires may be illustrated by the scales dealing with the quality of the patient's communication. The nursing questionnaire has a single scale for confused and unrealistic communication, while the therapist questionnaire has two, one dealing with the patient's ability to make verbal communications and the other with his ability to understand them. Essentially the same items appear on both questionnaires, but the item intercorrelations are different, presumably because the therapists pay closer attention to their patients' communications and distinguish the nature of unsatisfactory communications more precisely.

A cluster analysis was made of the scales on the therapist questionnaire, using data gathered in the January 1960 administration of the questionnaire. We did not find exact counterparts of the general clusters found with nursing personnel, but there were similar clusters.

One cluster consisted of the following scales:

Patient Behavior	*Therapist Behavior*
Approach	Friendly Attitude
Expression of Positive Feelings	Lack of Expression of Negative Feelings

(As before, the phrase "lack of" denotes a negative correlation.) This cluster resembles the friendly overtures cluster described above. Two of the patient behavior scales appear in both clusters. The differences between the two clusters are worth discussing briefly. One difference is the appearance of the "friendly attitude" scale under therapist behavior. This is similar to the "expression of positive feelings" scale on the nursing staff questionnaire, but is not quite the same (partly because of the inclusion of some additional items on the therapist questionnaire and partly because the therapists distinguished somewhat more precisely between expressing friendly feelings and expressing their own good mood). The expression of positive feelings does not appear in the nursing personnel equivalent of this cluster, simply because it was not correlated with the other scales on all seven units, but it was correlated with them on most of the units.

A second difference between the two clusters is the absence of active activities in the therapist cluster. There is no such scale on the questionnaire for therapists because of the rarity of such joint activities in therapist-patient interactions.

A third difference is that the nursing personnel cluster includes personal communication by both patient and staff member, but the therapist cluster does not include either of these. The reason for this will become apparent when we consider another cluster which is found in the therapist questionnaire results:

Patient Behavior	Therapist Behavior
Approach	
Personal communication	Personal communication

This is the missing part of the friendly overtures cluster.

It is as if the friendly overtures cluster breaks in two in the relationship with the therapist, this cluster and the preceding one being the two parts. (Actually, there is some tendency in this direction in the data of the nursing staff questionnaire, but it is not as strong.) In other words, personal communication and expressions of friendly feelings are components of interaction that often go together, but need not do so. The separation of these patterns in the therapist questionnaire results may be due to the attitude of many therapists toward expressions of feelings. Conventional expressions of friendliness are often superficial or insincere; therapists are less likely to express friendliness in such conventional terms and less likely to encourage such expression by their patients. For similar reasons, therapists may have somewhat more stringent standards for what they characterize as "personal communication" than nursing staff members and be less inclined to include somewhat superficial and conventional kinds of communication.

There is also in the therapist questionnaire data a cluster which corresponds roughly to the problem behavior cluster on the nursing staff questionnaire. This consists of the following scales:

Patient Behavior	Therapist Behavior
Problem Behavior	Use of Control Techniques
Demanding and Complaining	

The differences between this cluster and the one on the nursing questionnaire are that this one does not include lack of compliance by the patient nor lack of clarity of communication by the patient, while the problem behavior cluster on the nursing questionnaire does not include demanding and complaining. (The demanding and complaining items do appear on the nursing questionnaire, but do not correlate with one another highly enough to form a scale.)

Two other small clusters appear on the therapist questionnaire which may be somewhat related to the problem behavior cluster. One consists of the following items:

Patient Behavior	Therapist Behavior
Lack of Compliance	Use of Control Techniques (for patient's behavior during session)
	Expression of Annoyance

This clearly refers to the therapist's dissatisfaction with his patient's behavior during the therapy sessions and with resistance by the patient to the therapist's attempts to change the unsatisfactory behavior. The kind of patient behavior which provokes such a reaction does not appear in the cluster, possibly because the appropriate items were not included on the questionnaire or because the kinds of behavior that provoke this reaction are different for different therapists.

The other cluster consists of the following items:

Patient Behavior	Therapist Behavior
Demanding and Complaining	Lack of Friendly Attitude
Expression of Negative Feelings	

This sounds as though it arises from patient dissatisfaction with his therapist. This cluster is not simply the negative of the mutual friendliness cluster, although there is some tendency for patients who are high on one to be low on the other. There are some patients who are high on this cluster who do not show a consistent pattern on the mutual friendliness cluster. These two clusters refer to different kinds of problem situations in the therapeutic relationship.

Since these therapist cluster analyses are based on only one set of therapist questionnaires about a small group of patients, it is not appropriate to put much weight on these findings or to discuss them in any more detail here. (For further details, see the Appendix.) One general impression is that patient interest in the relationship and patient manifestation of problem behavior are very important determinants of the interaction with therapists as with nursing staff members. Another general impression is the therapists' more differentiated awareness of the character of the patient's behavior and of the interaction (as shown by the distinction between friendliness and intimacy, distinguishing two kinds of communicative ability, distinguishing two kinds of negative feeling, and distinguishing three kinds of problem interactions). Instead of two big clusters, the therapist questionnaire yields five smaller clusters, which strongly suggests that patient relationships with therapists are more varied and differentiated than their relationships with nursing staff (as well as that therapists have more differentiated perceptions). Of course this refers only to the average, but it is certainly what would be desired and expected. The relationship between a particular patient and a particular aide may be much more differentiated than the average, and a patient may have a less differentiated than average relationship with his therapist.

Comparison of patient standings on nursing staff clusters and more or less comparable therapist clusters do not show any general tendencies. For example, there are patients who are friendly with both nursing staff and therapist and patients who are friendly with neither, but there are also patients who are friendly with one but not the other. Similarly for problem behavior. The significance of similarity or difference of relationships with various people will be considered in more detail in examining the relationship patterns of individual patients.

We have described the general conditions affecting the development of patient-staff relationships involving Third Floor patients. The organization and functioning of the hospital insure the development of a significant relationship between each patient and his psychotherapist, both by providing for regular one-to-one interaction and by keeping the patient assigned to the same therapist for relatively long periods. The organization and functioning of the hospital provide the opportunity for significant relationships to develop between patients and nursing personnel, but whether this comes about depends much more on the initiative and activity of the individuals involved. Furthermore, significant relationships which do develop with nursing personnel are far less protected against interruption by the transfer or departure of either partner. The two most common themes of interaction between nursing staff and patients are conventional sociability and dealing with problem behavior, both of which seem to be initiated mainly by patient behavior. The conditions and consequences of these and other forms of interaction will be examined in detail in later chapters concerned with individual patients and their relationships.

BIBLIOGRAPHY

Cameron, N. & Magaret, A. (1951), *Behavior Pathology*. Boston: Houghton Mifflin.

Foa, Uriel G. (1961), Convergences in the Analysis of the Structure of Interpersonal Behavior. *Psychol. Rev., 68*:341-353.

VI

THE QUEST FOR CONSTANCY BY A STAGE MANAGER OF REALITY

Donald L. Burnham

THE CASE OF GLEN, with the complex vicissitudes of his relationships, illustrates the use of object redefinition and restructuring of reality as attempted solutions to a severe need-fear dilemma and object inconstancy.

BACKGROUND

Glen's wealthy and heavily matriarchal family lived in a western city of the United States. His father was largely a self-made business success who eventually owned at least two substantial companies. His fatal illness, when Glen was 23, was a major precipitant of Glen's psychosis. Glen's mother was the dominant influence in his life. She suffered from a goiter and was highly nervous. She was absolutely convinced of the rightness of her opinions and imperiously rode herd over the entire family.

The circumstances of Glen's birth explain much of his subsequent faulty differentiation and integration. He was the last of his parents' children to be born and the only male. He had three sisters, 13, 11, and 6 years older than he. His mother had had two miscarriages, each of a male fetus, and her pregnancy with him had been in jeopardy, reportedly because of her exertion in caring for her husband, then ill with influenza. During this time Glen's sisters were sent to stay with relatives. Glen was born a month later than expected and weighed nine pounds.[1] After nursing him for three months, his mother contracted influenza, and he was turned over to the possessive care of a nursemaid who "completely took over the baby." These factors combined to surround his birth and subsequent existence with an aura of precarious specialness.

His mother was extremely overprotective and clashed repeatedly with a nursemaid with regard to his care. After a year the nursemaid was fired, but rehired six months later; during this interval a succession of three others cared for him. When Glen was 4, she was again dismissed, ostensibly for allowing the child to ride a pony from which he fell, thereby provoking his mother to shout, "You are trying to kill my baby!"

This incident exemplified his mother's pervasive, anxious concern and protectiveness, which increased as he suffered recurrent bouts of asthma and bronchitis from the age of 4 to 14. Convinced of her indispensability, she supervised his every move, thus preventing him from developing autonomy and confidence in his own resources. Fearful that he might be kidnapped, she severely restricted his contacts with persons outside the family. Literally every moment of his day was directed by governesses and tutors until he was 10, and not until he was 15 was he allowed to leave the home premises alone. Only father's vigorous insistence overrode mother's fear of sending Glen to public school, but even then her overprotection continued. She engaged a tutor to supervise his homework, and two music teachers, one to give him lessons and the other to assist him at practice.

Glen was insulated from much of reality by his mother who, despite her controlling qualities, had difficulty saying "no" to many of his whims. She feared arousing his displeasure and led him to expect quick gratification of his wishes. Thus he failed to develop a normal capacity to tolerate frustration. By unrealistic praise—for instance, of his musical ability—she cultivated his narcissism. She also encouraged a readiness to transfer blame, endorsing his excuses for any failure or defeat. Concurrently he failed to develop realistic capacities

[1] During his psychotic illness Glen insisted that his gestation period had been 11 months, that of a horse. This was part of a major preoccupation and identification with horses.

for coping with stress. He shrank from all competition, physical or mental, while affecting an attitude of aloof superiority. At school he "knew more than his teachers," an attitude not substantiated by his spotty, mediocre performance.

Glen's mother made it difficult for him to establish a successful masculine identification. Uncomfortable about ever being in the position of frustrating Glen, she exerted discipline by using father as a bogeyman threat. Glen apparently accepted her definition of father as cruel, and nursed a memory of undetermined accuracy of father's having pushed him down a flight of stairs. He also claimed that his father had threatened to knock his teeth in.

Mother's and father's conflicting expectations of Glen interfered with his integration. An example was a planned camping trip. His mother was fearful that he would not be adequately supervised, that he might drown, get lost, or suffer other harm. His father clearly wanted Glen to make the trip, but left the final decision to him. When his mother "had hysterics," Glen chose to stay home, whereupon his father sharply rebuked him: "No son of mine behaves like a sissy! You have no courage." In addition, father repeatedly compared him unfavorably with other boys.

Glen failed in various ways to live up to his father's expectations. In preparatory school his grades were only fair, and he was discovered, with three other boys, engaged in some type of homosexual activity. Later he dropped out of college and made a pathetically inept attempt to work in his father's business, quickly deciding that it was beyond him. When he announced his wish to become engaged, his father retorted that since he had demonstrated no ability to support a wife, marriage was out of the question.

Contradictions and inconsistencies in father's behavior compounded Glen's difficulty in identifying with him. Though strong and assertive in his business, father usually deferred to his wife in family affairs. At times he regarded his children—especially Glen—as rivals for his wife's attention. He insisted that she accompany him on trips, and that the children be left behind. He suffered frequent migraine headaches and would insist that his wife and daughters remain continuously near to minister to him with cold, moist towels. This behavior contrasted sharply with the family myth characterizing him as fearless, and contradicted the standards of masculine strength and courage which he exacted of his son.

Father began to have episodes of cardiac palpitation when Glen was 9, and thereafter suffered gradually increasing disability. Family vacations in areas of high altitude were discontinued. More important, he progressively withdrew from contesting his wife's decisions, especially those concerning Glen. Glen may have interpreted his father's decline and withdrawal as evidence of the hopelessness of opposing his powerful mother—a theme of great importance in his subsequent illness.

Mother also interfered with Glen's identifying successfully with other men. She abruptly dismissed the longtime family chauffeur-gardener for putting gas in the car when she had forbidden Glen to drive it. His departure was a keen loss to Glen, for he had served in many ways as a substitute father and male identification model. Later mother interfered with Glen's friendships with other young men, especially those who might lead him into "dangerous" activities—motorcycle riding or swimming in cold weather. His eldest sister made a strong effort to combat mother's overprotection of Glen. She feared that he would be totally lost as a person if he were not helped toward at least a modicum of independence from his mother. By insistent urging, and with some support from father, this sister overcame mother's reluctance to allow Glen to attend a boarding school. At first he was very homesick, and school officials feared that he might kill himself. Both mother and sister visited the school. Mother wanted him to return home immediately, but sister persuaded Glen to stay. He settled down and ultimately completed a college preparatory course.

As stated earlier, his school record was marred by his involvement in some sort of homosexual activity. Although two of the four boys involved were expelled, Glen and the other were not, partly because Glen openly confessed. Glen wrote his father about the incident, asking that he not report it to mother. Significantly, his request was not honored, and at her first opportunity mother grilled Glen about the episode. Typically, she excused him as having been led astray by the others. Later, after Glen became psychotic, mother blamed his illness upon his having left home for boarding school, saying in effect, "If he had only stayed with me, he would still be all right."

ONSET OF ILLNESS

Glen became overtly psychotic when he was 23, after six months of noncombat Navy duty overseas. Before then he had served eight months at stations within the United States. At the onset of his psychosis, his father's health was distinctly worse, though it was another year before he died.

Glen voluntarily reported to the medical officers and the chaplain that he had "a strange feeling and crackpot dreams." On one occasion he left his post without permission and retreated to his bunk. In a new assignment as clerk to a medical officer, he smashed the doctor's instruments.

As he became more obviously ill, he complained that his sex organs needed treatment, that he was changing into a woman and about to go into labor. He was hospitalized in a catatonic state and required assistance to bathe and eat. Sporadically he wrote autistic dissertations on death and the possible use of hormones to restore his masculinity.

He spent about two years in Navy and Veterans Hospitals, after which he was discharged to his mother's custody. From the time of father's death, Glen pursued his never-ending quest for the perfect father. His concept of a perfect father included qualities of a heroic rescuer, patron saint, and guardian angel—in sum, someone like the description of God in the Twenty-third Psalm, which Glen once attempted to paint on the roof of his family's home.

He lived most of the next eight-and-one-half years at home with his mother. For the most part she denied that he was ill, despite his sitting blankly for hours at a time and requiring assistance to dress. She made continual efforts to revive his interest in playing the piano and other pre-illness activities. Gradually he became more active. At this time he initiated his plan to give a pageant-recital, a project which was ineffectually to continue for many years and which became an important identity fragment.

For a time he left home to purchase a ranch and raise horses. He became disorganized, however, and this enterprise came to an unsuccessful and costly end. Another abortive venture was a trip to Hollywood to seek employment as an actor. He engaged a series of agents to arrange auditions, but failed to keep the appointments they made for him.

His life at home was largely insulated from the world. He managed to establish a few acquaintanceships, but yielded to his mother's demand that he discontinue his friendship with one man, who, in her opinion, led him into dangerous activities. When he learned that this friend had died of cancer, he suffered a recrudescence of major psychotic disorganization. He tried to deny his friend's death by insisting that the man had been buried alive and should be immediately rescued from the grave.

Greater disorganization followed, upon which he was rehospitalized only to be released after three months, when his mother succumbed to his pleas that he be allowed to return home. A year later he was again hospitalized, this time at the insistence of the FBI after he had attempted to contact President Eisenhower, who, he was convinced, was withholding vital information about life-giving supplies obtainable from another planet. This and other fantasies of rebirth and rescue greatly preoccupied him at that time. Two months later he was transferred to Chestnut Lodge.

CIRCUMSTANCES OF CHESTNUT LODGE ADMISSION

At age 37 Glen was admitted to Chestnut Lodge for a trial of psychotherapy. His eldest sister, who years before had encouraged him to leave home for boarding school, was instrumental in arranging the admission. She feared that Glen would never recover if he remained near his mother, who, for her part, strongly opposed his leaving her to go to Chestnut Lodge. His sister accompanied him to the Lodge, and when she departed he literally clung to her.

Glen remained on Third Floor during the entire five years of our study except for the one day he spent on Hilltop I. Chlorpromazine, of which he was receiving 200 mg. q.i.d. on admission, was progressively diminished and, after 10 days, discontinued. Dr. Clark was his therapist throughout the period of our study, and Dr. Gibson his administrator for the first three-and-one-half years.

INITIAL PRESENTATION OF SELF

Glen introduced himself to the hospital staff with an engraved card bearing his name and the words, "Concert Pianist and Horse Trainer."

For most of the three months following this identity claim, Glen structured a reality in which the theme of unfulfilled need was pre-eminent. He pictured himself as weak, helpless, abandoned, and bereft of desperately needed supplies. Death was a central preoccupation. He said, "I've come here to be buried. . . . There is no hope for me. . . . I died as far as my life is concerned." Convinced that he had lost his sexual potency and with it all capacity for active endeavor of any sort, he felt that his body was disintegrating, and lay passively in bed much of each day.

Often he said that he should not eat, since food would only prolong his life of suffering. He begged the aides to end his misery by mercy killing and wondered aloud how he might provoke them to it. Less frequently he spoke of killing himself. Clearly sensed by his listeners was an underlying appeal for comforting responses.

Glen spoke plaintively of being abandoned by his geographically distant family and friends. He made fitful efforts to write to them, but quickly gave up, saying that the task was too much for him. His statements about God epitomized his feeling of loss: "Before, I thought He was helping me and I heard God-thoughts in the back of my head, but now He has abandoned me. . . . He is cruel, unjust, wicked; I wonder if He really exists; maybe He and Satan are the same."[2]

While bemoaning his helplessness and loss of suppliers, he none-theless began to grope for new suppliers in the hospital setting. At first this was an unselective reaching out to everyone within range, including even chance visitors to the ward. Along with pleas for pity were somewhat more hopeful importunities for friendship: "Say you will be my friend. . . . Please tell me I can get well, even if you don't mean it." His stereotyped repetition of these appeals had a possessive, clinging quality, as did his requests that staff members play checkers with him for hours on end.

Among the objects of Glen's clinging overtures was his therapist, Dr. Clark. At the outset of their relationship Glen openly avowed his object need—an avowal soon to be abruptly and stormily denied. He said, "I like you very much; please say that you like me as much,"

---

[2] This fusion of the ultimately good and bad objects, despite his struggle to keep them separate in his structuring of reality, exemplified Glen's severe ambivalence and object inconstancy.

following with a lengthy discourse to the effect that friendship and love between two men need not involve sex. It seemed as though he were inviting Dr. Clark to become his perfect friend and helper. He was eager that they agree completely on all topics. If Dr. Clark did not immediately agree with an idea, Glen would insist so challengingly that Dr. Clark felt coerced. Glen seemed unable to tolerate the slightest incongruence between his version of reality and that of his chosen friend. Clinging was further manifest in Glen's insistence that they shake hands at the beginning of each therapy session.

Glen also directed pleas toward Dr. Gibson for pity and help, and especially for male hormone injections to restore his lost strength. Usually, however, he quickly retracted this request, saying that it was already too late.

Though helpless despair was the predominant motif, it was broken occasionally by thoughts of a different cast. One, voiced shortly after admission, was a fear of "blowing up." Later, during his second and third months at the Lodge, came his various notions of rescue and rebirth. Hormone injections had this meaning for him. He began also to talk of other sources of vital supplies, frequently in terms of autistically constructed rebirth myths. He was convinced, for example, that the son of an aviation hero, alternately Lindbergh and Rickenbacker, had made a flight to Mars to discover supplies with which to replenish the Earth's depleted stocks and thereby avert world catastrophe. Glen contrasted the bounteousness of masculine Mars with the barrenness of the feminine Moon which he claimed had also been visited by space flight. In another myth he claimed foreknowledge of the imminent birth of a white winged colt whose great magical powers included restoring Glen's lost strength. Glen argued that the birth of the colt would not only confirm his prediction but would affirm the validity of all his beliefs.

As he began to recite these myths, his general behavior and attitude toward the hospital staff changed. Flurries of activity and assertiveness punctuated his mood of helplessness. He started playing the piano, and spent increasingly long times in the bathroom, where the aides suspected he was masturbating. His woeful supplication and clinging gave way to complaints more in tones of envy, anger, and vengeance. Where before he had viewed certain staff members as potential friends and rescuers, he now saw them as jailers and tormentors. Once he suddenly approached a male aide from the rear and began to choke him. Although he quickly stopped and apologized, the incident gave substance to his previously voiced fear of blowing up.

Another explosion was directed at Ed, a Negro aide, who, in urging Glen to get up from his bed of despair, met with initial success until, as a friendly gesture, he tapped Glen on the knee. Thereupon Glen struck him and shouted, "I don't need help from you or anyone else!" From that time on, Glen frequently cast Ed in the role of hated enemy.

Soon Glen's denial of need for help was also manifest in his relationship with Dr. Clark. In place of pleas for help, he now denied illness, patienthood, or any need for treatment. He tried to avoid therapy appointments, and made various attempts to reverse roles with Dr. Clark, once by trying to force the doctor to lie down to be psychoanalyzed. Clearly, fear now predominated over need.

Dr. Clark opposed Glen's attempts to avoid him by insisting that Glen keep their appointments, even with an aide present if Glen so desired. At first Glen became more fearful, voicing dread that the doctor would kill or rape him, and threatening violent retaliation. Later, however, in a brief interval of insight he said to Dr. Clark, "Sometimes you seem a true and loyal friend, at other times my worst enemy," adding that Dr. Gibson, too, seemed unpredictably changeable. Thus he epitomized his problem of object inconstancy.

Glen's shift from passive despair to active assertiveness, and from possessive clinging to fearful avoidance was further accentuated in the next phase of his hospital career.

REBIRTH TRANSITION

After three months at Chestnut Lodge, Glen suddenly seemed convinced that his rescue-rebirth, which he had presaged in self-comforting myths, now was an accomplished fact. In a manner akin to a swing from depression to mania, he literally rose from his bed of helplessness and loudly announced that he was going to practice the piano at least six hours a day.

Where before he had felt utterly bereft, he now felt abundantly supplied, not by proximate persons but by persons who were geographically distant or even dead. Almost all of these were men. He asserted that those who had died had been brought back to life, including his father.

Now cast in the role of principal helper was Lt. Grant, a police officer in Glen's home city. Glen's relationship with him was more autistic than shared. Their main real contact had occurred when the Lieutenant had been instrumental in hospitalizing Glen, for which Glen had classed him as an enemy. Now, however, he was transformed into a magic provider of advice, guidance, and protection against all enemies. Though Glen wrote and phoned the Lieutenant several times, he relied primarily upon "telepathic contact." As he described it, whenever he felt uncertainty, he waited for a prompt answer from Lt. Grant to arise in his mind. In this fashion he felt guided even in such seemingly small decisions as whether to go to the dining room for a particular meal.

The most important function attributed to Lt. Grant was the governing of Glen's relationships within the hospital—which persons were friends, which enemies, whom to approach, and whom to avoid. If Glen's feelings toward a person changed, he would attribute this change to instructions from the Lieutenant and say that the latter was about to arrive on the scene to rescue him from the Lodge and its evil staff. At other times Glen cast in the protector-rescuer role such authorities as Eisenhower, Truman, and J. Edgar Hoover. His sense of alliance with such powerful persons assisted him in denying any vulnerability, helplessness, or need.

Concurrently, he devalued Drs. Clark and Gibson and tried to avoid them. He would say, "Go away. I'm too busy writing to Lt. Grant to see you." He accused the doctors of wanting to kill him, of having sexual interests in him and in each other, and of being women who pretended to be men. He complained that Dr. Gibson was dominated by the charge nurse, and said, "She's more of a man than you are."[3]

That Glen's view of his mother shifted dramatically during this period seemed an important factor in his rebirth transition. Previously he had rarely mentioned her, though he had placed her in the role

[3] This was but one of many recastings of the central family drama in which Glen viewed father as subservient to mother. An essential quality of Glen's desired magic helper was that he be strong enough to stand up against women.

of his benevolent supporter. With his sudden sense of acquiring a male magic helper in Lt. Grant, he ventured to become angry at his mother in outbursts by letter and phone. Later he told others, "I felt as if a great weight had been lifted from me." Clearly his sense of rebirth was connected with feeling, albeit temporarily, free of her.

During this period Glen drew an additional sense of strength from a supposedly magic ring embellished by a winged horse figure associated with one of his rebirth myths.[4] He boasted that the ring made him invulnerable to hurt by the hospital staff, and endowed him with absolute power to bless or destroy them. His blessing was directed at particular male aides whom he was trying to enlist as magic helpers, in contrast to his earlier more diffuse groping for helpers.

RECRUITMENT OF NEW AIDES TO THE MAGIC-HELPER ROLE

Glen tried to recruit to the magic-helper role a series of aides new at the hospital and on Third Floor. So pronounced was this effort, that it became known by both clinical and research staffs as "the new-aide phenomenon." Glen sought to enlist each of this series of aides as a perfect friend. He would ask the intended recruit to sit and talk with him. For this he offered effusive thanks, and when the relationship was scarcely begun, would say, "I like you very much. Will you be my friend? Will you go to the movies with me, or on a drive to the mountains?" Charged with meaning was his overture, "Will you go to a ranch with me next summer? I would like to take you to a rodeo." A ranch was one place where he had known temporary freedom from the power of women.

Glen's choice of new aides as recruits for the perfect-friend/magic-helper role was both autistic and narcissistic. It was based more upon his wishes and fears than upon shared evaluation of actual encounters, and his idealized percept of the recruit contained projected aspects of his ideal self, such as youthfulness. To find a perfect friend was to attain his ideal self and to erase all earlier failures.

A function of the perfect-friend role was that of auxiliary ego which would serve as thinker and decision-maker for Glen, especially in the problematic area of relationships. He expected the recruit to

---

[4] This ring was but one of a variety of substitute objects to which Glen had recourse in attempting to escape his need-fear dilemma.

distinguish friend from enemy for him. He also wanted the chosen aide to be *his* friend exclusively, and constantly available.

He was usually careful to disclaim sexual interest in the recruit. Occasionally, however, he slipped into open overtures for physical intimacy, reaching for the aide's hand, touching his leg, or trying to hug and kiss him, while saying that he loved him.

These overtures revealed splitting processes, since they coincided closely with his avoiding Dr. Clark while vehemently accusing him of homosexuality. Once, for instance, he literally clung to an aide's hand while voicing fear and distrust of Dr. Clark. At times he agreed to keep a therapy appointment only on the condition that his favorite aide also be present.

A few of the new aides escaped being cast into the magic-helper role, two because on first impression Glen judged them as being "too friendly" and defined them as FBI agents trying to collect evidence against him. When another new aide aroused a frightening wish for closeness, Glen encouraged him to make friends with one of the veteran staff members.

RECURRENT CRISES OF OBJECT INCONSTANCY

Underlying Glen's quest for a perfect friend was his fundamental belief that the quality of the object literally and almost completely determined his state of being. This was a result of his faulty differentiation. He felt that the presence of good objects gave him a sense of comfort and competence which he felt unable to provide autonomously, and he sought constant contact with them. He felt that bad objects caused all of his internal upset and disorder, and he sought to avoid them. Success of this strategy was unlikely, because his need and fear were so poorly integrated within himself and within the compass of any one relationship that his object definitions were highly inconstant. Abruptly, a needed friend might become a feared enemy. He attempted to counter this inconstancy by splitting, redefinitions, and restructurings of reality. But these tactics were foredoomed to failure because they were so autistic. The result was a series of object inconstancy crises.

Again and again, Glen's definitions of objects changed as his need and fear oscillated. If he expressed need, he was likely to be seized by fear. If he expressed fear and hatred, his sense of need would emerge, accompanied by dread that he might destroy a needed object.

In a typical example of need-fear oscillation, Glen approached Dr. Gibson to say, "You will be annihilated today." Several patients nearby chimed in with complaints about Dr. Gibson, who remarked, "This seems to be open season on me." At this point Glen, as if fearful that the attack had gone too far, approached the doctor, clasped his hand, and embraced him, saying, "I want you to know that I don't hate you; I really love you." Then he immediately drew back, declaring that he was well and ready to leave the hospital. Later he asked to phone Lt. Grant and charged that Drs. Clark and Gibson were homosexual partners, only to recant quickly with an apology for saying such "nasty things."

For over three years Glen tended to alternate in defining first Dr. Clark, then Dr. Gibson, as "bad"—especially, bad because of their being "homosexual." He would tell one that the other had propositioned him, or accuse both of being sexual partners. This was but one pattern by which he structured his object world. Many other objects, good and bad, near and distant, were involved; their definitions shifted incessantly and abruptly in kaleidoscopic diffusion.

Extreme separation anxiety contributed to the inconstancy of Glen's object world. This was evident in connection with his doctors' vacations. When the first major vacation separation from Dr. Clark was imminent, Glen's anxiety mounted sharply. He tried to deny his fear of loss by devaluing both Dr. Clark and Dr. Gibson as women and perverts, and by asserting that his true friends were outside the hospital where he soon would join them. Nonetheless, he kept most of his appointments with Dr. Clark, and denounced him more in his absence than in his presence. One evening, in the midst of denigrating Dr. Clark to an activities worker, Glen suddenly asked, "Do you think Dr. Clark hates me?" The worker answered, "No, I don't," upon which Glen queried further, "Even after all those things I've said about him?" He added plaintively, "Dr. Clark probably wishes I would commit suicide." Later the same evening Glen said to an aide, "I don't want to push myself on anyone."

He asked Dr. Gibson to be his therapist while Dr. Clark was away. When refused, Glen complained to the social worker, in Dr. Gibson's presence, "How could someone I like so much be so nasty to me?"

Later he told Dr. Gibson in private, "I only pretended anger, because if I had expressed my true feelings of love, I would never be released from the hospital."

As Dr. Clark's departure drew closer, Glen defined him as even more noxious, and talked of beating him and serving cups of his blood to the staff at a party. Preoccupied with this idea for several days, he made such preparations as bringing a supply of paper cups from the recreation center to Third Floor.[5]

On the day he had designated for the beating, Glen was extremely anxious before his appointment with Dr. Clark, but the session proved uneventful. Later in the day, however, he attempted to go to the local police station, and violently attacked the aide who restrained him. For several days thereafter his definitions of Dr. Clark and this aide oscillated.

Another primitive defense against separation threat consisted of his stripping and exhibiting himself in the hallway. The meaning of this was obscure until a year later, when, in the face of another imminent departure by Dr. Clark, Glen voiced the idea of taking off his clothing and seducing the doctor, presumably in order to bind them inseparably together.

For their last appointment before Dr. Clark's vacation, Glen arranged a protective barrier of furniture between them. Immediately after this therapy session, he agitatedly paced the floor and asked the aides repeatedly, "Do you think Dr. Clark will be killed?" Next, in an apparent effort to quell separation fear, he wrote letters to distant helpers, including his mother and Lt. Grant. That evening he violently attacked the Director of Psychotherapy, of whom he had earlier requested a substitute therapist. For the duration of Dr. Clark's vacation the Director of Psychotherapy was a major target for Glen's displaced feelings, along with more remote and autistic objects such as President Eisenhower and J. Edgar Hoover. Meanwhile, Glen mentioned Dr. Clark only infrequently. Displacement was evident in several complaints about distant objects, such as his protest that President Eisenhower was more interested in being with a mistress than in helping him, clearly an indirect reference to Dr. Clark's vacationing with his wife.

[5] It seems probable that this represented a primitive psychotic urge to avert separation by devouring the object.

When Dr. Clark returned, Glen openly acknowledged having missed him and said, "I was lonesome; now I'm tired and need a year's mental rest." Ten days later, however, his separation anxiety again flared acutely when Dr. Clark phoned to change the time of their next day's appointment. Immediately, Glen demanded to see the doctor-on-call and threatened to attack an aide if the doctor was not there within 15 minutes. The doctor came and Glen calmed down temporarily, but his agitation returned when he saw Henry, the mute catatonic patient who is the subject of Chapter X, being tube-fed. Again he demanded to see the doctor-on-call. This time when the doctor arrived Glen ferociously struck him.

Glen used several strategies in an effort to deny and circumvent his object inconstancy and need-fear dilemma. One was his attempt to recruit new aides to the magic-helper role. Sometimes he was able to maintain a fairly constant definition of a new aide recruit for several weeks or even months. Eventually, however, a shift of object meaning would occur and idealization would then give way to disillusionment. In addition to Glen's internal instability, several reality factors contributed to the inevitability of disillusionment.

In the first place, most of the recruits were ill-equipped to fill the magic-helper role into which Glen cast them. They were young and relatively inexperienced, and he was a virtual stranger to them. Furthermore, their limited power in the ward situation made them less suited than others, such as the ward administrator and charge nurse, to function realistically as protectors and intercessors. This is not to say that Glen's constructs and recruitment procedures were entirely lacking in shared reality value, for many of his overtures to a new aide would evoke pleasant interest and friendliness. The charge nurse customarily warned each new aide against becoming too charmed by and "involved" with Glen. Her aim was to contain Glen's tendency to diffuse to new objects and to lessen the violence of his subsequent disillusionment.

In reality, of course, it was impossible for a recruit to fulfill all of Glen's expectations, particularly his insistent demand that the aide be continuously available and in complete agreement with him on all topics. Glen's urge for absolute congruence of opinions was intended to relieve his inner dividedness, but it caused endless complications in his relationships. He desired that the recruit and he agree totally with each other's evaluation of third persons. He deeply resented and tried for as long as possible to deny evidence of his friend's having any positive interests or relationships with persons other than himself.

Glen used splitting and displacement extensively in his effort to preserve ideal definitions of helpers. When disappointed by someone defined as a helper, he was likely to become angry at another person whom he had cast in an enemy role. Usually, each new aide recruit, as he realized the impossibility of fulfilling Glen's expectations, would become increasingly uncomfortable and less confirming of Glen's claims to ordinary friendship, let alone those to perfect magical friendship.

In the meantime Glen became less able to deny discrepancies between his autistic definition and the aide's actual capabilities and inclinations. Under the weight of cumulative evidence, Glen's idealization would collapse and he would redefine the aide as an enemy. The immediate precipitant of disillusionment might in itself be of minor significance. For instance, Glen once started to leave the dining room without his required escort. When a heretofore idealized aide attempted to restrain him, Glen attacked ferociously, and for many months periodically redefined the aide as an enemy. He would suddenly hug the aide in a manner which varied unpredictably between gentleness, roughness, and a curious amalgam of the two.

These abrupt object redefinitions were less determined by the object's actual behavior than by shifts within Glen, such as sudden consciousness of unintegrated primitive sexual or dependent urges. When this happened, the object would be reclassified as a dangerous id stimulant rather than as a reliable auxiliary ego. This was the usual fate of Glen's relationships with new aides.

Another major strategy by which Glen tried to alleviate his object inconstancy was to claim help from persons outside the hospital. These included a host of proximate and distant persons whom he attempted, with varying degrees of autism to recruit. Some he had actually known; others he hadn't, and they might never have even heard of him.

These extrahospital role recruits comprised four major categories. One consisted of entertainment world personages, whose significance in part concerned Glen's concert pianist ambitions. A second consisted of persons in the horse-breeding world, in which Glen also had aspirations. The third consisted of persons in spheres of government and law enforcement, toward whom Glen looked for strong, lawful order, both internal and external. In this group were various judges, lawyers, and police officers, as well as J. Edgar Hoover, President Eisenhower, and the state Commissioner of Mental Health. The fourth was highly autistic and consisted of the sons of famous fathers, such as Lindbergh and Rickenbacker. These figures were associated with Glen's wish somehow to revise his memory of his father and their relationship, a wish also reflected in his occasionally thinking of himself as Jesus.

Glen's strategy with regard to these extrahospital relationships was to claim help from them while denying any dependence upon more proximate and real persons. Repeatedly he told Dr. Clark, "As long as I have one good friend, I have no need for others." He was likely to turn to distant autistic helpers whenever he was disappointed by the responses of proximate helpers or threatened by feelings of hurt, frustration, loneliness, or personal insignificance.

Since his definitions of autistic helpers were determined even less by the objects' actual behavior and responses than were his definitions of proximate, real objects, he often could idealize them for longer periods of time. He overlooked unresponsiveness from them, and magnified the slightest show of interest into confirmation of his claims of perfect friendship. For example, he wrote repeatedly to ask a distant autistic helper to become his theatrical agent. After many weeks, the only response he received was a polite, brush-off, form letter. Instead of feeling rebuffed, he literally danced with joy. He proceeded to mimeograph and distribute copies of the letter to members of the hospital staff with the triumphant tone of "I told you he was my devoted friend."

At other times he reasoned that third parties, usually women, prevented his helpers from responding. Despite the kernel of truth that a secretary might in fact block direct access to a helper, this grievance basically derived from his mother's earlier interference with his achieving closeness and identification with his father. This motif recurred in various forms—for instance, in his protest that the charge nurse dominated Dr. Gibson and rendered him unhelpful.

An even more autistic attempt to preserve constancy was Glen's assumption of personal responses where there were none in actuality. This was most evident regarding two television personages whom he cast in prominent helping roles. They were Groucho Marx and the announcer of his program, George Fenneman. This program featured a secret "Magic Word" which Glen adapted to his need for direction. He would seize upon the Magic Word, fit it into his most pressing immediate concern, and autistically elaborate it into answers to his uncertainty and indecision. For instance, if in conflict about Dr. Clark, he was likely to emerge from watching the program with assumed directives as to whether and for how long he should meet with the doctor the following day.

The extreme autism with which Glen tried to maintain a sense of being nurtured was illustrated when, during the program preceding Fenneman's vacation, Glen became convinced of a magic message containing a clue to Fenneman's vacation address and a promise to send money which would enable Glen to join him there.

Despite such tactics, however, Glen's definitions of distant magic helpers did not remain constant. Some inconstancy crises were precipitated by the object's actual behavior, as when Lt. Grant, who had featured so prominently in Glen's rebirth period, finally wearied of Glen's frequent letters and phone calls and wrote to say that he wished no further communication. Glen tried at first to deny the reality of this rebuff, then blamed the Lieutenant's wife for interfering, and next declared the Lieutenant worthless and of no further interest. A rush of ideas of magical rescue followed, including plans to resurrect a dead friend and to appeal to the local police to replace Lt. Grant. Soon, however, he became fearful that the local police, too, were against him. It was at this time that he "discovered" George Fenneman and Groucho Marx as magic helpers.

Other inconstancy crises seemed to have no connection with the object's actual behavior. President Eisenhower was in rapid sequence defined as a heroic rescuer, homosexual seducer, member of a horse-stealing plot, and potential murderer of Glen's sister. Urges to appeal for the President's help were supplanted by ideas of arresting or killing him, followed by wishes to apologize and make amends by inviting him to dinner. Fear of the President's supposed seductiveness was replaced by a plan to send a telegram saying "I surrender," and then by hasty retraction of the plan.

His definition of the police was similarly inconstant, in accordance with his need-fear oscillations. One day he would view them as protectors against the doctors, the next day as enemies in league with the medical profession. For a time he misperceived an aide as a policeman to whom he looked for protection whenever Dr. Gibson was near. At other times he feared that if he ventured from the protective hospital the police would abduct or kill him. In attempting to quell his fear he looked incessantly for a superordinate authority: the local police to arrest the doctors, the state police to discipline the local police, the FBI, or the President.

Still another strategy by which Glen sought to avoid object inconstancy was his recourse to a wide assortment of substitute objects —a ring, pictures, and clothing—which served as magic talismans and fetishes. Pet animals, including a kitten and several turtles, also substituted for people. A plan to resurrect a pet bird, dead for several years, was a recurrent preoccupation.

Another set of substitutes was an endless series of exhibitionistic plans and projects, including a pageant-concert, a television appearance, a lavish dinner party, a court hearing, and a garden display. Each of these, he was convinced, would vindicate him in a triumphant show of his worth to the world. These plans consumed countless hours, but tended to remain largely in the realm of self-comforting talk. Their magical and autistic quality became increasingly apparent as they became increasingly elaborate and unusual. Even initially modest and realistic plans underwent such endless autistic changes and postponement that they seldom reached actual execution and testing in shared reality.

Magical word play had much substitutive value for Glen. He derived a spurious sense of mastery from playing with the names of persons who upset him, often by giving them animal names. For a time he termed the hospital "Dr. Doolittle's Zoo," and listed this as the return address on his outgoing mail. Composing poems and limericks ridiculing others also afforded him distraction and temporary comfort.

As with his other categories of helpers, Glen's substitute objects were inconstant. His magic ring, initially a source of comfort and power, suddenly became fearsome to him. He asked the staff to place it in safekeeping to protect him from its dangerous power. Another time he asked to have the ring's insignia removed, hoping thus to restore its goodness. His definitions of other substitute objects underwent similar vicissitudes.

In his quest for constancy, Glen never completely abandoned shared reality relationships in favor of autistic constructions and redefinitions. Rather, he tended to shuttle back and forth between autistic and shared object worlds as his need and fear oscillated. When his fear was mobilized in shared reality, he would find temporary relief in autistic relationships. However, genuine fulfillment of object need was impossible in autistic relationships, which, by definition, were devoid of actual gratifying responses from the other persons. His unfulfilled need would force him back to the shared object world where opportunities for genuine response were greater, but where vulnerability and fear were also greater. In shared reality he was confronted by inevitable inconsistencies and frustrations. Unable to integrate them, he would be flooded by intolerable, disorganizing feelings. This would prompt his retreat again to autistic relationships, thus continuing the cycle.

The treatment task was somehow to break this cycle by containing and integrating Glen's need and fear within actual relationships in shared reality. Only then could he achieve genuine object constancy. His tactics of diffusion, splitting, and redefinition could bring him only temporary *pseudo* constancy.

STAFF ATTEMPTS TO PROMOTE CONTAINMENT
AND INTEGRATION

The question of how best to promote integrative containment raised uncertainties and tactical problems. In the face of Glen's periodic waves of fear and avoidance, Dr. Clark was uncertain as to how vigorously and absolutely he should insist that Glen keep all their appointments. For the most part Dr. Clark pursued a policy of firm insistence that they meet. Several times in the first two years of their relationship he literally had to stand his ground against Glen's efforts to shove him out of the room and out of his life. Early in their relationship this was likely to arouse Glen's intense anxiety and violent protests, but these responses diminished appreciably in the course of treatment. Occasionally, Dr. Clark arranged to have an aide present, a measure which seemed to relieve Glen's anxiety. Infrequently Dr. Clark allowed Glen to skip one appointment while insisting that subsequent ones be kept.

As administrator, Dr. Gibson faced the difficult decision concerning the degree to which limitations should be imposed on Glen's tendency to diffuse to a wide variety of relationships. What range of mail, phone, and vis-à-vis contacts should he allow Glen? Dr. Gibson decided that Glen should have at least some opportunities to test the reality of his object definitions, whether good or bad. If Glen were barred from actual communication, he could not do this, and his autistic assumptions might further proliferate. Accordingly, Dr. Gibson allowed Glen considerable freedom of communication, except when he appeared likely to make seriously menacing threats or be excessively a nuisance or cause himself and his family extreme embarrassment. He allowed Glen less freedom when he was obviously upset and bent upon markedly autistic recruitment attempts. When Glen seemed receptive, Dr. Gibson would suggest that he deal with more proximate real objects rather than displace his feelings to distant ones.

The ward staff employed various containment tactics. One was the charge nurse's warning to new aides that they be wary of accepting too readily the role of magic helper which Glen tried to assign them. Another was the staff's urging Glen to discuss directly with Dr. Clark or Dr. Gibson those matters that he seemed to be displacing from them. His responses varied from acquiescence to fearful recoil and stormy denial that the doctors had any significance in his life.

Another containment tactic was to bring together good and bad objects, with Glen sometimes present, sometimes not. An example of this was Dr. Clark's occasional inclusion of an aide in therapy sessions with Glen. Dr. Gibson arranged several conferences between himself and various extrahospital persons whom Glen had cast in special roles. Glen's usual response to these containment moves was first intense anxiety, then relief. As treatment progressed, he occasionally suggested such moves himself.

Sometimes a distant helper would attempt containment measures. For example, when Lt. Grant learned that Glen claimed, in avoiding Drs. Clark and Gibson, to be following his orders, he wrote Glen, denying having given such orders, and urging him to cooperate with the doctors. Glen's first response was a flurry of fear, avoidance, and intensified definition of the doctors as noxious. A few days later, however, he confided to Dr. Gibson more of the manner in which the magic-helper Lieutenant's suggestion had upset him. He said, "I can't stand Dr. Clark. . . . No, that's not so; I like him very much." Then, shaking his head, he said, "I don't know how I feel, except that I'm less upset in your presence than in Dr. Clark's." He added plaintively, "Probably both you and Dr. Clark would prefer Lt. Grant as a friend to me, although I can't be sure."

At another point Lt. Grant asked Glen to cease trying to contact him. Glen reacted by redefining Lt. Grant as bad. Dr. Clark, in turn, questioned Glen's abrupt redefinition of the Lieutenant, saying, "Don't completely write off that relationship; Lt. Grant has been important and helpful to you." Glen became angry, and the next day refused the doctor admittance to his room, saying, "Lt. Grant says you are not the kind of person he would allow in *his* house, so I am not going to allow you in *mine*."

This was typical of the anxiety and anger Glen displayed whenever his object definitions were questioned. Repeatedly, Dr. Clark commented upon Glen's tendency, with premature and absolute certainty, to classify others as good or bad before they had demonstrated their actual attitudes and intentions. Dr. Clark urged Glen not to jump to conclusions, but to test his assumptions first.

He also tried to help Glen recognize that the rapid shifts of his object definitions stemmed from the mercurial changeability of his feelings and self-evaluation. Dr. Clark pointed out Glen's oscillations between crushing despair and unbounded confidence, and cited the rebirth transition phase as an example.

During the first two years of treatment, Glen usually denied that he or his definitions were changeable. He insisted either that the other persons had changed drastically or that his mood had been influenced by external agents such as drugs. However, beginning in his second year of treatment he became increasingly able to acknowledge awareness of the inconstancy of his feelings.

RELATIONSHIP QUESTIONNAIRE REPORTS ON GLEN

The relationship questionnaire was administered seven times within two years—the third and fourth of the five years spanned by our study of Glen. The reports indicated that during these two years Glen ranked quite high, compared with other Third Floor patients, in the frequency of his approaches to ward staff members, of his talk to them about both personal and impersonal matters, and of his expression of both positive and negative feelings. He presented relatively little problem behavior and required correspondingly infrequent control efforts by the ward staff. As a whole, the ward staff tended to be less active in approaching and expressing feelings to Glen than he to them.

From the first six administrations of the questionnaire, only one significant change was reported in this overall pattern. This was a progressive drop in the reported frequency of his expression of negative feelings toward staff members.

The seventh administration of the questionnaire happened to coincide with one of Glen's most severe object inconstancy crises. He told an aide, "This is the worst time of my life. I'm having terrible trouble with women." The degree of his upset was reflected in the questionnaire reports. In his relationships with the ward staff, he was reported as more frequently avoiding them, while approaching them almost as often as before. Presumably, this indicated fluctuating approach-avoidance rather than consistent withdrawal. At the same time, he was reported as more frequently talking but with less clarity, more frequently manifesting problem behavior, and much more frequently expressing negative feelings.

From the same administration of the questionnaire, an interesting sidelight on the special-helper role also was obtained by comparing the report of an aide whom Glen had at this time at least partially cast in this role with the pooled reports from all ward staff members. According to this comparison, Glen approached this aide with much greater frequency, avoided him less, talked to him more extensively with greater clarity and with much more, though equally frequent, expression of positive and negative feelings. Of himself the aide reported that, compared with the ward staff average, he more frequently approached, talked personally, and expressed positive and negative feelings to Glen. These findings seem to indicate that Glen's attempts to recruit special friends from among the aides were not entirely in the realm of autistic redefinition.

From data sources other than the questionnaire, it was possible to discern several major patterns in Glen's hospital course. These included his increased tolerance of need for proximate objects, greater capacity to locate so-called badness in himself, and more acknowledgment of the significance of women in his life.

INCREASED TOLERANCE OF NEED FOR PROXIMATE OBJECTS

Glen's progress toward containment and integration was sporadic and interspersed with periods of retrogression. Apparent insight would be followed by recrudescence of wildly autistic notions. Periods of relative calm and comfort were interrupted by violent outbursts of anxiety and rage. This was reflected in the course of his hospital privileges. Periods of being free to move about the grounds and to make occasional unaccompanied trips to the village shopping area alternated with periods of restriction. This sequence recurred many times, and the periods of unaccompanied privilege status gradually lengthened.

Perhaps the most important measure of progress was Glen's changed attitude toward need for proximate objects, especially for Drs. Clark and Gibson. Though still prey to inconstancy, he dropped much of his denial that the doctors were significant to him. Early in his hospitalization at the Lodge, some of his expressions of attachment were oblique, such as his claim that his distant helper, Lt. Grant, had advised him to accept being a patient. He spoke of finding security by "hibernating in a sturdy chestnut tree," and after joining the hospital's drama group he said, "Being part of a group effort is more important to me than how well the production goes."

Nonetheless, for the first two years he denied more than he admitted attachment to Dr. Clark, and spoke of his reliance upon distant and autistic friends. At the same time, he showed interest in his therapy sessions and would frequently request extra appointments. Occasionally, at the end of a therapy session he would say, "Gee, is the time up already? Do you have to leave now?"

Intermittently, he acknowledged that he found it useful to talk with Dr. Clark. An instance occurred when he learned that Dr. Gibson planned to talk with his sister. At first highly agitated and accusatory in a diffuse and autistic fashion, he calmed after he told Dr. Clark, "I'm afraid of Dr. Gibson's meeting with my sister. . . . I don't hate you doctors, because you are sick and I don't get mad at sick persons.

You know, in spite of all I say about Dr. Gibson, I still believe he is my friend." At the end of this therapy session, Glen gave Dr. Clark a light embrace and said, "I do appreciate your coming to see me. It helps to talk to you. I feel good now."

Further evidence of his partial acceptance of need was his asking Dr. Clark for help with various body ailments, among them toothache and loss of hair. Previously, he had been unable to speak of anything which might indicate that he was not in good and youthful health. Dr. Clark responded with simple factual advice and assistance in arranging for appropriate care, and was privately pleased that Glen so clearly acknowledged him in the role of doctor.

Still, this acknowledgment of need was inconstant and interrupted by flurries of fearful avoidance. But frequently he did take more direct responsibility for his avoiding behavior. Instead of saying that he was acting on orders from outside, he was more likely to say, "You make me uncomfortable and I want you to stay away." He told Dr. Clark that he preferred a "strictly business," impersonal relationship, and that having frequent appointments upset him.

Glen's oscillations of need and fear gradually became more capable of containment within particular relationships and with shorter time spans. Swings from need to fear and back again would occur within one therapy session rather than over a span of weeks. Sometimes when his fear mounted, rather than break off the contact, he might say, "This talk is making me uncomfortable. Let's move out to the hallway." His increased capacity for containment was accompanied by more explicit statements of ambivalence and inconstancy: "Dr. Clark, you are of some help to me, but it doesn't compare to the greater harm you do. . . . You know, it's puzzling—I was all set to baptize[6] you if you came to see me today, but now that you're here, I don't feel that way, and I'm even somewhat glad to see you. . . . What did you mean last time when you said you felt friendly toward me? That sounds queer."

Once in a burst of denial and projection he said, "*You* can't trust anybody; *you* don't dare to, but I don't have that problem. I have true friends like Lt. Grant and Mr. Fenneman." When Dr. Clark countered, "Glen, I believe you have found that on occasion you could trust

[6] This referred to his throwing water, which for over a year he periodically employed as an avoidance tactic, with the rationale that it would cool off the sexual and aggressive impulses of the noxious object.

me a little bit," Glen protested, "You're a liar; that's not so; you're untrustworthy." Again Dr. Clark countered, "I don't believe you, Glen; I know good and well that you have experienced some trust in me." Then, as he rose to leave, Dr. Clark extended his hand and was somewhat surprised when Glen gripped it firmly.

In another sequence of need-fear oscillation, he one day talked freely to Dr. Clark, but the next day first tried to throw water on him, then took himself to the shower to cool off. He then returned and talked cooperatively, only to become upset and threatening toward the doctor on the third day. On occasion he would say, "I don't want to see you today; go away," but if Dr. Clark waited in the hallway, Glen was likely to emerge after 10 or 15 minutes and say, "Oh, are you still here? Well, since you are, we might as well talk."

The Third Floor staff noted that in the process of containment Glen slackened his efforts to contact distant magic helpers and partially relinquished some of his substitute objects. He also made moves to bring Dr. Clark and various of these other objects closer together. For instance, he asked Dr. Clark to join him in phone calls to several distant persons, including his mother. He gave the doctor a copy of a letter about his plans for a musical pageant. In a further effort to consolidate his objects, he requested that Dr. Clark and several of his favorite aides write to Mr. Fenneman, his autistic magic helper.

These moves toward containment and integration were still likely, however, to be followed by resurgences of diffusion, splitting, and object redefinition.

Glen's relationship with Dr. Gibson followed a similar pattern. He would acknowledge need indirectly by complaining, for example, that the doctor had not been interested enough to watch him perform in a play. More directly, he would acknowledge need by expressing great appreciation and asking to hold his hand briefly after Dr. Gibson had prescribed for a mild physical illness. At a Third Floor picnic at the swimming pond, perhaps stimulated by the informality of the occasion, Glen made a startlingly direct sexual overture to the doctor. When they were somewhat apart from the group, Glen said, "I still want you. Just what do I have to do to have you?" Dr. Gibson responded that Glen did not need to give special services or gifts in order to maintain their friendship. Surprisingly, Glen did not follow his overture with the usual wave of fear, anger, and avoidance, but with sustained moderate friendliness. At other times, however, friendly moves were quickly supplanted by redefinition of Dr. Gibson as loathsome.

Jealousy, a less direct expression of his need, occurred in several episodes. One of Dr. Gibson's psychotherapy patients boasted to Glen of how friendly he and the doctor were. The following day Glen redefined Dr. Gibson as noxious and assaulted him. For several weeks thereafter he avoided Dr. Gibson but could not stop talking to the aides about him. He wrote a letter to the Commissioner of Mental Health denouncing Dr. Gibson, but promptly tore it up, saying that he really wanted to be friendly. He made word-play emendations of his definition of Dr. Gibson, such as, "He's not responsible for all my troubles, only ninety per cent of them."

He was similarly jealous of Dr. Clark's other patients, particularly an older man who had been the doctor's patient longer than himself. He accused this man and Dr. Clark of having a sexual relationship.

Another bout of jealousy was set off when Dr. Gibson became the psychotherapist of Frank Sacco, another Third Floor patient, whose severe autism and limited verbal communicative capacity called for therapy tactics which included play and physical contact. Glen expressed his jealousy of Frank to one of the aides: "Do you like Frank better than me?" To another he said, "I don't bother you by asking you to go for a walk with me. Mrs. (sic) Sacco has already bothered you enough by his hollering."

To Dr. Gibson Glen said nothing directly about Frank, but revived an earlier charge that Dr. Gibson had attacked him. After several repetitions of this charge, Dr. Gibson commented, "Judging from your complaints, I gather you feel I'm not paying you enough attention and you want more contact even if it's in the form of a fight." With abrupt indignation Glen shouted that Dr. Gibson had just sexually propositioned him.

For the next two months Glen was awash with ambivalence and inconstancy. First he would announce that a distant helper had assured him that "Dr. Gibson is O.K. and knows his stuff"; then suddenly he would redefine the doctor as noxious. Toward aides he had assigned the special-friend role he was similarly ambivalent, telling one, "I'm going to baptize you because you're the only person here that I like," and another, "I love you, but you frighten me. I'll smash your teeth in. . . . You're queer."

As this episode of ambivalence and inconstancy subsided, Glen voiced his need more directly: "I have no friends—maybe only two or three out of the three billion persons on earth. . . . People scare me; I can't be certain of them. . . . You don't know what it's like to be so lonely." He was openly grateful for minor indications of others' interest in him, such as an aide's asking if he had slept well, another's talking with him or suggesting a walk together, a student nurse's sewing name tapes in his shirts.

An index of greater acceptance of need was a change in Glen's reactions to separation. In the third year of treatment, as Dr. Gibson was about to leave on a trip, Dr. Clark said to Glen, "You probably will miss him." Somewhat surprisingly, after Dr. Gibson returned, Glen confirmed this prediction, adding that he now was more certain that Dr. Gibson liked him and that he had decided not to write the Commissioner of Mental Health complaining about Dr. Gibson. That same year, when Dr. Clark's summer vacation approached, Glen complained of insufficient advance notice and half-playfully said, "I'll be out of here and back home before you leave on your vacation."

Later the same year, Glen made a visit home. Upon his return to the Lodge, he greeted Dr. Clark warmly and said, "I missed you and I'm glad to be back," only to assert the next day that he wanted to return home. In the ensuing period of angry avoidance of Dr. Clark, Glen said, "I feel as if I were in two places at once." Then, apparently in an effort to overcome his sense of dividedness and to achieve peace with both "parents," he reavowed his goal of becoming both a horse trainer and concert pianist.

At a later time, his mother urged that he be transferred to a hospital nearer her. Glen's response was to issue a "Thirty-day Notice." This was his word-magic twist on the usual "Three-day Notice" of intent to leave the hospital, with the difference that he wanted an injunction to *prevent* his leaving.

In the fourth year of Glen's treatment, Dr. Gibson left Chestnut Lodge to join the staff of another hospital. Initially, Glen reverted to old defensive patterns. He devalued Dr. Gibson and busily wrote and recited scurrilous limericks about Dr. Gibson's dereliction and cowardice in running away. He displaced his feelings by complaining to the state police that the municipal police were shirking their duties. Soon, however, he was able to acknowledge the pain of losing Dr.

Gibson and to reestablish occasional positive contact with him by mail and phone.

In the months immediately following Dr. Gibson's departure, Glen's relationship with Dr. Clark entered a chumlike phase. They worked many hours side by side in a garden which for Glen was something of a world of his own. They shopped in the town for seeds and other garden supplies. Concerning this shift in the doctor-patient relationship, Glen commented, "You know, this is funny, you working along with me here, helping me." He turned to Dr. Clark, as to an older brother, for various types of direct advice.

On his side, Dr. Clark experienced this changed relationship with some discomfort. When he found himself agreeing to help Glen establish contacts with a lawyer and a local judge, he expressed concern to staff colleagues that this might lead to a "paranoid twosome." However, this concern was allayed by the rationale of helping Glen to test the reality of his life situation, including the limits and circumstances of his hospital confinement.

Despite greater tolerance of closeness to Dr. Clark, Glen's clinging-avoidance oscillations continued. On the day following an especially friendly and communicative therapy session Glen was likely to voice doubt that he should continue to talk with the doctor. He said, "You help me some, but you also cause me trouble. . . . I want an office where I can hang up a sign reading, 'Glen Smith, Pianist, Office Hours 1-5 p.m., Do Not Disturb.'" Yet in the course of such denials of dependency, he frequently spent the entire hour talking with his doctor. This was in distinct contrast to previous extended avoidance when his fear was mobilized.

INCREASED CAPACITY TO LOCATE BADNESS IN HIMSELF

Another important indicator of progress and need-fear containment was Glen's heightened awareness of badness within himself. Badness comprised any source of distress or upset. Earlier Glen had attempted to relegate all badness to the outside and then to avoid or destroy it. He once propounded a scheme to assemble all his enemies in one spot at an appointed hour and destroy them, presumably so that he could thenceforth live in comfort.

Increasingly, he was able to acknowledge internal distress such as loneliness. Plaintively, he said to Dr. Clark, "I don't have any friends. What is it that goes wrong? Why don't people like me?" Gradually, he blamed his difficulties in relationships less completely on the treacherous inconstancy of objects and more upon his own contribution. One evening he surprised fellow-members of the drama group by saying, "I guess I've been doing what Dr. Clark tells me I do, being antagonistic when I really want to be friendly. I'm afraid that if I'm too nice to people right away they might misinterpret my feelings." On another occasion he admitted to the charge nurse that he had angrily challenged Dr. Gibson because he wanted to put the doctor on the defensive before asking for ground privileges.

He was more able to notice internal factors in his becoming upset, instead of relying so completely upon denial, displacement, and projection. Previously, if invited to visit his sister, he was likely to say, "I'd better not. President Eisenhower might become upset and try to assassinate her." Now he could say, "I'm afraid to visit her. I get excited very easily; in fact, that is a major cause of my illness." He observed that even in trying to write to his sister or his mother he was likely to become too distraught to complete the letter.

Glen began also to distinguish between two types of upset: (1) "physical trouble" caused by enemies, and (2) "emotional trouble"—literally a sick feeling—caused by friends coming too close. The cause of the "most trouble" he attributed to his closest friend. Accordingly, he preferred "strictly business" relationships.

He discussed with Dr. Clark many instances of closeness triggering fear. One occurred when a favorite aide asked him outside to see the car the aide had just purchased. Although at first Glen enjoyed this very much, he suddenly became agitated, convinced that passersby were suspicious of what was happening between him and the aide, and fled back to Third Floor.

Although, as in this incident, he still employed defensive projection, Glen gradually acknowledged that a large part of his fear was due to inner conflict, not all to the assumed noxiousness of the object. This was clearly evidenced by changes in his attitude toward the annual summer cottage trip made by Third Floor patients. The first year he refused to make the trip. The second year he made the trip but returned several days early, complaining of general misconduct of the staff at the cottage. The third year he voiced concern that others might not want him along, but after debating with himself for more than a week, finally decided to put aside his fear and to go. At the cottage he functioned quite well, with notable efforts to be helpful and to manifest concern for whether other patients, particularly Henry, had enough to eat.[7]

Intermittently, Glen's capacity for self-criticism increased, perhaps partly in response to Dr. Clark's persistent interpretations of his tendency to deny any vulnerability to being hurt. Glen often admitted feeling utterly isolated and outcast. Still tinged with denial were such self-criticisms as: "I may be nuts, but I'm not insane. . . . I know I'm no saint. . . . I know I sometimes act like a jackass, but I don't care. . . . I jump to conclusions, and I'm likely to say the wrong things." (He once taped his mouth shut in an effort to control his impulsive talk.) When Dr. Clark commented, "You sound as if you want to be the hub of the universe," Glen responded, "Well, it sounds ridiculous when you put it that strongly." To an aide friend he spoke of his need to objectify his anxiety, saying that being prevented from carrying out an intended action, such as a phone call, gave him something outside himself on which to pin his discomfort.

An interesting shift in Glen's localization of badness was concretely manifest in his uses of water. For over a year, he periodically threatened to "baptize" Dr. Clark and others, with the conscious purpose of cooling them and cleansing them of their badness. Less conscious was his wish for physical intimacy, as when he called Dr. Gibson "filthy scum," adding, "You are so dirty—I should give you a bath." Subsequently, when upset in sessions with Dr. Clark, he would excuse himself to take a shower in order to regain control of himself. Earlier he had said that *others* needed dirty cobwebs washed from their heads; now he said *he* needed this treatment.

In less metaphorical terms he told Dr. Clark, "Something is wrong with my reasoning; sometimes I say the wrong thing or get the wrong idea about a situation; I can't be absolutely certain of some of my ideas." As his conflicts became more contained, he said, "At times there seem to be two voices in the back of my head, one saying one thing, another saying something contrary." He also described "two kinds of thinking" and acknowledged feeling confused. Often he

---

[7] This solicitude, almost an apology, contrasted conspicuously with his earlier violent attacks upon aides who fed Henry.

coupled such self-criticisms with criticisms of Dr. Clark, "I have trouble with my thinking, but you are doing nothing to correct it."

An earlier way station toward acknowledgment of internal problems was his statement that a deranged person was pursuing him and he was unable to escape. He became more aware of attributing poorly integrated aspects of his self to others. He realized that when he said of Mr. Fenneman, "He upsets me. . . . I never can please him, never can accomplish all he wants me to," he referred, in part, to his own perfectionistic standards, which often paralyzed him with fearful indecision. As projection lessened, he said, "Sometimes I think Fenneman and I are the same person; he knows me better than I know myself." At the same time, Glen became more aware of Mr. Fenneman's functioning as a screen for feelings displaced from Dr. Clark.

Projection of sexual urges lessened. Early in treatment, during his first furor of accusations toward his doctors, Glen had suddenly said, "I have a confession to make. Really, I am the one who is a cocksucker. But it's only a matter of wanting to kiss; I never wanted to bring on an ejaculation." This startlingly abrupt dissolution of the projective process was only momentary, as he quickly reverted to denial and projection. It had, however, revealed something of the nature and intensity of his object need, which was more oral than genital.

Later he occasionally remarked to an aide friend, "Love is different for insane than for normal persons." Much later he more consistently acknowledged sexual impulses as arising from within himself, though this was still partly denied and distorted. For a time his acknowledgment took the rather bizarre and exhibitionistic form of a homemade "chastity belt" which he wore in an effort to control sexual urges— without success, it might be added, since the aides observed him frequently masturbating during this period.

Sporadically he acknowledged directly that he felt sexually attracted to various men, including several of his favorite aides and his autistic helper Fenneman, and attributed this to internal urges rather than to toxic external influences.

During his fifth year of treatment Glen became especially friendly with one aide, to whom he was able to reveal more of his sexual problems. He said to the aide, "My trouble is with women. I can't get along with them, so I'm going to have to get along without them.

I'm really a eunuch; sex makes me ill, and I have nonsexual intercourse." He defined "nonsexual intercourse" as orgasm achieved simply by looking at a person or by mental contact. He then asked the aide, "What do you think of Mr. Fenneman?" When the aide replied, "Just another guy on television," Glen first retorted, "Well, you're not as good a friend as I had thought," but then quickly asked, "Do you think less of me for telling you these things?" The aide's answer, "No, I'm glad you felt able to talk about them," seemed to relieve him.

On another occasion he told the aide of an attempted sodomy attack on him in childhood. Though also confiding some of these painful secrets to Dr. Clark, he still partially split his need and fear. On the same day he might hurl contempt and threats at Dr. Clark, then turn to his aide friend and ask to rest his head in his lap. If the aide, in an effort to counter this splitting, urged Glen to talk more freely with his doctor, Glen was likely to retort, "He's not a doctor, and I'm not a patient."

WOMEN IN GLEN'S REALITY

Glen had enormous difficulties in integrating his feelings toward women. This was reflected not only in his relationships with women but also in the roles he allotted them in his structuring of reality. Both aspects changed in the course of his treatment. His actual contacts increased, and women were represented in his reality more directly and with less autistic definition.

These changes were particularly noteworthy in his attitude toward his mother. Despite her overriding significance in his life, Glen said remarkably little about her during the first two years of treatment, though he was in telephone contact with her every week or two. A notable exception was his outburst of anger toward her in association with his rebirth transition period. In general, he seemed unwilling or unable to say very much directly about her. This was true to a lesser degree concerning his sister, who lived nearby and who visited him quite regularly. Of his other two sisters he said very little and had virtually no contact with them. Within the hospital during this time, he had limited relationships with the charge nurse and the social worker assigned to Third Floor. For the most part he avoided women patients.

While remaining largely uncommunicative about his mother, he spoke fairly often of various persons who were targets for feelings displaced from her and his sisters. Most prominent among these targets was a Mrs. Muirfield, who owned a horse-breeding farm. Glen had once sold her a horse, but otherwise his definitions of her were almost entirely autistic.

He distorted Mrs. Muirfield's buying his horse into the belief that she had stolen it from him and a rancher friend. This, in turn, became the core of a delusional system, elaborations of which recurrently preoccupied him. It was clearly a displacement from his belief that his mother had interfered with his friendship and identification with men.

Glen's definition of Mrs. Muirfield was not constant, however. At times he defined her as a friend instead of a noxious agent. Once, upon receiving a Christmas card from her, he began to think of marrying her. Glen's awareness that he was displacing feelings from his mother and sister to Mrs. Muirfield gradually increased from his initial, almost total unawareness, but the displacement process never completely disappeared.

Glen also displaced feelings onto the mother of another Third Floor patient. He autistically defined this woman, who frequently visited her son, as a pernicious, unfaithful wife who had concealed the true paternity of her son.

Not infrequently, Glen made even more autistic displacements, linking his internal preoccupations to nationally newsworthy persons and events. For instance, he charged President Eisenhower with failure, because of undue influence by various women, to do his duty. This, of course, was the same accusation he made toward Dr. Gibson and the charge nurse. The father-substitute significance of the President was further evident in Glen's idea that the Vice President was like a son and needed the President's protection.

The displacement of Glen's ambivalence toward women sometimes set off delusional productions so complex and tortuous that to untangle them was extremely difficult. Once while riding in a car with his sister and her husband, he was suddenly seized by the fear that a passing taxi driver was, at the behest of Mrs. Muirfield, trying to kill him. For several weeks he was preoccupied with a kaleidoscopic shuffling of his object world. He alternately defined Mrs. Muirfield as enemy and friend, and autistically and inconstantly defined numerous other persons as for or against her designs toward him.

Only later did his thoughts return to his sister. For a time he feared that she and Mrs. Muirfield were collaborators against him and perhaps even sexual partners for each other. Then he conceived a plan for a dinner party including his sister, Mrs. Muirfield, and their husbands. His stated motive was to establish peace and harmony. In this unrealistic notion, one could discern an underlying urge to bring together and integrate the scattered and split objects of his diffused need and fear.

Another episode of labyrinthine delusional displacement involved a crisis which Glen precipitated by anonymously phoning the FBI to say that a bomb had been planted at his sister's home. When he was identified as the source of this alarm, Drs. Clark and Gibson held separate talks with him. Insisting that the danger to his sister had been real and imminent, he was convinced that a mysterious woman had planted a bomb in order to divert attention from her illicit relationship with President Eisenhower.

Subsequently he explained that it had all started with his suddenly feeling very ill. At first he conjectured that this was the result of Mr. Fenneman's anger at his not being more friendly with women. Then he was seized by the overpowering conviction that a bomb was endangering his sister. This idea superseded all other possible explanations for his feeling ill. As if to consolidate this changed explanation, Glen wrote dutifully to Mr. Fenneman to report his beliefs about the bomb.

During the next month Glen incessantly and kaleidoscopically restructured his interpretation of the incident, shifting the identities of the presumed culprit and intended victim. He first redefined J. Edgar Hoover as the culprit rather than rescuer and agent of lawful control. Then in rapid sequence he designated a number of men and women both near and far as the culprits, among them several agents of control, including the Commissioner of Mental Health and Dr. Gibson. His charge that they were unreliable and corrupt seemed a projection and repersonification of his unreliable inner control system.

Next he reached the fearful reformulation that the intended victims were himself and Chestnut Lodge, and that the culprit was a former

"Mr. America" whose picture he had seen in a *Strength and Health* magazine.

Finally, as this frantic episode subsided, Glen gave several indications that his mother was the probable prototype for his initial assumption that a woman was the agent of the bomb threat. He explicitly voiced intense fear of her. The wildly autistic diffusion of the whole episode evidenced how difficult it was for him to integrate the full range of his feelings toward her.

Glen made earlier and more durable progress toward integrating his feelings about his sister. During his third year of treatment his relationship with her became increasingly important, and women in general were allocated more important roles in his object world. When his sister invited him to stay at her home overnight, he commented, "This is the first time in a long while that anyone has invited me out just for friendly reasons. No one likes me." On another occasion he was able to say directly to her, "You know, despite all the trouble I've been to you, I believe you do love me," and to accept her answer, "Oh, Glen, of course I do." Such openness was still exceptional, however.

Holidays prompted Glen to become more aware of a sense of need for supplies from his sister and mother. One Thanksgiving his sister said she would like him to come for dinner, but only if he promised not to talk about his wild notions, such as a space trip to Mars. Glen reacted first with a brief flurry of anger; then he quickly concocted a plan for inviting several celebrities to a large dinner party at the Lodge. For several days he was so absorbed in the details of this plan that he seemed almost to deny completely the hurt from his sister.

At the approach of his third Christmas in the hospital, Glen said angrily of his mother, "She has me locked up here because she doesn't like me and wants to protect my sisters' social position. She likes them better than me." Although twice phoning her and venting anger directly, he quickly displaced his anger to one or another of the nurses. At this time he seemed able only fleetingly to focus his feelings squarely on his mother.

Another Christmas he placed an evergreen branch in his room and comforted himself by announcing, "Well, I'm not home with them, but at least I have the Christmas tree here."

He would amplify even such small expressions of interest as a simple greeting card into an indication of deep friendship, though he might earlier have defined the sender as a bitter enemy. A card from a former student nurse at the hospital sufficed to launch him on an autistic plan to marry her, a sequence of events identical with that noted at another time concerning Mrs. Muirfield.

Gradually Glen spoke more directly about his mother to Dr. Clark and Third Floor staff members, though his image of her was ambivalent and inconstant. He might say to Dr. Clark, "She is insane and unreliable," but tell an aide the same day, "My mother is my only friend and the only person I can trust." Here he epitomized the root of his need-fear dilemma: he felt his mother to be his only source of support—but she was unreliable. His inability to integrate this contradiction was evident in his stating its opposite poles to separate listeners.

Dr. Clark made repeated efforts to interpret this problem to Glen, who was extremely touchy about the doctor's introducing the topic. Dr. Clark once suggested that Mr. Fenneman's supposed supervision of Glen's every move seemed similar to the supervision maintained earlier by mother; Glen responded, "This is different. He's my friend." When the doctor asked, "Does that mean you were not so sure of your mother's friendliness?" Glen recoiled with, "Now you're twisting my words. I didn't mean that at all. How dare you insult my mother!"

At another point Dr. Clark suggested, "You seem to want me and Dr. Gibson to protect you from the powerful women." Glen promptly denied any such wish and turned against Dr. Clark, saying that in any struggle against women the doctors would be unreliable and as helpless as minnows against whales. Apparently what he took as an invitation to join forces against the women mobilized even deeper fear of them.

On the other hand, he was likely to be equally upset by what he interpreted as suggestions that he become friendlier with women. Some of these suggestions were actually made. Others were projections of his own awakening interest in friendship with women. Plaintively he said that those who urged this on him were expecting too much. It was noteworthy, though, that his fear of women now was based less upon their supposed intrinsic noxiousness and more upon his fear of intimacy with them: "My trouble is with women. I can't get along with them, and the idea of sex with them makes me sick."

His difficulty in integrating sex into his relationships with women was further manifest in ideas that if he married he would arrange that a friend father any children his wife might want so that he could remain immaculate, devote himself primarily to music, and totally avoid sex.

A fundamental problem for Glen was how to integrate simultaneous friendships with men and women. He seemed to feel that to be friendly with one automatically incurred the other's enmity. Early in treatment his predominant concern was that women interfered with his efforts to establish perfect friendships with men. Later he expressed fear that his men friends might desert him for women. The thought of one of his male magic helpers being sexually intimate with a woman caused Glen intense discomfort. He mentioned this concern regarding Mr. Fenneman and several aides, but never regarding Dr. Clark. Significantly, this concern about his helpers' possible intimacy with women occurred when he himself was becoming more friendly with several women.

Glen was greatly upset on learning that one of his men friends had paid a visit to his mother. He seemed to feel that his mother and his friend should have remained in separate compartments of reality. His mother's contribution to this problem was dramatically manifested during his first visit home. The visit went quite comfortably for both Glen and his mother until he decided to make a call upon Lt. Grant. When his mother objected, Glen flared in anger, called her unreasonable, and the next day lapsed into a recrudescence of many of his delusional notions.

At times he found himself in great conflict over whether a man or a woman offered the better prospect of friendship. In one bout of such conflict he tried to decide whether Mrs. Muirfield or his former rancher acquaintance was his true friend and should have possession of his valued horse. Finally he said, "I hope that when this is all over, the three of us can sit down and be friends forever," thus allegorically expressing his deep yearning for harmonious integration of his family, a wish which he still had difficulty formulating and sustaining in terms of his actual family.

As Glen spoke more directly about his mother, he was able to partially integrate hostility toward her. In his fourth year of treatment he reported to Dr. Clark a dream of pushing her down a flight of stairs. This was a striking switch from his earlier report, of undetermined accuracy, that when he was a boy his father had pushed him down the stairs. For the first time he also complained to Dr. Clark that his mother had interfered with his successful pursuit of a musical career. Such direct complaints about her still were fleeting and quickly displaced to others, including his sister, whom he accused of forcing his mother to have him locked up.

In the final year of our study he somewhat more consistently voiced conflicting feelings about his mother. Once he called her insane and the cause of all his troubles. Periodically he indicated partial awareness that his recurrent belief that Mrs. Muirfield had cheated and robbed him was displaced from his mother. Dr. Clark helped him to realize that he habitually used identical phrases to describe them. He separately mimicked each by raising his fist and saying, "I've got the power and there's nothing you can do about it," and he called each "a powerful hatchet woman." His awareness of this displacement would periodically lapse, however, as he reverted to elaborations of his delusional system about the horsewoman's plots to destroy him, or to other displacements, such as the belief that another patient's mother was endangering Washington and was about to collapse the Capitol dome. Concurrent with these delusional relapses he threatened to attack the administrative physician and various male aides.

In the meantime, Glen's contacts with some of the women patients gradually increased, and he became rather friendly with several. One he escorted on occasional evening dates and to lunch with his sister. Another, a fellow-member of the hospital drama group, he would join for bridge games and lengthy conversations. Despite their partial anchorage in shared reality, however, these relationships were extremely tenuous and liable to autistic distortion and disruption whenever Glen's need or fear mounted suddenly. Need might take the form of unrealistic fantasies of marriage, only to be abruptly supplanted by a wave of fear, rage, and distancing maneuvers.

One summer several women patients temporarily occupied rooms on Third Floor while their rooms elsewhere were being remodeled. Glen reacted with intense fear that he would become ill if he left his room. He wanted to appeal to the Commissioner of Mental Health and to various distant helpers to correct the "immoral situation." He spoke of asking the local police for protection and permission to sleep in the police station. Fairly soon, however, this wave of fear subsided.

Glen was able to establish a moderately stable relationship with the Third Floor social worker and would sometimes turn to her when he redefined Dr. Clark as noxious. She discouraged Glen's impulses to flee completely from his doctor, and helped him to see that his abrupt redefinitions stemmed less from the doctor's actions than from shifts in his own feelings. The social worker's impression of her relationship with Glen was that he cared less about her as a person than as an audience or listening post.

He was superficially friendly with several student nurses whose temporary assignment to the hospital made congeniality with them relatively safe. His relationship with the charge nurse became somewhat more stable, although still prey to resurgence of feeling that she interfered with the friendships he had established among the doctors and aides.

Résumé of the Integration vs. Diffusion Struggle

We have described Glen's repeated attempts to restructure reality in order to create an object world of ideal goodness and constancy. The leitmotif of these restructurings was his quest for a perfect father-magic helper to protect him from dangerously powerful and malevolent women. He sought relief from his need-fear dilemma by extensive use of diffusion, splitting, and autistic redefinition, as well as by clinging to a variety of substitute objects. These unrealistic mechanisms foredoomed his relationships to the very inconstancy which he sought to circumvent. His diffusion and splitting worked counter to the containment and integration which the staff sought to promote as the necessary basis for genuine constancy.

As Glen and the staff pursued their different ways toward constancy, a series of object inconstancy crises occured. Again and again, as his need and fear oscillated, his definitions of objects abruptly changed and his relationships were disrupted. A related problem concerned his intense reactions to separation. He attempted to defend himself by denying need for proximate and real objects and by looking instead to distant or autistic objects to fulfill his need.

Gradually he became more able to tolerate and acknowledge need for proximate objects, especially for his psychotherapist, Dr. Clark. This correlated with his increased ability to contain waves of need and fear within single relationships and within relatively short time spans, with less recourse to massive and lengthy diffusion and to gross re-definitions of objects.

A closely associated significant change was his increased capacity to locate and tolerate badness within himself. He shifted from attributing badness to toxic intrusions from outside to attributing it more to his easily disturbed feelings; that is, his use of projection lessened.

These changes further coincided with his permitting women more of a place in his reality structure as he progressed toward integrating his need and fear of them. He was able to think and speak more directly of his intense ambivalence toward his sister and his mother instead of constructing autistic versions of the family drama with other persons in the salient roles.

Despite these definite moves toward containment and integration, however, much remained that was disappointing. Retrogression alternated with progression. Periodically he reverted to tactics of diffusion, splitting, and psychotic restructuring of reality. It was not always easy for the treatment staff to keep in mind that this pattern is usual with such a sick patient.

Glen's acknowledgments of need and friendly feeling for proximate objects, particularly Dr. Clark, continued to be followed by waves of fear and avoidance. Late in the last year of our study this was manifest to the extent of his seriously assaulting Dr. Clark, the administrative physician, and the Director of Psychotherapy, while during the same period declaring sexual attraction toward several other men, including a currently favorite aide. Thus he still used splitting, despite the partial success of the staff's efforts at containment and integration.

He also continued his periodic recourse to certain of his stereotyped delusional notions—the belief that his horse had been stolen, that a long-dead friend and a pet bird were still alive, and that various agents of law and order were corrupt and aligned against him. At these times he still wove current public news events into his restructurings of reality, linking them to his internal preoccupations.

For the most part, despite sporadic reshuffling and some new recruitments, he employed much the same cast of characters for these restructurings. He continued in his efforts to recruit new aides to the role of perfect friend. Similarly he continued to plan and replan a concert in an attempt to establish his identity as a musician, and prove his worth to the world. His clinging reiteration of this and similar plans still functioned in a substitute object capacity.

Nonetheless, it was noteworthy that his reversions to diffusion, splitting, and restructuring of his object world became briefer and episodic rather than obstinately continuous. As he gained in awareness, tolerance, and containment of a greater range and depth of feelings, he placed more reliance upon proximate, real objects and less on distant or autistic objects. Whether Glen might have made greater progress toward containment and integration had different treatment tactics been employed, we do not, of course, know. As it is, the gains he made must be counted definite but limited.

Postscript

Following the period of our study, Glen continued in treatment with Dr. Clark for another two years, with disappointingly little further change. Dr. Clark finally decided to terminate his therapeutic relationship with Glen and another therapist took over for a year and a half. Then when Glen's mother died after a long illness, he became increasingly disturbed, and at his family's request was transferred to a Veterans Hospital.

There he soon became an outpatient and lived in a rented house with a former Chestnut Lodge aide as a companion. Two months later, however, the companion was drafted into military service, whereupon Glen's condition deteriorated into apathy and inactivity. Against the advice of his VA physician, he sought and received electroshock from another doctor. Following this he dropped most of his remaining restructurings of reality and became overtly depressed. He was invited to perform in a charity concert, but, to his family's puzzlement, declined.

Two months after the shock treatments, Glen announced to his housekeeper that he and a young man friend, a recent acquaintance, were going to buy a gun. This they did, despite the housekeeper's efforts at warning others to prevent them. The friend stood by as Glen ended his tormented life. Whether the friend believed this to be the best service a "magic helper" could give Glen we do not know.

VII
DAN: A BOY IN SEARCH OF MANHOOD

DONALD L. BURNHAM

DAN, THE YOUNGEST OF THE PATIENTS in our study, was 19 when admitted to Chestnut Lodge. In an earlier hospitalization he had said, "I have never been a man because I was never shown how to be one. . . . My parents prevented me from becoming independent by overprotecting and babying me." His efforts to make the transition to manhood were impeded by a severe need-fear dilemma which, despite his attempted denial, rendered him dependent and ill-prepared for autonomy. He employed various combinations of clinging, avoidance, and redefinition in his quest for constancy and control of his object world.

BACKGROUND HISTORY

The history, as obtained from Dan, his parents, and previous medical records, was spotty but supported his claim that he had been overprotected.

He was from a wealthy Jewish family which held a socially prominent position in the southern city where they lived. His only sibling was a brother, two years younger. Dan defined himself primarily in terms of family membership. The prestigious maternal line was a source of special pride, but also of a set of nearly impossible achievement ideals. At least two of his three given names were maternal family names. He regarded his maternal grandmother, who had lived

160

with his parents since his infancy, as commander of the household. Her cousin Abe, a bachelor, also was a dominant power in the family and in the entire community as well. Dan worshipped him as a hero.

In contrast to his idealization of members of the grandparental generation, Dan depreciated his parents. His father, a compulsive, cautious man, shared something of this view; he regarded his family of origin as low-class nobodies but his wife's as wealthy somebodies. Father seemed less impressed by having worked his way through college than by later joining his in-laws' family business. During several years of courtship he postponed marriage, wanting first to establish his financial independence. He had met his wife, 10 years his junior, when he was teaching her Sunday school class.

Dan's mother was an only child. She was tall and, as a girl, felt shy and socially awkward, but after going away to college became more self-confident. She worshipped her father and felt that she had been spoiled by him. She was less fond of her mother. In the first years of their relationship she adored her husband-to-be, much as she did her father. She would suffer from crying spells, which she attempted to conceal, particularly from her husband, who, in emphasizing strength, hard work, self-improvement, and will power, was extremely intolerant of such "shameful weaknesses" as crying.

Dan was described as a "placid, good, quiet baby" who seldom cried. Reportedly he toilet trained himself at an early age, and was so fussy about cleanliness that he wanted several changes of clothing a day.

Several significant separations marked his infancy and childhood. First, his mother was hospitalized for abscessed breasts shortly after his birth, and he was left in the care of a nurse. Then, when he was two, his brother was born, and uterine hemorrhaging delayed his mother's return from the hospital. When she did return, her time was completely monopolized by this baby brother who was such a "terror" that mother felt called upon to sleep in his room for several months in an effort to placate him. Mother didn't think Dan had noticed the special attention given his brother, but this seems most unlikely. During treatment he often spoke of having turned to others, such as his grandmother and the gardener, in the absence of his mother.

Dan had further separation difficulties in connection with school. He apparently enjoyed nursery school, but on entering kindergarten, he pleaded to stay home, complaining that the teacher expected too much of him. His mother sided with him and intervened with the teacher.

At 10, Dan went away to summer camp and was very homesick, though, according to his parents, he enjoyed camp in subsequent years.

During childhood he reportedly had many playmates but no close friends. He was friendly, but passive and shy in initiating friendships. Elementary school went fairly well, though in fourth grade he had difficulty with a teacher who required that each child in the presence of the entire class, grade himself in conduct. One day Dan came home in tears and covered with hives, saying he had graded himself with a D. In an effort to comfort him, his parents took him out to dinner that evening. In eighth grade he was transferred to a private school. Subsequently he claimed that his parents had arranged this in order to prepare the way for his brother to attend this school later and that this was typical of their scheming to plan his whole life. He also vividly recalled his father's demand that he fight with a schoolmate for his rights, saying angrily, "No son of mine will be a coward!"

Dan felt that his brother resembled his mother more than he did, and that both parents, especially mother, favored this child. He considered his brother very dissimilar to himself. The parents described their other son as a model youth and an excellent student, who, unlike Dan, openly confided in them.

In Dan's third year of high school his problems became more conspicuous. He did poorly in his studies and felt unpopular with classmates, especially girls. His only friends were two similarly troubled "lone wolf" boys. At home he locked himself in his room. After several months of this behavior, Dan told his father of his fear that excessive masturbation might be the cause of his poor school performance. Father suggested body-building exercises, but was sufficiently concerned to ask the advice of a surgeon friend. This man recommended psychiatric consultation with Dr. Jones, who became Dan's first psychotherapist.

During the next year and a half Dan visited Dr. Jones once or twice weekly. The doctor, though he suspected schizophrenia, diagnosed an "adolescent reaction" because he felt more comfortable doing psychotherapy with a patient of the latter diagnosis. Dr. Jones reported that Dan needed "someone to point out reality to him and particularly someone with whom he can identify and use in place of a father."

Dan told the doctor that his family had overprotected him and had given him so much that he had never learned to struggle and to cope with things himself. In the home he became increasingly antagonistic toward his parents whom he cursed, at first under his breath and then aloud. He was especially hostile toward his mother and scarcely spoke to her except to mutter through clenched teeth, "You bitch!" His antagonism spread to include his grandmother and the gardener, previously perhaps his closest friends.

For the most part his family passively endured his behavior and tried to overlook or deny it as much as possible. Several relatives suggested that Dan was seriously ill, while others urged a dose of strong discipline.

Meanwhile Dan barely scraped by in school, but when graduation approached, he became more overtly disturbed. He dressed slovenly and limited his food intake so severely that he lost almost forty pounds.[1] Finally one night he repeatedly washed his underclothes in the toilet and several times drove off wildly in his car, returned, and soon drove off again, as if desperately uncertain whether to stay or flee. He was hospitalized for a month and received a tranquilizing drug.

While in the hospital, Dan decided that if he could avoid his parents by going to live with Cousin Abe, his problems might be solved. Upon his leaving the hospital this plan was put into effect. He saw his parents only once in the next two and one half years. For the next three months he lived with Cousin Abe and managed to graduate from high school.

He worked that summer as a waiter at a camp in another part of the country. Upon returning to his home city he debated, with much indecision, whether to enter college there or in another city. He finally decided on the latter, though his protest that he wanted more independence seemed partly a cover for his fear of separation. He also expressed the concern that if he didn't leave Cousin Abe, he might become too dependent on him.

---

[1] A maternal relative of a previous generation was said to have literally starved himself to death.

Dan did poorly in college, both academically and socially, and was asked to leave before the end of his first year. He preferred to explain his failure on the basis of a playboy attitude rather than on sheer inability to concentrate. For a time during this year he consulted a psychiatrist recommended by Dr. Jones and received a tranquilizing drug in addition to some psychotherapy. This doctor's diagnosis was "obsessive-compulsive character neurosis, with brief periods of psychosis."

In the face of his college failure, Dan decided to make a man of himself by joining the Marine Corps. Meanwhile he angrily refused to communicate with his parents, who were increasingly troubled about him. At their behest a rabbi friend of the family contacted Dan and sternly rebuked him with such communications as: "You are destroying your parents by your hostile attitude. . . . Your father is depressed and your mother has aged terribly. . . . I don't understand why you do these things." The rabbi urged him to visit his parents.

Dan's reaction was mixed—he was tearful and angry, but felt "more like a human being than I ever had in my life." In connection with Dan's heightened sense of personal identity in this encounter, it probably is significant that the rabbi's attitude contrasted sharply with the parents' usual inability to oppose Dan firmly. Dan felt that the rabbi would not have dared talk to him so strongly had Cousin Abe been present as a protector. As it happened, Cousin Abe added his urging to the rabbi's, whereupon Dan agreed to see his parents, but insisted on a brief meeting in a hotel rather than at home. These conditions typified his efforts to assert mastery and to deny dependency though he claimed that he made these demands in order to counter his parents' possessiveness. His parents timidly acquiesced. Rather than oppose or exert authority over him, they usually turned to outside authorities such as doctors, teachers, and rabbis.

Dan's subsequent account of this visit was that his father made an ineffectual effort to dissuade him from enlisting in the Marines by offering him a car and freedom to come and go as he desired if he would forget about enlisting and stay at home. Dan refused, left the meeting, and shortly thereafter reported for recruit training in the Marine Corps. Later Dan complained to his therapist at Chestnut Lodge that his father should have recognized that he was still too

much of a boy for military service and should have absolutely forbidden it—not, of course, the wish Dan had expressed at the time.

Shortly after completing recruit training, Dan was sent to a noncombat overseas duty station, where he soon became increasingly
upset. He appealed for help, first to Dr. Jones, then to his father. Dr.
Jones referred him to a local civilian psychiatrist who saw him twice
and prescribed a tranquilizer, but reported that he gave "a quiet and
healthy impression."[2] Actually Dan was on the verge of panic, with
ideas of reference and fears of homosexuality. He wrote frantically
to his father, who, though alarmed by the irrationality of Dan's letter,
restrained his first impulse to fly immediately to Dan's aid. Instead
father consulted Dr. Jones, and on his advice wrote Dan urging him
to buck up and be strong. Later Dan complained, "He should have
realized that I needed more than advice."

Shortly thereafter Dan presented himself to a medical officer, saying
that he was ill, possibly from a frontal lobe brain tumor, and requesting skull X-rays, EEG, and lobotomy. He also complained that his
barrack-mates were talking about him, accusing him of cracking up,
being insane, being a baby, and needing to be sent to the stockade. He
was promptly hospitalized and told the hospital physicians, "I fought
off the suspicion that somebody was trying to kill me. . . . I have
never been a man because I was never shown how to be one. . . .
My parents prevented me from becoming independent by overprotecting and babying me."

In the succeeding nine months Dan was treated in several military
hospitals overseas and in the United States. He received 15 electric
shock treatments and chlorpromazine. Hospital reports described his
talking of suicidal urges and of his need for a father figure with whom
to identify.

Treatment at Chestnut Lodge was recommended to Dan's family,
and it was arranged that simultaneously he be transferred there directly
from the military hospital and discharged from the Marine Corps. On
hearing of this rather unusual plan, Dan protested that it would only
continue his family's overprotection and domination and further delay
his accession to independent manhood.

---

[2] Repeatedly the degree of Dan's illness was underestimated, doubtless partly
because of his efforts to conceal and deny it.

INITIAL PHASE OF CHESTNUT LODGE TREATMENT

Fearful of upsetting him, Dan's parents preceded him to Chestnut Lodge in order not to be there when he arrived. Upon admission he protested that the hospital was an extension of his parents' noxious influence and that he planned to escape as soon as he received his military discharge pay. He claimed that when he had been in the military hospital his father's visit had caused him a relapse with suicidal urges, and that his main goal was to dissociate himself completely from his parents and his past.

Dan strained to appear manly. He grew a mustache. He wore parts of his Marine uniform and spoke of reenlisting under another name. He boasted of sexual interest in women and made awkward overtures toward several student nurses and women patients.

Contrary to his manly pose, however, he told the Director of Psychotherapy and others that he was a spoiled child, ashamed of his college failure, and fearful that others would see him as puerile, weak, dependent, and unable to control himself. If he couldn't eliminate his childishness, he wanted to conceal it. He wished especially to dominate women and make them feel as small as they had made him feel.

Though he told the Director of Psychotherapy that earlier he had been ill with delusions, hallucinations, and the belief that he was two other persons, he tried to minimize his present degree of illness in a manner that was overly candid, pseudosophisticated, almost exhibitionistic, and distinctly counterphobic. He blamed his illness on psychiatrists and voiced a general fear of them. He complained that psychiatrists viewed him as a "schizophrenic" rather than as a person, and that psychotherapy placed the doctor in a superior position. He added that previous therapy had caused him to lose interest in girls and to feel depressed, and that psychiatrists always tried to talk about his past, whereas he wished to dissociate himself from it. He did acknowledge, however, that he liked the idea of a doctor's scheduling time regularly to listen to him, though he feared that giving in to this desire would weaken him.

Dan's relationship with his first Chestnut Lodge psychotherapist, Dr. Asch, lasted only two months. At the outset he protested that he did not want psychotherapy, fearing it would make him weaker and less able to control himself. Nonetheless, the first interview seemed unusually warm and Dan appeared to talk freely, almost eagerly, about himself. Dr. Asch felt strongly identified with Dan and was uncannily reminded of himself at the patient's age. The next day, however, Dan announced that he would tolerate only 10 minutes with the therapist, and for the next two months saw progressively less of him to the point of almost total avoidance. Dan retracted his initial liking for Dr. Asch, who he now claimed was so intolerably similar to his father that he caused greater upset as well as increased frequency and loudness of hallucinated voices. The sequence of initial approach followed by avoidance seems clearly referable to the intensity of Dan's need-fear dilemma.

Toward Dr. Gibson, his administrative physician, Dan alternated between relative friendliness and antagonism. With other hospital staff members Dan handled his ambivalence by splitting; he approached some and avoided others. Most of those he approached were somewhat peripheral in the hospital staff structure: student nurses affiliated with the hospital for only three months, activities staff members, and ward staff members on the evening and night shifts. His wish to avoid the mainstream of hospital activity also prompted some day-night reversal of his usual sleep pattern, and with one or two temporary exceptions he avoided close contacts with other patients.

To the student nurses he eagerly and insistently spoke of himself and his problems. Later he said that this was with the hope of impressing them by his charm, intelligence, and wit, and of obtaining from them confirmation of the pleasantness of his personality. He used multiple substitute listeners to reinforce avoiding his therapist, just as earlier he had turned from his mother to various substitutes.

The Director of Psychotherapy consulted with Dan concerning his adamant avoidance of Dr. Asch. When asked what he wanted to do, Dan answered that he wished to stay at Chestnut Lodge because he found it helpful to talk to the nurses and aides. At the same time he admitted that his feelings toward Dr. Asch were not completely negative and that not all psychiatrists were totally bad. He had considered Dr. Jones an ally. He acknowledged some liking for Dr. Gibson and averred that if he must have a therapist at Chestnut Lodge, he would prefer him. Since Dr. Gibson had no therapy time available, Dr. Bailey was assigned as Dan's new therapist.

Before proceeding to describe the development of this new relationship, we should mention two concurrent events. One was the discontinuance of the chlorpromazine, 800 mg. daily, which Dan had been receiving on admission. It was discontinued because it was uncertain whether it was any longer benefiting him and because it was desired that his condition without the drug be evaluated. The other event was the discovery during Dan's second month at Chestnut Lodge that he had a duodenal ulcer. A Sippy regimen was prescribed with which he cooperated surprisingly well, and in a manner contradicting his protests that he wanted and needed no help or treatment from others. The ulcer healed rapidly without recurrence.

RELATIONSHIP WITH DR. BAILEY: INITIAL PHASE

Dan's first reaction to Dr. Bailey was to reiterate that he had no wish for a therapist and that by forcing one upon him the psychiatric profession would only ruin him. At his insistence the initial interview with Dr. Bailey lasted only 45 seconds, during which he kept his back turned and carefully avoided eye contact, as though fearful that the doctor might get to or into him through his eyes.

Dr. Bailey scheduled four therapy sessions a week. Since Dan refused to come to his office, the doctor came to Third Floor for their appointments. Sometimes they met in Dan's room, sometimes in the hallway, depending on Dan's mood. Dr. Bailey did not try to force a relationship, but also did not completely accept at face value Dan's protests and avoidance tactics. For instance, when Dan asked him to leave, Dr. Bailey would delay doing so until Dan became more convincingly insistent. When Dan objected to talking about his past, Dr. Bailey responded that they didn't have to, that their first task was just to get to know each other.

For the first two or three weeks Dan preset limits of a few minutes for each of their meetings. Significantly, however, he usually allowed their sessions to last twice as long as his announced limits; also, he lengthened them daily, though he continued to protest and to avoid eye contact. In the third week of this relationship, the longest session was 20 minutes and the total time together during that week 70 minutes.

Dan articulated various reasons for his reluctance to enter this new relationship: it might make him more anxious and perhaps again psychotic; it might take away his will to fight and his interest in women; it might force him to give in to childish dependent urges and to the control of others.

While for the most part avoiding Dr. Bailey, Dan talked extensively to members of the Third Floor nursing staff, whom he considered of equal, if not greater, importance than the doctor. This was corroborated by questionnaire reports obtained on Third Floor patients at this time. The reports on most of the patients indicated that their relationships with their doctors were distinctly different from those with the nurses and aides. In Dan's case, however, there was very little reported difference—less, in fact, than in the case of any other Third Floor patient.

Gradually Dan tolerated longer meetings with Dr. Bailey and even grudgingly acknowledged that he could talk to him "one degree better" than to Dr. Asch. He added, "At least you don't remind me of my father." When their relationship was a month old, it reached a dramatic turning point. For a full hour Dan spoke to Dr. Bailey of many of his innermost feelings. Then he recoiled in fear. He told activities staff members, "Well, they've got me now. . . . Dr. Bailey upset me so much today that I feel I will have to commit suicide." The next day he said he had been so upset that he had masturbated seven times the previous evening. Dan's fear that if he opened himself to the doctor he would be invaded and captured clearly indicated his lack of differentiation and his need-fear dilemma.

His lack of integration also was manifest. He was especially fearful that he might lose control of his poorly integrated anger. He complained to Dr. Gibson that Dr. Bailey had said that it was all right to be angry and that this contradicted what his first psychiatrist, Dr. Jones, had told him. Because of his inner dividedness, Dan was greatly upset when his significant objects appeared at odds with each other in their opinions or advice. Dan would devote hours to efforts to persuade Dr. Bailey to make his ideas more congruent with those of Dr. Jones. Undoubtedly this reflected his inability to integrate inconsistencies and contradictions between earlier intrafamilial objects.

During the second and third months of his relationship with Dr. Bailey, Dan continued to waver between need and fear. At times their contacts were minimal and Dan was stubbornly negativistic and uncommunicative. At other times he was warmer and more approachable.

Meanwhile he maintained considerable interaction with ward staff members. The relationships associated with the Sippy ulcer regimen seemed to afford him an acceptable vehicle for expression of some of his dependency needs.

Dan increased his contacts with Dr. Gibson and expressed preference for his specific administrative directions over Dr. Bailey's less directive manner. This, of course, contradicted his oft-repeated wish for total independence, as did his statement that a more organized and regulated Veterans Hospital would be better for him than the relative freedom of Chestnut Lodge.

During this period Dan worked for a time on the hospital grounds crew, partially in the hope that this would prove his readiness for quick discharge from treatment. He abruptly quit, however, when the grounds manager inadvertently touched on his dread of being regarded as childish by calling, "Hey, boy," to him. Later, at Dr. Gibson's urging, Dan returned to work at this job, but only sporadically. He tore up a paycheck because he felt that since it had indirectly come from his father's payments to the hospital, to accept it would mean accepting his father's influence.

Briefly Dan worked in the canteen which was both managed and staffed by patients until his repeated "borrowing" from the cash drawer was discovered. When, despite warnings, it did not stop, he was fired. He hinted that he had wanted this money because it was untainted by his father.

Throughout this phase of his treatment Dan continued to disclaim affiliation with his parents, refusing to write and saying that he didn't want to hear from them. He also spoke of changing his name. When an aide offhandedly remarked that everyone needs a family, Dan became extremely upset, demanding that Drs. Bailey and Gibson meet with him and the aide in order to obtain retraction of the aide's remark. Dan resented his father's paying for his treatment. He spoke repeatedly of engaging a private lawyer and a private psychiatrist, obtaining his release from Chestnut Lodge, and getting a job on his own. Again and again he set deadlines for his departure, announcement of which seemed to enable him temporarily to feel in control of his destiny.

RELATIONSHIP WITH DR. BAILEY: SECOND PHASE

During his second six months at Chestnut Lodge, Dan was increasingly preoccupied with seeking a magic helper who not only would protect him but would arrange a world in which he could both achieve his ideal self and obtain freedom from his need-fear dilemma. At this point he still considered Cousin Abe his likeliest magic helper and described him as follows:

> He wields tremendous influence on other people, not through his wealth, but through his power and influence. He came along and, without saying so, he got my family off my back, the police, and the school. . . . He gradually got it over to people that I was to take a responsible position in whatever environment I was in, on his order that they were to accept me this way, and that I had as good a chance as anybody of working out an existence within or without the family, anywhere I would choose to have it. . . . Why do I speak of this now? Because I do need somebody's influence to help me now. Not his personal influence, but somebody who wields enough power to get across to all these people who are scared, including me, and scared of nothing really, that I need somebody's power and influence to say, "Will you listen to Dan, give him the help he needs."

He continued to devalue his father, although he recalled a family story of his father's diving through the air to catch him when he had been hurled from his unattended baby carriage as it careened down a steep hill.

Within the hospital Dan seemed to consider various persons as possible recruits to the magic-helper role. For instance, early in treatment he regarded the senior evening aide as an intermediary between himself and other members of the Third Floor staff, saying, "He is a great liaison at explaining things such as my problems to the staff."

Dan progressed unevenly toward perceiving Dr. Bailey in the role of helper. His need-fear dilemma and associated object inconstancy caused periodic crises and swings from approach to avoidance. For the most part he attempted to preserve a percept of Dr. Bailey as a good object. Frequently he accomplished this by casting others in bad roles and attributing his discomfort to them, almost as if his percept of Dr. Bailey received an increment of goodness in proportion to the badness he allocated to third persons.

Dan categorized objects as absolutely good or absolutely bad according to the feelings he associated with them. To good objects he attributed his feeling strong, independent, self-controlled, and generally good. To bad objects he attributed his feeling weak, dependent, poorly controlled, and generally bad. Further, he believed that these feelings were caused by the objects' intrinsic goodness or badness, not by processes within himself. In categorizing objects he usually forced them into his definitions while overlooking their actual personal characteristics.

Dan tried to keep his good and bad objects separate. Uncertain of the constancy of good objects, he approached them cautiously, ready to flee at the first sign that they might be changing into bad objects. In efforts to preserve the goodness of objects, he set limits and conditions on their contacts with him. He wanted them available when he needed them, but they were to leave whenever he began to feel tense. Fearful of depending on any one object, he tried to recruit a corps of supportive objects among whom to spread his need. He was convinced that one bad object could contaminate his entire environment by "organizing others into giving me the wrong kind of recognition." From others he dreaded responses of criticism, disapproval, resentment, and fear. This dread of external badness was fed in large part by his projection of repudiated aspects of himself and his constant fear that they would return to him.

Periodically his diffuse sense of badness around him became focused upon a particular object. Then Dan would become acutely phobic and struggle desperately to avoid the focus of badness. In the succeeding section we shall describe three such episodes.

First Bad Object Crisis

This crisis, in the sixth month of Dan's hospital stay, involved his casting his father in the role of acutely noxious object while he moved toward greater acceptance of Dr. Bailey in the role of helper. The crisis was precipitated by a visit from his parents, neither of whom he had seen for over a year. Dr. Gibson and the Third Floor social worker, after discussion with Dan, had arranged the visit, thinking it unwise to agree even tacitly with the fear side of Dan's ambivalence and his absolute avoidance of his parents. Dr. Gibson also hoped that actual contact might modify Dan's all-bad, *in absentia* definition of his father.

Father seemed partly to accept this definition and voiced fear that the visit might harm Dan and make him violent. Since Dan refused to go downstairs to meet his parents, the social worker brought them to Third Floor. When father extended his hand in greeting, Dan abruptly struck him and shouted, "Take him away or I'll kill him; I'll tear him apart!" In an aside he growled, "You old bitch!" at his mother.

The parents immediately left the ward, and after consultation with the social worker decided against trying further to talk with Dan. It was a year before they visited again.

For several days Dan was diffusely angry. He avoided almost all staff members and tolerated Dr. Bailey's presence for only five or 10 minutes at a time. He threatened to kill the social worker if she ventured near him. Within a week, however, he resumed talking frequently with Third Floor staff members, asked to see the social worker, and tried to enlist her help in an unrealistic plan to free himself from his family by paying his own hospital expenses.

He talked at length about his father. At first he said, "I would like him to come again in two or three weeks. Then I'll be able to control my feelings and I'll talk with him. Of course, that will be the last time I will see him. I'll have my last say and tell him to stay out of my life forever." For the next several weeks Dan repeatedly avowed that soon he would be self-controlled enough for another visit from his father but each time would change his mind and request further postponement of the visit. Finally he reverted to insisting that he wished never to see his father again.

While focusing his fear and anger on his father, Dan began to perceive increased goodness in his doctor. For the first time he came regularly to Dr. Bailey's office. He stayed longer and talked more, and even began many sessions by shaking hands. He credited Dr. Bailey with being the first psychiatrist he had known who was not intent on forcing him back to his bad family. In fact, he seemed to view the doctor as partly replacing Cousin Abe in the role of good protector against his family.

Nonetheless his relationship with Dr. Bailey continued fraught with ambivalence and inconstancy. Unable still to fully contain his feelings within the one relationship, he periodically turned to a corps of auxiliary listeners. Especially after confiding fears of inadequacy and weakness to Dr. Bailey was he likely to seek out a nurse or an aide to say that Dr. Bailey was having an effect on him and, in the next breath, to announce a date for his departure from Chestnut Lodge.

Dan was explicitly ambivalent about his doctor. On the one hand he would talk about wanting to transfer to a VA hospital where he would not be required to have a therapist. On the other hand he would ask whether Dr. Bailey would consent to continue as his therapist if he transferred to another hospital. Periodically he maintained that he needed no therapist but only some assistance with practical daily affairs and his major project of leaving the hospital soon. Occasionally he tried to get Dr. Bailey to intervene with others to change rules and other factors affecting his daily life. He openly admitted, "I am aware of wanting you to tell me what is best to do." He partly relieved his ambivalence by declaring that he liked Dr. Bailey as a person but not as a therapist, in effect splitting him into two objects.

In explanation of his ambivalence Dan said he was aware of fearing a close relationship with anyone. He dreaded that he might come to like and need the doctor more than the doctor needed him. It upset him whenever he felt that Dr. Bailey had influenced him in any way, whether calming or disquieting. He reiterated his idea of moving about from place to place in order to avoid close attachments, which to him were traps. Fear of entrapping closeness often led to sudden shifts in the meaning of his significant objects, as the next crisis will illustrate.

SECOND BAD OBJECT CRISIS

This crisis was featured by Dan's relationship with Miss Smith, a student nurse. She became important to him during the subsidence of the upset evoked by his parents' visit. At first he was attracted to Miss Smith, making friendly overtures and offering confidences to her. Soon, however, he began to redefine her as overprotective and similar to his mother. This feeling became so strong that even details such as her shoes and hair style reminded him of his mother. This in turn seemed to prompt him to give Dr. Bailey a more differentiated description of his mother, of whom he had previously spoken only in brief, stereotyped, and banally complimentary terms.

Dan complained that both Miss Smith and his mother aroused the wrong type of feelings in him. He added that Miss Smith liked aspects of his self which he detested and, moreover, that she put undesirable qualities into him. He perceived his poorly integrated unacceptable feelings, particularly anger, as toxic intrusions from her. For instance, when he grasped her arm with unintended roughness, she said, "You want to hurt me, don't you?" He interpreted her remark as an attempt to put poisonous anger into him. Later he became aware of the internal source of his anger and said, "She recognized the violence in me before I did."

As his unintegrated feelings threatened to overwhelm him, he felt he was on the brink of panic and complete loss of control of destructive forces, all of which he attributed to Miss Smith. He begged that she be sent away from the hospital and considered escaping on a vacation trip. Then he restricted himself to Third Floor in the hope of insulating himself from her toxic influence. Even then, however, he felt influenced from a distance by thought transmission and television, and after Miss Smith left the hospital he continued to complain of residual influence that interfered with his feeling well and being comfortable with others. Ward staff observations of Dan during this period indicated that he was hallucinating. He spoke to the air as if addressing another person, and would turn up his portable radio's volume, apparently in order to drown out hallucinated voices.

Gradually this wave of fear subsided, and when new student nurses arrived to begin their three-month psychiatric training period, Dan's need was again manifest. Rather than avoiding, he approached them in a casually boastful and sexually suggestive manner. He told male aides that he would go to a whorehouse if only he had the price of admission, as if to deny his recent near-panic at finding himself too close to Miss Smith. Paradoxically, he seemed particularly drawn to the new nurse whom he perceived as most similar to Miss Smith. He aroused strong reciprocal feelings in many of the nurses. One said, "If it would help Dan, I would gladly let him hit me." Another observed that he seemed to want her attention when she was with someone else, but lost interest when she was with him. He himself commented, "I miss you when you are off duty, but you make me uncomfortable when you are near me. It's a case of not being able to live with you or without you."

THIRD BAD OBJECT CRISIS

Several factors combined to set the stage for this crisis during Dan's tenth month at Chestnut Lodge. First, against his wishes he was transferred to Hilltop, a semi-open building. Next, he was soon to be separated from Dr. Bailey, who planned to be away for a week or two while his wife had a baby. In addition, two nurses important to him were planning to be away. When, as these separations neared, Dr. Bailey was twice late for appointments, Dan threatened to fire him, saying he should be available whenever needed.

When Dr. Bailey departed on leave, Dan began to avoid the day shift ward staff members, while remaining relatively sociable with the evening staff. At first his complaint about the day staff was diffuse, but soon he focused upon Mr. Davis, a Negro aide, as the specific source of his discomfort. This fear crystallized when the aide offered Dan help for a foot infection and refused to comply immediately with Dan's brusque order that he leave the room.[3] Thereupon Dan redefined him as a bad, toxic object to be avoided at all costs. Dan refused to leave his room when Mr. Davis was on duty, and one day when the aide worked two consecutive shifts Dan smashed several windows. Dan demanded that the charge nurse order Mr. Davis to stay away from him. When she answered, "I'm not going to go along with your wish to rearrange the world," Dan promptly redefined her as bad and called her "an overprotective, seductive, teasing nymphomaniac, just like my mother and Miss Smith." His phobic avoidance of Mr. Davis and the charge nurse soon spread to reinclude the entire day staff and shortly thereafter to encompass the evening staff as well.

In the midst of this phobic reaction were several indications that denied need underlay Dan's fear. One day the charge nurse brought a lunch tray to his room. At first he berated her and said she was trying to make him ill. Then he suddenly softened and said, "I don't know whether I love or hate the ward staff; I'm afraid I might begin to care too much." On another occasion his denied dependent urges

---

[3] This infection had developed when Dan had secluded himself in his room to avoid the day staff and had stopped bathing. Dirtiness was extraordinarily significant to him. Though he feared it, as witnessed by his childhood compulsive cleanliness and his repeated washing at the onset of his overt illness, he also valued it as a symbol of masculinity and defiance of the dictates of women.

were dramatically revealed in projected form when he rushed outdoors to attack a nearby grounds worker who he thought had called him "mama's boy." Still further evidence was contained in his statement that Mr. Davis was like his father in wanting to force his submission. He added, "If you brought my father here and put him in bed with me, I would have a breakdown; if you removed him, I would be all right." Dan also recalled that earlier in a staff-patient meeting he had been so upset that he had fled the room when Mr. Davis had glanced at him in a friendly, "between you and me" manner.

Dr. Bailey was away for five weeks, much longer than he had anticipated. After his return, Dan complained at length to him about the bad Mr. Davis and others, but carefully omitted any criticism or expression of displeasure at the doctor's long absence. With significant vehemence Dan rejected Dr. Bailey's suggestion that their separation might have contributed something to his upset.

Dan continued to define Hilltop as intolerably bad, like his parents' home. After repeated appeals to Dr. Bailey and to the higher authority of the Director of Psychotherapy, he was returned to Third Floor. For several weeks he refused to venture outdoors during the day for fear that he might encounter Mr. Davis or other staff members from Hilltop, but soon he seemed appreciably more comfortable, though still somewhat seclusive and neglectful of his body and clothing.

Toward Third Floor staff members he was ambivalent. He alternated between approaching and avoiding the charge nurse; occasionally he said that she reminded him of Miss Smith. He seemed both to want and to resent her attention. One day she insisted that he bathe and brush his teeth. To her surprise he willingly complied, but shortly afterward threatened to knock out her teeth and said, "Some day I'm going to have to kill you." With the aides he was similarly contradictory, sometimes demanding that they leave him alone, at other times literally cornering them and insisting that they listen to him.

SECOND YEAR OF TREATMENT

At the beginning of Dan's second year at Chestnut Lodge his relationship with Dr. Bailey had developed to a point where it was demonstrably different from most of his relationships with Third Floor staff members. Evidence of this was contained in questionnaire reports made during the fourteenth month of his stay. According to these reports the frequency of his personal communication and expression of positive feelings had increased in his relationship with Dr. Bailey, but had decreased in his relationships with ward staff members. These changes are shown in Figure 1.

At this time Dan was approaching his twenty-first birthday, highly significant to him as the point of transition from dependent childhood to independent manhood. He announced unrealistic plans for quick financial independence and discharge from the hospital, but at the same time voiced doubts that he could achieve these goals, and added that he might become a permanent patient in a VA hospital.

Dan also campaigned for a visit from Cousin Abe and Dr. Jones, his first psychotherapist; he hoped they would arrange his release from Chestnut Lodge, and, further, that Cousin Abe would legally adopt him. He said that his father was the one who was sick, incompetent, and in need of hospitalization, and he didn't want his bad parents to know that his good helpers were going to visit.

Cousin Abe and Dr. Jones came to visit, but disappointed Dan by strongly recommending that he continue at Chestnut Lodge. He was further disappointed by undeniable evidence that Cousin Abe was far from omnipotent; in fact, his general health and memory were failing and he was lonely and unhappy. Dan even wondered whether he might become mentally ill—a fear of substance, since the old man had suffered at least one major depression.

Dan's more realistic view of Cousin Abe was associated with greater acceptance of Dr. Bailey as a source of help and possible direction. This shift was so pronounced that he openly regretted his previous resistance to therapy, wanted to make up for lost time, and spoke of perhaps needing treatment for two more years. He no longer tried to avoid or cut short the sessions, but instead was distinctly annoyed when anything interrupted them.

Separations of any sort upset Dan, and he more openly sought inseparability. Often on Fridays he would say to Dr. Bailey, "I hope you have a pleasant weekend; mine is going to be miserable." On Monday he might plaintively say, "It's been 48 hours since I last saw you," or, "Did you hear anyone talking about me while you were away?" He seemed to want reassurance that Dr. Bailey had not completely forgotten him while they were apart. A deep-seated fear was

FIGURE 1. Questionnaire Scores for Dan

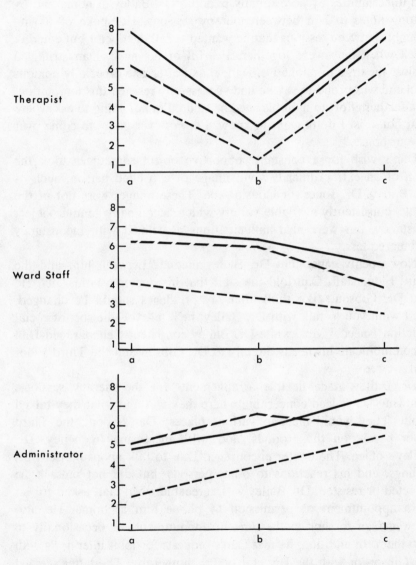

Approach by patient ————————

Personal communication by patient — — — — —

Positive feelings expressed by patient — — — —

a - 3 months after admission

b - 6 months after admission

c - 12 months after admission

that during separation the relationship might totally disintegrate or that Dr. Bailey might be destroyed. Dan tried to relieve these fears and uncertainties by occasionally phoning Dr. Bailey at home and by writing notes to him between therapy sessions. He spoke of having thoughts between sessions that he wanted to tell the doctor but couldn't recall when they were together. Fearful of his need, Dan struggled against the urge to phone Dr. Bailey, and after one especially anxious weekend was proud to say he had successfully resisted this temptation. In a further effort to fight his need he said, "I'm *not* going to ask where your house is. I don't want to know. I'm *not* ever going to come over to your house."

Dan's wish for a constant supportive object sometimes took the form of an extraordinarily vivid image of a needed person, such as Dr. Bailey, Dr. Jones, or Cousin Abe. These images were not of the stable, consistently available variety which accompany genuine object constancy, but were near-hallucinations associated with inconstancy and feared loss.

Now openly eager that Dr. Bailey mediate between him and the Third Floor staff, Dan told the staff that his doctor was his ally. He told Dr. Gibson, "*We* think that my privileges should be changed. . . . I want you to talk with Dr. Bailey; he'll tell you the sort of social situation I need." Meanwhile Dr. Bailey consistently encouraged Dan to communicate his needs directly to Dr. Gibson and the Third Floor staff.

Dr. Bailey made flexible arrangements for the therapy sessions, following Dan's lead concerning where they met and what they talked about. They would meet in various places: Dan's room, the Third Floor porch, on the grounds, and, with increasing frequency, Dr. Bailey's office. The doctor encouraged Dan to talk about himself, his feelings, and his reactions to other persons, but did not press if he objected or resisted. Dr. Bailey was agreeable when Dan asked for an extra appointment or permission to phone him at home. He also allowed Dan to shorten the time of appointments or occasionally to skip them. In addition, he met Dan's requests for joint interviews with Dr. Gibson or with the Director of Psychotherapy. The latter seemed to function as a court of appeal for Dan, who still was hesitant to rely completely on Dr. Bailey as a helper.

Dr. Bailey's flexibility was further manifest in his willingness occasionally to exchange roles with Dan. For instance, during the height of his fear of the noxious aide, Mr. Davis, Dan complained, "You don't understand just how it is. . . . Tell you what I'll do—I'll show you just how Mr. Davis upsets me. You lie down on the bed just like I was doing, and I'll go over to the door and knock and come right in without even waiting for you to say anything, just like Mr. Davis did a few days ago." Dr. Bailey agreed to this suggestion, and their role-playing not only usefully clarified Dan's conflict with Mr. Davis but also was manifestly enjoyable to both Dan and Dr. Bailey.

Dan gradually became more aware of his various attempts to control the frequency, duration, and quality of his encounters with Dr. Bailey and others. With regard to diffusion and splitting, he told the charge nurse, "Perhaps I have enough money to have two doctors. Then I could keep my relationship with Dr. Bailey pleasant; whenever I was angry or felt like complaining, I could talk to the other doctor."

For a time he achieved an approximation of this idea in the form of a relationship with Mr. Cohen, a medical student who was serving a three-month externship. Dan approached Mr. Cohen with clinging eagerness to talk. He said, "You remind me of my brother; he's a premedical student." Dan assumed that Mr. Cohen's assignment to Third Floor was specifically designed to meet his need for extra help. They spent many hours together in talk, walks, and shopping trips. Another staff member commented, "You two seem to have adopted each other."

Mr. Cohen soon came to feel, however, that the relationship was for the most part one-sided. Dan was at pains to state who he was, with particular emphasis on his family's prestige, but showed litttle interest in Mr. Cohen as a person, treating him mainly as a listener. One day, in an experimental mood and determined to gain some reciprocity in the relationship, Mr. Cohen insisted on talking about himself and what was on his mind. Dan was startled and impatient, and only grudgingly consented to listen. As Mr. Cohen subsequently put it, "Dan treated me as just a projection of a shadow and as a mechanical listening post rather than as myself. . . . Other than to get me to agree with him, he had no interest in my opinions."

Dan tried to control all aspects of this relationship. He wanted to know in advance exactly when Mr. Cohen would be available to him and was intolerant of anything that might come between them. He became disturbed when Mr. Cohen was attentive to others, especially if they were bad persons in Dan's eyes. One day such a patient interrupted a chat between Dan and Mr. Cohen. The latter turned only briefly toward the intruder, but when he turned back to Dan, he was met by, "Talk to one of the aides before you talk again with me." Knowing the literalness of Dan's ideas about bad objects contaminating the good, Mr. Cohen complied and then said, "There, am I clean enough to talk with you now?"

During most of their relationship Dan preserved a predominantly good definition of Mr. Cohen and partly denied the importance of Dr. Bailey. Then, as Mr. Cohen's departure from the hospital approached, Dan devalued him, saying, "You know, you're no help to me; in fact, you may even be harmful." Once, on a shopping trip he even refused to borrow money from Mr. Cohen for a minor purchase. Concurrently he restored Dr. Bailey to grace: "He's the only helpful person." As soon as Mr. Cohen left, however, Dan missed him and asked the Director of Psychotherapy for a replacement.

During his second year of treatment Dan made definite progress toward clarification and lessening of his need-fear dilemma. He became more accepting of his need. He became aware, for instance, that despite his oft-stated wish to be free of his parents, his primary definition of himself was in terms of family membership. While disavowing affiliation with his parents, he perceived others as resembling them, and he tended to replicate his family in current relationships wherever he was. His bitter complaints about overprotection were counterbalanced by conscious wishes for guidance and regulation by others, as in his stating, "I feel more my real self when someone gives me clear, strict orders."

Dan's belief that others literally determined who he was far exceeded normal need for identity confirmation. He said, "I have a true self and a phony self, and others determine which one I am at any particular time." This included whether he was man or boy, male or female, and strong or weak, as if these identity elements were fed into him from the outside. He said that rough or insulting responses made him feel more real and manly because they demonstrated that he had no need or wish to be tenderly handled or to return to the sheltered existence of a little boy.

Dan regarded "recognition" from others as vital nutriment for his self, and he required it in proper form and dosage. He feared too much or too little recognition and was uncertain whether he wanted to be a special "somebody" or an average "nobody." The intensity of his hunger for recognition was strikingly manifest one day as he watched on television the President of the United States recognizing the latest astronaut hero. Dan blurted out, "I'd like to throw acid on that space hero and shoot the President! . . . If I went out in a blaze of infamy, at least I wouldn't be forgotten!"

Another problem was Dan's fear of simultaneous recognition from several persons; this clearly seemed derived from his inability to integrate his parents' differing expectations of him. Father was scornful when Dan was timid and unaggressive or, in father's eyes, weak and cowardly. Mother, on the other hand, was greatly distraught whenever Dan displayed anger. The result was a pair of incompatible self-images —his weak self and his angry self. He formulated this as follows: "There are two different images of me. Part of the time people are scared of me and think I am powerful, and the other part of the time they think I am real little and they are angry at me."

It also was true that in the past others, including his family and several doctors, had underestimated the severity of his illness and his capacity for homicidal rage. Part of his quandary was how to get others to take seriously his capacity for violence and yet not be frightened away from him.

Dan's dependence upon and vulnerability to the influence of others were further manifest in his beliefs regarding transmission of emotions. Believing that persons literally poured bad feelings into each other, he tried to dump his unpleasant emotions into others and to avoid persons who might dump theirs into him. In other words, he tried to maintain a one-way flow of feelings in his relationships, giving the other person little encouragement or opportunity to spill troubled feelings into him and avoiding sustained contacts which might invite a two-way flow of feelings. This was much of the basis for his efforts early in treatment to diffuse his feelings among a corps of listeners rather than to contain them within the doctor-patient relationship. Occasionally he spoke of needing even more listeners: "I need more outside outlets. I must have a dumping place for my fears, otherwise I'll become submerged. . . . I'll have to leave and find outside contacts." At other times he considered withdrawal his only remedy: "I'm having too intense feelings and my blood pressure is going up, so I must stay away from people for a while." A frequent fear was that feelings which he had passed to another person might return to him, either directly from the other person or via a bucket brigade of several persons.

Only gradually and unsteadily was he more able to contain his feelings within his relationship with Dr. Bailey. At first, as we have noted, this was accompanied by bad-object crises. In the second year of treatment there were no full-blown crises, though from time to time Dan was moderately fearful of various persons whom he defined as noxious. Occasionally he located badness further away in the adjacent town, especially during the month when he shopped there almost daily as part of his hospital canteen job. He complained to Dr. Bailey that townspeople were talking about him and asked that he accompany him into town to verify this. Dr. Bailey complied, and upon their return told Dan that he had observed no unusual attention or talk, and suggested that Dan's intense self-consciousness might account for his feeling that there had been. Dan agreed that this might be, and seemed relieved.

Dr. Bailey's willingness to serve as a partner in this reality-testing venture was part of his general effort to encourage Dan to test reality rather than automatically assume personal relevance in all surrounding events. Frequently he suggested that Dan might have misheard or misinterpreted something. He was quick to confirm or refute many of Dan's assumptions, especially those concerning what the doctor might be thinking.

Dan fluctuated in his ability to locate inside himself what he considered bad and dangerous and to feel less vulnerable to outside influence. Concerning his wish to achieve comfort by moving from place to place, he tolerated Dr. Bailey's blunt statement: "I'm getting rather bored with your continual requests to transfer to other hospitals; you are always viewing the grass in the other yard as greener." After a burst of angry denial, Dan agreed that this had often been true in the past, but now he was resolved to face frightening situations and had been thinking of going over to Hilltop to visit Mr. Davis. He carried out this resolve and developed a rather friendly relationship with the formerly noxious aide.

At other times Dan reverted to his belief that external badness caused his troubles. His uncertainty about this was evident in his saying,

> I know that even if things were perfect—that is, not organized—inside this hospital, I still couldn't stay here, because the town outside is organized against me. *You* might say "Well, if it weren't for these people there would be someone else," or *you* might say, "He's organized them himself." But this is not true. I guess, though, that I'm going to think it's organized against me wherever I go, until I'm rid of my fears. I will say this, though: part of the time I'm right. Third Floor has always been organized.

Despite this complaint about Third Floor, Dan continued to prefer its relatively controlled atmosphere to the laissez-faire of other wards. It fact, three times when he was transferred to a semi-open ward, he became so uncomfortable that he was returned to Third Floor.

Nonetheless, Dan's recourse to avoidance, as a universal remedy for discomfort lessened. He abandoned his previous plan to become an itinerant laborer constantly on the move, never in one place long enough to become attached to anyone. He realized that a flaw in this plan was that it would deprive him of his needed "recognition." To be truly anonymous, to be nobody, threatened him with annihilation. Furthermore, he lacked sufficient genuine autonomy to carry off this plan.

Dan also became aware of several self-defeating aspects of his strategy of arranging a favorable help-harm balance in his object world. His attempted unilateral control and imposition of definitions tended to depersonalize others, as when he treated them as receptacles into which to dump his bad feelings and his repudiated traits, or as replicas of past objects. Similarly depersonalizing was his expectation that others—with whom, through pseudocandor, he initiated relationships—be mechanical listening posts rather than persons with their own needs to express feelings and opinions. Early in treatment he had voiced a view of others as tools in a grandiose analogy which indicated his estimate of the magnitude of his struggle to produce a good self. He had said, "As Winston Churchill said to Franklin Roosevelt in 1940, 'Give us the tools and we will finish the job. But without equipment we can't do a thing.'" As treatment progressed he became more sensitive to others' needs to be persons, not tools.

Dan became increasingly aware that his self was shaped not entirely by outer recognition but also by inner processes. He relinquished some of his belief that if everyone would treat him respectfully as an equal and a man, he would automatically become a man. As he became more autonomous and differentiated from his surroundings, he also gained in his ability to integrate previously repudiated aspects of his self, particularly his dependent need and his anger.

Early in treatment he had considered dependent need an intolerable weakness. His fear of being seen as a "mama's boy and crybaby" had at times been so intense that it had assumed the form of hallucinations and ideas of reference. The role of patient had been objectionable to him because it had connoted weakness and passivity and he had tried to set himself apart from other patients, especially those who showed "weakness" by open displays of emotion. Painfully sensitive to any real or imagined failure by staff members to accord him recognition as a full equal, he had protested that he should be treated as a person, not as a patient, and had responded favorably when occasionally placed in a helping role such as providing assistance to a sicker patient. Sometimes he had attempted to reverse roles with Dr. Bailey and to speak of what he would do as a psychiatrist.

Dan had tried to defend against "weakness" by extensive denial of hurt, sensitivity, and passive longings. He had exerted much effort to avoid situations that might evoke these feelings, while straining to maintain a pose of active, masterful strength. Dan also had employed negativism to deny that others could influence him, for many months neglecting his personal grooming in order to demonstrate independence. Any suggestion that he bathe or shave had been resented as implying that he couldn't care for himself.

As therapy progressed, his defensiveness lessened. At times his acknowledgment of "weaknesses" was strained and counterphobic. For instance, he might stand in the hallway and shout, "I'm a coward and a homosexual! There, you can put that in your records!" At other times, though, he spoke more simply to Dr. Bailey and others of his loneliness, hurt, and urges to cry. He admitted feeling physically weak and envying others' accomplishments, particularly his brother's success in college. If even a casual passerby appeared well dressed and confident, Dan felt a sickening wave of inferiority.

He relinquished much of his defensive grandiosity. He said, "I realize now that I'll never be a big shot," though still he occasionally comforted himself with fantasies of becoming a heroic soldier, a great lover, a football star, or a famous physician, or with a negative identity wish to be an obscure bum.

Dan revived a boyhood interest in sketching, earlier abandoned out of fear that others might consider it unmanly. Dr. Bailey encouraged this renewal of interest and responded positively to Dan's offer to show his sketches to him.

In place of denial of need for others Dan openly acknowledged intense loneliness. He became aware of using his portable radio as a substitute for persons, and he voiced his envy of others who seemed to establish relationships easily. Sometimes the mere sight of others in close conversation would fill him with tearful rage and trigger ideas that they were talking about him—scant relief from his sense of being left out. He recalled the pain of thinking that his brother was much more included in the family than he, a sharp contrast to his earlier protests that he wanted no part of his family.

Further integration took in previously unacceptable anger. Dan now saw anger more as an internal process and less as a toxic intrusion from the outside. He voiced fears of killing others, especially children, and divulged a fantasy of a cross-country killing spree. He recalled in detail his earlier rage toward his family and how it had spilled out into obscene gestures and insulting remarks toward others.

Dan's progress toward integration of anger correlated with his discovery that his relationship with Dr. Bailey did not collapse if he became annoyed at the doctor, though he still tended toward caution and guardedness in his expressions of anger. Once he suggested meeting in his Third Floor room rather than in the doctor's office in order to test Dr. Bailey by hurling insults at him. The contrivedness of this arrangement was typical of Dan's defenses against uncontrolled rage, but Dr. Bailey agreed to try it. When the time came, Dan was able only to mutter nearly inaudible curses, reminiscent of earlier behavior with his family.

On other occasions Dr. Bailey was able to assist Dan toward fuller expression of his feelings by commenting that his manner often seemed to contradict his words. Dr. Bailey also pointed out Dan's defensive displacement of feelings to third persons. A portion of Dan's anger remained unintegrated, as witnessed by his telling Dr. Bailey that he *thought* he had overheard his roommate say, "God damn Dr. Bailey!" Clearly Dan had further progress to make in integrating his need and fear of his doctor.

As mentioned previously, this involved his difficulty in integrating his weak self and his angry self. He feared that if he revealed too much of either of these selves, his relationships would collapse. At times this led him deliberately to create a bad first impression rather than to risk subsequently spoiling an initial good impression. Gradually he came to see strength and weakness in more relative and less categorical terms. This lessened the previous gap between his perceived self and his unattainable absolute ideals.

His view of his parents changed. He now saw them as rather troubled persons who had done their best with their mixed strengths and weaknesses. His image of each parent became more differentiated. He spoke favorably of his father's determination and tenacity, but still criticized him for not providing sufficient advice and direction. He recalled that when asked for advice, his father usually referred him to someone else. He considered his father to be overly concerned with proper appearances and the opinions of others, fundamentally lonely, suspicious, and fearful that others would take advantage of him.

Dan was further troubled by his father's inconsistencies, such as dressing impeccably in public but sloppily at home, and proclaiming the ideals of strength and self-determination while deferring to his mother-in-law as the head of the family. Adding to Dan's confusion about masculine and feminine roles was his observation that his father indulged and protected his mother in a manner that Dan envied and desired for himself.

Dan's sensitivity to his father's contradictions was conspicuously reflected in his relationships with hospital staff members. He wished his doctors to be perfectly consistent, and complained that Dr. Gibson refused when he requested increased freedom but granted it when he didn't request it. Dan was troubled when staff members disagreed regarding attitudes and policies toward him. He said he preferred the more experienced aides because they were more certain of themselves and accordingly more consistent.

His percept of his mother also became more differentiated. He saw her as easily upset and tending to withdraw or to dissolve into tears if threatened by a disagreement. He also pictured her as very attractive to all men—except himself.

After nearly two years at Chestnut Lodge Dan wrote his grandmother that he no longer blamed his parents for his illness. His parents responded to this indirect but welcome message by visiting him a month later. This visit differed vastly from the previous one, when his assault on his father had plunged him into a bad object crisis. This time he feared that he might cry when he saw his parents; as a precaution he asked Dr. Bailey to be present. When his parents arrived, he was able to greet them with warm embraces. After a while he asked Dr. Bailey to leave, and spent the next four hours in pleasant interaction with them. In their relief and joy his parents became temporarily distraught, whereupon Dan assumed a protective calming role. The success of this visit did not mean, however, that his fear of and anger toward his parents were completely gone. Periodically he continued to blame them and to assert that despite their protestations to the contrary they had never really wanted him.

Dan's progress toward greater differentiation and integration correlated with his focusing more of his need and fear on Dr. Bailey. Still he experienced periodic recrudescence of fear and urges to avoid all objects, but as his fear-avoidance and fear-rage sequences became more conscious, they became correspondingly more controllable. He realized something of the degree to which his wishes and fears shaped his definition of others, to wit his statement, "I'm going to think it's organized against me wherever I go, until I'm rid of my fears." He expressed his need more directly in open overtures for companions, and no longer derogated dependence on others as hateful weakness. Occasionally he even asked an aide to shave him. As his denial of illness and patienthood lessened, hope replaced despair. He abandoned defensive talk of a quick departure and announced that he might stay five years to complete treatment. Despite some remaining stereotypy in his structuring of an object world, he indicated partial resolution of his need-fear dilemma when he said, "I think mental health is halfway between dominating others and being dominated by them." His transition to manhood seemed partly accomplished.

VIII
THE NEED-FEAR DILEMMA OF
A WOULD-BE CATALYST OF
WORLD INTEGRATION

Donald L. Burnham

THIS IS A STUDY of William Gabriel Alberto Richter. He suffered a severe need-fear dilemma which he attempted to relieve by various combinations of object clinging, avoidance, and redefinition. His names, chosen by his mother, reflected his family's dividedness and disharmony and his faulty integration. His father called him Bill, while his mother called him Alberto or Al. She also emphasized an association with Saint Gabriel, a linkage which later contributed to his urges to save the world. He preferred to be called Alberto.

BACKGROUND

Our information concerning Alberto's life prior to his admission to Chestnut Lodge is spotty and derived from his fragmentary and often incoherent accounts, previous hospital records, one interview with his brother, and another with his former wife.

His family consisted of his father, mother, a brother two years older and named for father, and a sister one year younger and named for mother. His mother had been previously married and widowed, with one son eight years older than Alberto. Father headed a manufacturing business established by his father and subsequently carried on by

190

Alberto's brother. Alberto's sister was for many years a paranoid schizophrenic patient in a state hospital.

Alberto described his family as deeply divided, particularly between the worlds of business and art. Father he considered a typical businessman, a bad type, and a harsh disciplinarian who violently beat and even threatened to kill him. Nonetheless, on occasion he spoke tearfully of loving father and of envying his brother, who was father's favorite.

Alberto identified closely with his mother, whom he regarded as completely opposite from father—artistic, warm, intelligent, and religious. He claimed that she had disliked father on first meeting and later had barely tolerated him. Alberto's former wife shared his preference for his mother and described her as "a very wonderful, beautiful, and attractive person," and his father as "stodgy, opinionated, and stubborn."

Alberto's brother recalled mother's exuding a consumingly intense love from which he sought insulation, while her favorite, Alberto, reveled in it and in her great expectations for him.

Mother was uncomfortable in her husband's world and very conscious of having a different cultural background than he. Her nostalgia for the past was epitomized by her arranging parties at which everything—menu, decorations, entertainment, and even guests' costumes—were designed to recreate a small private world of past gentility.

She also wished for a world of universal love and denied evidences of hostility and disharmony. She told Alberto, after his father had beaten him, "Don't mind, your father really loves you," as if to say that he should immediately dismiss any resentment from mind. Concerning his sense of conflict between the worlds of business and art, Alberto recalled that when less than 10 he had seized a knife one evening at dinner, threatening to stab himself, and announcing his intention to become an artist rather than enter the family business.

Early in school both he and his sister scored exceptionally high IQ's and were included in a nationally publicized study of gifted children. However, his school record was erratic. In college his classroom attendance was irregular, and he left abruptly in the middle of his senior year. Subsequent explanations varied. He said that after trying unsuccessfully to convince his professors of the importance of his personal discoveries,[1] he had left school because he had "more important things to do." His ex-wife recalled, however, that his involvement in a homosexual scandal had been a factor. Of this he made no mention, although he spoke vaguely of an incident in his teens with a church sexton, which had been associated with an "echo experience," a peculiar sensation of "floating about four inches off the ground" during a church service.

After leaving college Alberto worked in the family business for a year or two, following which he spent 10 years in stage and film productions as an actor, costume designer, and director's assistant. He then married and returned to work in the family business.

His marriage was unusual in many respects. He and his wife, 12 years younger than he, were only slightly acquainted prior to marriage. They had met when she and her mother, a family friend, came from their home country to visit in the United States. At the time, his ex-wife recalled, Alberto seemed more interested in her mother than in her. After she returned home, he proposed marriage.

In an interview at Chestnut Lodge his ex-wife said that though two sons had been born to them, their life together had been "one bizarre episode after another." Her friends were divided about his eccentric ideas and actions. Some considered him odd, but very talented and insufficiently appreciated. Others considered him a minimally talented fraud whose achievements were mostly talk and whose eccentricities had been undeservedly noticed and praised.

Alberto was much preoccupied with matters usually considered the wife's responsibility, like party arrangements and house decor. He flew into violent tirades when these were not exactly as he wished. For several years a man friend, who seemed psychologically very important to Alberto, was a member of the odd household.

Meanwhile Alberto worked in the family business and was deferred from military service. Though he contributed positively to product design, he wrangled incessantly with his father and brother. He felt that they treated low-ranking company workers unfairly and, further, that they were dissatisfied with his work performance. He did

---

[1] During his stay at Chestnut Lodge, Alberto was greatly preoccupied with his discoveries, about which he talked repeatedly in stereotyped, cryptic phrases, such as "the identity of art and religion," convinced that if others only would listen, his ideas could transform the world.

not heed his wife's repeated urgings to leave the company and study architecture. Ultimately his brother became head of the company and fired Alberto.

According to his ex-wife, despite his declaration of great love for his mother, Alberto did little to sustain contact with her, leaving this obligation to his wife. Upon his mother's death, he showed minimal overt reaction; however, his marriage deteriorated further. His outbursts of rage were more frequent, and he took to insisting that food at the family table be served in communal dishes to guard against his being selectively poisoned.[2] He increasingly isolated himself from his wife and sons and finally left the house. About a year after his mother's death, his wife divorced him and took custody of the children. Following this, he was openly and consistently hateful toward her. For a time he sporadically took his sons for outings, but soon even this contact ceased, and he disappeared from the city.

His former wife returned to her home country and heard nothing more of him until a year or two later, when her brother chanced to see him on a European city street. He apparently remained in Europe about two years, during which time his father died, three years later after the death of his mother.

We know little of Alberto's life in Europe beyond his vague description of a skiing accident which resulted, he said, in a fractured vertebra and an injured knee. During this time he became convinced that the CIA had a special interest in him and was directing "beams" toward him.

FIRST HOSPITALIZATION

Acting upon his delusions, Alberto returned to the United States and sought a White House interview to determine whether the CIA "beams and caps on his brain" had been authorized by the President. He was immediately taken to a federal hospital, where he remained for seven months before transfer to a state hospital. He stayed there for the next four years, except for a brief unsuccessful trial visit with a cousin. The doctors at the state hospital diagnosed his illness as paranoid schizophrenia and described him as aloof, haughty, unco-

---

[2] In Alberto's childhood his parents had suspected attempts to poison his father during a period of company-union strife.

operative, and consistently denying illness. Electroshock treatments effected little or no change, and he refused to take chlorpromazine, partly because he considered that taking medicine would have been an acknowledgment of illness. This was his condition when, at age 47, he was transferred to Chestnut Lodge.

CHESTNUT LODGE ADMISSION

Alberto was admitted to Third Floor and Dr. Hein became his therapist. Our study of Alberto spanned three years, which we have divided into three phases of approximately six, 21, and nine months. Each phase represented a different type of attempt to relieve his need-fear dilemma and a different definition of himself.

Phase I: World Savior

Alberto's appearance was striking. He was dressed simply in dark blue and gray, his hair resembling a monk's tonsure, and his eyes deep-set and piercing. He spoke softly with earnest, almost priestly solemnity in impressive-sounding but obscure phrases. Early in treatment he poured out a jumble of autistic and cryptic thoughts amid which, however, listeners were able to discern, with gradually increasing clarity, his reiteration of the theme that he was good, kind, gentle, religious, and artistic. In his disconnectedness he circled back again and again to proclaim his devotion to the mission of bringing integration, peace, and harmony to the world.

Alberto's vision of the world's disunity seemed to derive directly from his view of his family's dividedness. With strings of stereotyped labels he spoke of his father's side of the family as a "German —British—Yankee—big business—Teddy Roosevelt—Communist— dictatorial control system," and his mother's as "Mediterranean— warm—artistic—intelligent—religious." The only break in his adulation of his mother was a brief parenthetical comment that his brother had accused him of murdering her, which he, of course, denied.

Alberto's absolute good-bad classification of his family extended to his entire object world, to each new person he met, and beyond, to clashes between good and evil, beauty and ugliness, art and business, East and West, white and colored races, and Buddhism and Christianity, all on a global, even cosmic, scale. In sum, his entire reality structure was pervaded by this good-bad conflict.

Alberto proclaimed numerous vague, grandiose, utopian schemes for healing the world. He spoke of establishing and subsidizing various artistic, religious, and educational institutions, and delivered long, difficult-to-interrupt monologues strewn with autistic, stereotyped notions about "the identity of art and religion; a dancing contest for ladies over 60; an Ave Maria contest; a rock-and-roll jazz mass; a plan to unite religions by building three monasteries on adjacent hills; a three-track system; and unification of the black, brown, and white crescents." To some observers he gave the impression of using this talk as a vacuum filler, as if he were thinking, "I know none of this makes sense, but I don't care." In the main, however, he was intensely driven and serious, especially when he said, "I am catalyst to the world. I *will* bring about integration." At this stage he seemed minimally aware of his need for integration of his inner world.

In his self-defined role of world savior Alberto felt victimized. Time and again he reiterated his innocence: "I am a good man. I want only to spread kindness in the world. I am not vengeful." Concurrently he emphasized the badness of his surroundings. He feared influence by electricity, food, cigarettes, and clothing, and absolutely dreaded direct contact with bad others. Contending that mental hospitals were particularly noxious and in the service of malevolent forces that opposed his life's mission, he repeatedly demanded immediate release.

Alberto voiced manifold wishes for more effective control of external badness. He wanted a benevolent superordinate control system different from the "German—British—big business control system" typified by his father. He said that the Justice Department should regulate psychological testing, that the FBI should curtail various malefactors, and that the American Medical Association should more strictly control psychiatrists and psychologists, including Dr. Hein.

Picturing himself as minister to the world's needs, Alberto denied that he had needs which anyone in the hospital might fill, and claimed that legions of friends and allies awaited him outside the hospital. He contradicted these denials, however, in many demonstrations of need toward Dr. Hein. In the first two weeks of their relationship he spoke with surprising candor of his desire for personal closeness, in distinct contrast to his previous hospital reputation of aloof, hostile suspiciousness. While reiterating that all mental hospitals were bad, he allowed that Chestnut Lodge perhaps was not quite as bad as previous ones.

Almost from the outset, clinging was prominent in Alberto's behavior toward Dr. Hein. He began and ended each therapy session with a handclasp, often of an engulfing sort. Once when he included the doctor's cuff link in his grasp, he exclaimed happily, "Oh, that was a good one!" Frequently he attempted to prolong therapy sessions by lingering in the office doorway while he continued to talk, or he would leave and momentarily return, saying that he had neglected to mention something. At other times he would accost someone outside the office and say, "Let me tell you something that I wasn't able to finish telling Dr. Hein just now." Occasionally he would approach the doctor and hug him, once abruptly declaring, "I love you. You are different from my father and brother." Along with all this clinging, scarcely a therapy hour passed without Alberto's reiterating his wish to leave the hospital.

Mostly he defined Dr. Hein as good. When he occasionally complained, "You are cruel to hold me in such a bad place," his emphasis was more on the place than on the doctor. Now and then he spoke critically of the doctor to others, but in the next therapy session he would apologize, as if to repair any damage his criticism might have done to the doctor and the relationship.

The depth of his fear of losing a positive relationship was apparent in his reactions to separation. As he left the doctor's office he was likely to say, "You *will* be sure not to let them harm me, won't you?" In the third month of their relationship, Dr. Hein informed Alberto that because his wife was having a baby, he would have to be away for two weeks. Alberto said anxiously, "You will be back, won't you?" Then, as if to deny jealousy or anxiety, he added, "Perhaps I could be a baby-sitter or tutor for your children." This form of role reversal, in which he proffered help rather than expressing fear of its loss, was repeated in the face of subsequent separations.

At other times Alberto quite candidly spoke of his loneliness and sense of loss. Once he told Dr. Hein, "I have no one." On another occasion, in the midst of protesting that he was not a patient, he paused and then said, "You are a psychologist.[3] Psychologists are

---

[3] Alberto used the terms "psychologist" and "psychiatrist" interchangeably without specifying why he sometimes used one and sometimes the other.

interested in frustrations. My greatest frustration is the divorce from my wife and the loss of my two sons." He also spoke sadly of the loss associated with the sale and change of name of the family business. Tearfully he referred to his age and a feeling that everything good was irretrievably lost in the past, but then denied this feeling by urgently requesting prompt discharge so he could get on with his world-saving work.[4] Another frequent request was that he be allowed to return to his home state—this voiced in a manner which suggested that fundamentally he hoped that to do so would restore his lost supportive relationship with his mother.

In his relationship with Dr. Gibson, Alberto was ambivalent. At the outset he said, "I trust you. . . . Please protect me; don't let them drug me and abuse me. . . . Probably, though, I can't trust you and you'll disappoint me." Ambivalence and need-fear fluctuation continued to mark their relationship. Virtually each time they met Alberto would ask or demand permission to leave; his manner was so stereotyped that Dr. Gibson considered it almost a ritualized greeting gesture. At the same time, however, Alberto averred his wish to cooperate and to follow the rules. Often he tried to prolong their interviews and to talk of matters more appropriate to a psychotherapeutic relationship.

Alberto quickly defined the Third Floor staff and patients as noxious. He called the patients stupid, filthy, and evil, and the staff no better. He pressed Dr. Gibson for unaccompanied grounds privileges; when they were granted, he spent most of each day away from Third Floor, returning there only to sleep.

Alberto's splitting of his need and fear was opposite to Dan's, which we described in Chapter VII. Initially Dan avoided his therapist and clung to the Third Floor staff. Alberto did the reverse. Questionnaire reports indicated minimal differences between Dan's relationship with his therapist and his relationships with nursing staff members. The reports on Alberto showed that his relationship with Dr. Hein was very different from his relationships with nurses and aides.

In avoiding Third Floor, Alberto spent much time wandering alone about the farther reaches of the grounds, apparently deep in thought. Less frequently he hung around the Recreation Center, maintaining

[4] Cf. Chapter XIII for a discussion of time perspective in the hospital careers of schizophrenic patients.

a distance from others and only rarely approaching the periphery of groups there. Sometimes he curled himself in a corner on the floor, using his jacket as a pillow. Occasionally he busied himself in solitary housecleaning chores, emptying ashtrays and tidying the furniture. When offered a regular job, though, he refused. Whenever someone from Third Floor came to the Center, Alberto shrank away.

Third Floor seemed associated in his mind with delusional fears of contamination. Seldom, if ever, would he bathe there. Instead, he bathed at the Center in a most bizarre manner: he stood at a sink and for hours on end, fully dressed, soaped and rinsed himself and his clothing. In the process he used dozens of paper towels and frequently obstructed the toilet in attempting to dispose of them.

He was so reluctant to remove or change his clothing, including the tennis shoes which he habitually wore, that had the staff not periodically insisted upon a change, he might have worn the same garments until they rotted on his back. He slept in his clothing and carefully avoided getting under the bed covers, apparently fearful of their possible noxious influence.

When tested by the psychologist in her office, he told her that he welcomed the opportunity to escape Third Floor, if only temporarily. Designating her as good, he talked volubly and clingingly. He reacted similarly to chance visitors to Third Floor, as if they afforded him respite from the noxious regular inhabitants.

His definition of Third Floor was not completely bad, however. In the fourth month of Alberto's stay, Dr. Gibson spoke to him of possible transfer to Hilltop. Surprisingly, Alberto replied that he preferred to remain on Third Floor. He hinted that this was partly from loyalty to Dr. Gibson and partly from fear of change. It also seemed likely that some of his fearful avoidance of Third Floor had been designed to deny the magnitude of his needs. In any event, the proposed transfer was abandoned for the time being.

While avoiding Third Floor and the mainstream of hospital activity, Alberto had recourse to a variety of substitute objects. His clothing served in this capacity. As previously mentioned, he was exceedingly reluctant to part from his old and familiar clothing even by undressing at night, and he literally dreaded contact with new clothing. Later he explained to Dr. Hein that certain articles of clothing were like persons to him and gave him a sense of comfort by their closeness to his body. Among other substitute objects were two pet dogs at the Center to which he talked at length, while assiduously avoiding persons.

A substitute activity was his writing literally thousands of notes in large flowing script on huge sheets of sketch paper. He wrote protests against hospitals, pleas for rescue, and cryptic allusions to his various world-unity schemes. These were addressed to a large assortment of persons, not so often by name as by vague, grandiloquent, autistic titles symbolic of power in some religious, educational, or government organization. Less autistic, though still obscure, were notes he sent to his brother, who was his trustee. Alberto appeared to derive a comforting sense of object contact from writing these messages; of relatively little concern to him were whether they reached their destinations and whether he received answers, although he pestered Dr. Gibson about mailing them.

Children at a nearby public playground formed another group of substitute objects. For as long as they would listen, Alberto harangued them with the avowed purpose of inculcating goodness and inhibiting badness in them. They seemed to regard him with curiosity at first, but stopped listening when the novelty wore off. Despite the autistic, unilateral nature of these relationships, they helped Alberto to retain a sense of object contact and mitigated his sadness at separation from his own children.

The treatment staff debated how vigorously to counter Alberto's strategy of relying on substitutes while avoiding more realistic relationships. They questioned whether to try, by rescinding his unaccompanied grounds privileges, to force him into greater interaction with staff and other patients. The consensus was against restricting him, since his relationship with Dr. Hein seemed to be developing well under a nonrestrictive policy. The same relatively laissez-faire policy was followed concerning his participation in hospital activities. He seemed determined to avoid anything which might signify his accepting the role of patient.[5] He resisted efforts to assign him a regular cleaning job at the Center, although informally he did this work. He also refused to join the hospital drama group, despite his earlier professional experience in dramatics. Similarly, he refused to join art

[5] For further discussion of this type of problem see Chapter XIV on Identity Definition and Role Demand.

classes, despite his avowed intense interest in art. The staff's judgment was that as he became better integrated and less fearful, he would avoid less and participate more.

In the meantime Alberto regularly attended his psychotherapy sessions and was eager for as frequent meetings as possible. According to Dr. Hein, during this period he mainly "just sat and listened to the patient's rambling discourses," trying occasionally to get in a word or two to focus and clarify the feelings of despair, defeat, and uselessness which underlay Alberto's world-saving schemes. He also sought to increase Alberto's awareness of the anger which was not completely hidden by his insistently defining himself as kind, gentle, and loving. Alberto's stereotyped demands for release were met by the doctor's now and then reasserting his belief that Alberto needed a hospital. Less regularly Dr. Hein said, "I have no intention of abandoning you," which seemed simultaneously to startle and to reassure Alberto.

As their relationship developed further, Dr. Hein interpreted Alberto's defensive use of obscure talk to keep others at a distance, and his deliberately changing the subject to avoid anxiety. When his apparent fear, sadness, and discouragement were commented upon, Alberto usually was quick to deny such feelings and to call the doctor a stupid fraud. Occasionally, however, his response was quiet tears.

Phase II: Vulnerable Supplicant

In this phase Alberto relinquished much, though not all, of his self-designated world-savior role and spoke more openly of his need for help and of his fears that he might be changed into a dangerously violent criminal. Cautiously he ventured into shared relationships within the hospital and relied less upon peripheral, autistic, and substitute objects. For instance, his message writing about his world-unity schemes diminished noticeably. Periodically, however, there was a recrudescence of his autistic grandiosity, frequently after weekend separations from Dr. Hein.

His efforts to dispense benevolence took new forms. Rather than wanting to endow monasteries, he was more likely to offer simple gifts, particularly to Dr. Hein, less frequently to Dr. Gibson; these included flowers, postcard reproductions of paintings, candy bars, and neckties. When Dr. Hein questioned the necessity of this gift giving, Alberto responded, "I would die if I couldn't give gifts; right now it is the only thing I can do in the world." Unspoken was his deep underlying wish that someone give to him.

A special type of gift was his "Holy Ghosts"—decorative arrangements of dried grass, twigs, wild flowers, and weeds which he gathered, bound together, and presented rather ceremoniously to Dr. Hein, Dr. Gibson, and a few other favored persons. The giving of the Holy Ghosts was clearly a symbolic expression of his wish for a harmonious Trinity. He was greatly disappointed if the intended recipient failed to recognize immediately which Holy Ghost had been designed specifically for him. This was but one indication of his wish for closeness and harmony so complete that no verbal communication would be necessary. Often he pleaded, "You do understand, don't you?" If Dr. Hein said "No," Alberto would become greatly distressed.

His wish for closeness took a variety of other forms during this phase of treatment. He frequently tried to prolong the therapy sessions, and eagerly approached whenever he saw Dr. Hein outside his office. Dr. Hein usually allowed time for a few minutes' chat and occasionally, on days when they had no appointment, dropped by to say hello to Alberto. Sometimes Alberto wistfully said, "I wish we had more time together. . . . If we could just lie in the sun together for several hours."

Often he expressed his need and longing for closeness in a primitive sort of pantomime. Prostrating himself on the floor, he would reach out to touch Dr. Hein or his clothing, and would twist himself into bizarre postures suggestive of abasement and supplication. Frequently such a performance directly followed his voicing criticism, annoyance, or disagreement, for which he felt he should make immediate atonement.

Early in this phase of treatment Alberto reported frequent dreams of ill-defined, lurid sexual activity, often of himself in "oral copulation" with another man. At first he insisted that these dreams must have been "induced" from the outside. Later, as his denial of inner sexual urges lessened, he made frankly sexual overtures to Dr. Hein and complained that the doctor's only response was embarrassment. Concurrently he reported fewer sexual dreams and no longer insisted that they had been "induced." To him a homosexual relationship was less a form of genital activity than an expression of yearning for a mother-infant type of pregenital intimacy. In support of this interpretation were such statements: "My mother was a wonderful homosexual. . . . Yesterday, Dr. Hein, when I put my head on your chest, all those feelings of fear and distrust went out of me."

While yearning for closeness, he also feared it. He told Dr. Hein, "We must not sit together on this bench; people might think we are in agreement." Dr. Hein's mere hint that Alberto might feel slight friendliness toward him would trigger a long diatribe beginning with, "But, Dr. Hein, you are an evil man. . . ." Alberto often stressed their separateness and differences: "I am a religious, artistic man; you are a business man and a doctor. We have nothing in common. You have no artistic sense whatsoever. . . . I want to leave this place."

On the other hand, his reactions to separation further revealed the intensity of his need. He would ask Dr. Hein, "Can't I come with you and your family on vacation?" and then would hastily add, "I will *not* miss you when you are gone." At least once he asked, "Will you adopt me as your child?" but partially reversed this by treating the doctor in a distinctly maternal, protective manner. As weekends or longer separations approached, he would beg, "Please don't let 'them' harm me with drugs or electric shock while you are gone. . . . I am afraid when you are away. . . . I wonder whether you are faithful. . . . Don't say good-bye; say good morning." Even minor changes in appointment times were likely to evoke these fears.[6]

Alberto's wish for inseparability was graphically displayed toward certain substitute objects, particularly a small silver pitcher with which Dr. Hein watered plants in his office. Alberto was convinced that years before in a different setting he had given this pitcher to the doctor, a belief clearly reflecting his wish for a long-continuing, constant relationship. Frequently he would cradle and caress the pitcher. He clung similarly to his old coat and described with deep feeling the comfort he gained from enfolding himself in it and feeling his arm in intimate contact with the sleeve. His clinging to these substitute objects also seemed a way of saying to Dr. Hein, "This is what I want from you."

Also indicative of need was his verbalization of wishes for direc-

---

[6] See Chapter XII for further details of his struggle with separation anxiety, including his poignant statement of vulnerability, "Sometimes I feel like a newborn infant whose life could be snuffed out at the whim of others."

tion, support, and reassurance from Dr. Hein. He would ask, "Is it all right to smoke these cigarettes? . . . Should I eat this food?" He refused to wear a new coat that had been purchased for him and tried to tear it up until reassured by Dr. Hein that it would not harm him. Likewise he refused penicillin for a serious foot infection until Dr. Hein persuaded him that it was safe. Anything new or unfamiliar was likely to evoke his dependence. When requested to fill out a research questionnaire, he immediately asked, "Does Dr. Hein say it is O.K. for me to do this?"

The degree of his dependence was revealed in the following sequence: On a shopping trip he became tense and reached out to touch a bra displayed on a store mannequin. The accompanying aide cautioned that this was socially inappropriate and suggested they leave. Alberto cursed angrily but reluctantly complied. On subsequent inquiry from Dr. Hein about this incident, he said, "Doctor, you don't think your strength goes out to me when I'm out *there* (in the outside world), do you?"

A still more literal, though indirect, expression of his need for supplies of goodness was his suggesting that cancer might be cured by transfusing blood from a healthy person. Now that his denial and projection had lessened, he feared that he might have incurable badness within himself.

He voiced a fear of being turned into a criminal. Since he considered criminality and anger synonymous, this fear became more pronounced as he grew more aware of his anger. He began to vent anger at various distant and autistically defined objects, like "the German—British—Communist control system"; collective targets such as mental hospitals, doctors, and psychological testing programs; and various individuals, particularly his father, brother, and ex-wife. His mother usually remained exempt from his anger, although he bitterly recalled ill treatment from a nursemaid. He also labeled as bad a branch of his mother's family, the Wiggers, and another vaguely associated group, "the Z men."

Within the hospital Alberto aimed anger at several objects, including the nurses and aides collectively, and the two physicians who had admitted him to Chestnut Lodge. His principal target, however, was Frank, a severely autistic Third Floor patient. Frank's bizarre gestures and animal noises aroused loathing in Alberto, who feared animality in himself. To a lesser degree than Glen (see Chapter VI), Alberto also was jealous of Frank's having Dr. Gibson as both administrator and therapist.

Occasionally Dr. Hein was the object of Alberto's anger, though at first only in sporadic, dissociated bursts. He might suddenly interject into a neutral sentence a barely audible, "I could kill you." To Dr. Hein's "Who, me?" Alberto was likely to reply hastily, "Oh, that was just an aside." So great was Alberto's difficulty in integrating anger that if Dr. Hein encouraged further discussion of an angry statement toward even persons remote in time and space, Alberto often would deny having made the original statement. Since his thoughts were so unintegrated, he probably was completely sincere in saying that he had no memory of an immediately previous expression of anger.

He made many poignant statements of his fear of anger: "Hate is a terrible thing; it will destroy me. . . . I might become violent and murder someone in the Justice Department. . . . I can't stand to hate; I can feel my Civil War ancestors inside me.[7]

Fundamentally, Alberto dreaded that his anger would disrupt vital relationships. Once Dr. Hein commented after an open display of anger, "It must be upsetting to feel that way." Alberto answered, "Yes, you're the only thing I have."

He tried to defend against the dreaded loss of relationships by splitting off his anger and dividing his percept of the object. He told Dr. Hein, "You're all right as a person, but as a psychologist you are dirty and stupid. . . . I can stand you as a person to talk to, but as a doctor you are no good and should have your license taken away." Sometimes he attributed his changeable percepts to the surroundings: "It is different when I see you outside the office; I like you in one place but not in another." Or he blamed peripheral contextual elements: "I don't like the furniture of this office. . . . How can I like someone whose taste in clothing is so bad? If only you would wear nicer ties, then I could like you all the time."

Alberto used a variety of other defenses against the disruptive effect of anger. We described earlier his moving closer and trying to touch the doctor after flashes of anger. Or he might take a conciliatory over-

---

[7] His reference to the Civil War symbolized the family discord and conflicting identifications which contributed to his faulty integration.

ture: "Could we look together at the pictures in your new calendar?" He also used cognitive defenses such as *déjà vu* percepts and redefinitions of the doctor. Part-similarities, such as a facial mole, were enough to convince Alberto that Dr. Hein and previously known persons were identical. Periodically he redefined the doctor as "one of the Wiggers" or as "a Z man," and accordingly a bad person. By defining him as someone else when perceived as bad, Alberto for the most part preserved a good image of Dr. Hein.

Alberto's percept of Dr. Gibson also was split: "There seem to be two Dr. Gibsons, one quite handsome, the other ugly. . . . I've known him from before, too." For a time he insisted that Dr. Gibson was an FBI man who years earlier had interrogated him. This redefinition was a concretized metaphor, since it was evoked by Dr. Gibson's sharply questioning Alberto about his reported window-peeping at the nurses' residence. In expressing a sense of distance from Dr. Gibson as the FBI agent, he simultaneously denied estrangement from Dr. Gibson as Dr. Gibson. At other times he openly envied what he presumed to be Dr. Gibson's close personal friendship with Dr. Hein.

For the most part, Alberto continued mostly to avoid the nurses and aides and to define them as noxious. Near the end of his first year at the Lodge his unaccompanied grounds privileges were cancelled for approximately a month (following a protest from the parents of a child to whom he had talked at the nearby playground). This forced him into somewhat greater interaction with Third Floor staff. Questionnaire reports indicated that at this time he and the staff members more frequently approached, talked, and expressed positive feelings to each other, though he was rated as communicating with less clarity than previously. It appears that their increased interaction with him gave the staff greater opportunity to discover his disorganized thinking.

After a month's restriction his unaccompanied grounds privileges were restored. Three months later, questionnaire reports from Third Floor staff indicated that the frequencies of Alberto's interactions with them had returned nearly to the levels reported prior to the period of privilege restriction. This suggests that his increased interaction while restricted was more a temporary by-product of administrative control than a durable change in his relationships.

Meanwhile Alberto established a few relationships elsewhere in the

FIGURE 1A. Questionnaire Scores for Alberto Richter:
Patient's Behavior Toward Ward Staff

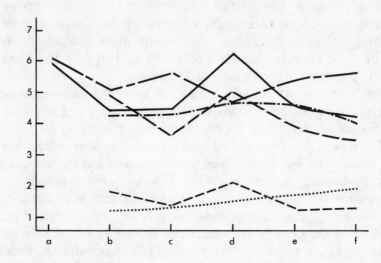

Approach ————————————   Positive feelings expressed — — — —
Personal communication — — — — — —   Negative feelings expressed —·—·—·—·—··
Clarity of communication — ——— —   Problem behavior ···

a - 3 months after admission   d - 11 months after admission
b - 6 months after admission   e - 15 months after admission
c - 8 months after admission   f - 17 months after admission

hospital. At the Center he became somewhat friendlier with several
Activities staff members. Two other significant relationships were
those with the charge nurse of an open cottage, and the elderly lady
who operated the hospital switchboard on weekends. Alberto sometimes would talk for hours to one or the other of them.

Twenty months after admission he was transferred to Hilltop, a
move that earlier he had refused. Now he accepted it quite readily,
with surprisingly little overt reaction to separation from Dr. Gibson
and Third Floor staff and patients. Though he retained his unaccompanied grounds privileges, he avoided the Hilltop staff less assiduously
than he had avoided the Third Floor staff. In fact, he began to establish significant relationships with a few particular staff members who
themselves were somewhat on the periphery of the staff group—a

FIGURE 1B. Questionnaire Scores for Alberto Richter:
Nursing Staff's Behavior Toward Patient

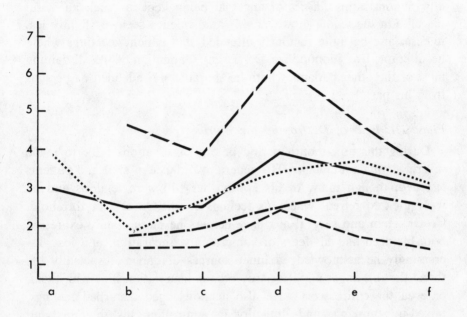

Approach ————————

Personal communication — — — — — — —

Positive feelings expressed — — — — — —

Negative feelings expressed —··—··—··—··—

Control ···················

a - 3 months after admission   d - 11 months after admisson

b - 6 months after admission   e - 15 months after admission

c - 8 months after admission   f - 17 months after admission

Japanese nurse temporarily affiliated with the hospital and two West
Indian Negro male aides who worked the evening shift.[8]

His relationship with Dr. Erling, the Hilltop administrator, was

———

[8] Alberto's interest in these staff members was reminiscent of his reported special
interest in low-ranking employees of his family's business.

essentially similar to his relationship with Dr. Gibson; he harangued him with long monologues that were clinging yet simultaneously sprinkled with protests that he didn't belong here, that this was a prison, not a hospital, and that he was not a patient, while occasionally demonstrating flashes of anger at being kept in "such an awful place." On the whole, however, his ambivalence seemed slightly less intense, and he quite regularly attended staff-patient meetings where he attempted to monopolize Dr. Erling's attention while disdaining most of the other patients whom he sporadically redefined as persons from his past.

Phase III: Fear of Destroying the World

During this nine-month period of our observations Alberto made several significant changes. His general avoidance of staff and patients lessened, though many of his approaches still were tenuous and he was quick to retreat when his feelings reached a certain threshold. To Dr. Hein and several auxiliary helpers he more openly expressed both his need and his fears of vulnerability, separation, and loss. Increasingly he acknowledged inner sources of danger, especially the threat that his anger might destroy others, his relationships with them, or even the entire world. He also acknowledged disturbed feelings, mixed-up thinking, and difficulty in controlling his thoughts and actions. By no means did his denial and projection cease completely, but they did become less total and less constant.

These improvements, several of which had begun earlier, were substantially aided by his receiving trifluoperazine hydrochloride; this was initiated in his thirty-second month at Chestnut Lodge and continued for the remainder of our study. A major benefit from the drug was the damping of Alberto's floods of anxiety, thereby permitting him to make more sustained object contacts and to consider more reflectively his painful emotions and thoughts instead of abruptly fleeing.

He continued manifold expressions of need toward Dr. Hein. For a time these included undisguised sexual overtures and attempts to embrace the doctor, who, after trying gentle dissuasion, finally quite brusquely repulsed these advances. With a hurt, hangdog look, Alberto responded, "You needn't be so nasty about it." Thereafter his sexual overtures were rare, and usually he would stop himself, often by saying, "I guess I smell bad; I need a bath."

Uncertainty about his personal attractiveness oscillated with uncertainty about the doctor. One day, gazing intently at Dr. Hein, he said, "Your eyes are pretty," and then added, "The lines in your face are nice," meanwhile fingering the lines of his own face. Abruptly he followed this with, "You look terrible—so angular—awful." Next, his eyes suddenly on an overhead cobweb, he declared, "I have to get that before it becomes too angular." Later in the hour he spoke more directly of the changeability of the doctor: "There seem to be several of you. Sometimes you are very likable, sometimes a dreadfully loathsome, dirty bastard." Immediately he shifted to self-criticism: "In college the professors ridiculed me. . . . I am a failure . . . just a mess of dirty ashes."

In another therapy session Alberto crawled on the floor toward Dr. Hein and attempted to embrace his legs, saying, "I feel great sadness in my heart." He compared their eyes as if uncertain of their colors, but hoping they were identical. Suddenly he turned to a wall mirror and, as if seeing himself for the first time in a long while, exclaimed, "I look terrible!"

Intense oral hunger was prominent. Sometimes as he voiced his desperate sense of need, Alberto would bare his chest and would denounce fraudulent women who dyed their hair and wore "falsies." When he saw Dr. Hein carrying a small thermos bottle of coffee in the crook of his arm, he remarked wistfully, "You baby the bottle but not me." Dr. Hein asked, "You would like to be cuddled?" Alberto answered, "Cuddled but not coddled."

As his separation anxiety lessened, he became more able to describe it. Once he made a gesture of breaking the telephone cord. Dr. Hein asked, "You feel cut off at the end of our hours?" Alberto replied, "Yes, it gives me a feeling of anguish. The good feeling I have when I am with you leaves me when I am away from you. I try to picture you; sometimes I have wonderful conversations out there on the lawn with your image." On the eve of weekends Alberto might comment, "It will be a long time before Monday, but I'll see you then." Or as he checked their next appointment time, he would add, "I will wait for your return." Alberto handled the third summer vacation separation from Dr. Hein differently than the previous two.

He arranged for an interim therapist and also wrote notes to give to Dr. Hein on his return, thus more openly acknowledging his doctor's importance to him.

He also was clearer about using substitute objects to counteract separation anxiety. During a therapy session in his room he said, "Please don't look away from me; it makes me feel abandoned." Then he picked up his blanket and hugged it, saying. "I've given this a very bad name—I call him 'Boston Blackie'—but he is my friend. My coat also keeps me company."

Alberto continued to depend openly on Dr. Hein for advice and reassurance, especially when fearful of some new external influence. He accepted new clothing, unfamiliar medicines, and a summer cottage stay with a staff-patient group only after Dr. Hein's assurances that they would not harm him.

Gradually he expanded the range of trusted persons. With one of the previously mentioned West Indian aides he ventured to shop for new clothing, and, most remarkably, agreed to major dental repairs under general anesthesia after exacting the aide's promise to remain with him throughout the operation.

He developed another important relationship with a woman older than he, who taught ceramics at the Center. Initially he stood at a distance watching her work and muttering to himself. Occasionally, without addressing her directly, he loudly denounced her work as artistically inferior. For her part, the teacher keenly sensed his excruciating loneliness, but waited for him to feel ready to move closer. After many months he began to speak more directly to her and to evince tentative interest in attempting some potting. He quickly added that he would be unhappy at being *under* her direction, but warmed appreciably when she said that she expected she could learn from a person of his artistic abilities.[9] He asked if he could help her decorate some bowls before they were fired, and was greatly pleased with his efforts, saying, "Well, it's not much, but it's better than nothing."

This relationship became increasingly important to Alberto. At first he seldom mentioned it to Dr. Hein, apparently wanting the two

9 The West Indian aide had expressed a similar positive valuation of, and willingness to learn from Alberto, a contrast from traditional role expectations which emphasize the patient's need to receive to the exclusion of his capacity to give (Cf. Chapter XIV).

relationships to remain in separate compartments of his object world. Gradually this lessened.

Even more drastically compartmentalized was the relationship between the ceramics teacher and Frank, the animal-like patient whom Alberto abhorred. When Frank suddenly embraced her at the Center one day, Alberto shouted vehemently, "Take your hands off her, you dirty, filthy, despicable criminal!" His absolute separation of good from bad was similarly shaken when he saw a sculpture of artistic merit which Frank had created.

Alberto's definition of the ceramics teacher was predominantly positive, except when his fear was aroused by too much closeness. For instance, if she spontaneously reached out to pat his arm, he might flare into a tirade of vilification. Through his relationship with her, Alberto became more integrated into the main stream of Center activities, as when he helped her make saki cups for a Japanese party at the Center.

Concurrent with his greater acceptance of proximate persons, Alberto more openly voiced grief at losing persons distant in time and space. Speaking sadly of his parents' deaths, he said that had his mother not died, he might never have been divorced. At her request, he did not see his former wife during her visit to the Lodge, but on learning of it, he admitted missing as well as hating her. He even half-convinced himself that her visit had been prompted by a wish to remarry him.

He reacted strikingly to photographs of his sons which his former wife had left with Dr. Hein. At first he denied that these were his sons and made a charge of "trick photography." He debated lengthily whether to take possession of the pictures, and finally decided to leave them in the doctor's office for fear he might destroy them. For the next several days he looked at them during each therapy session, and alternated between allowing that perhaps one of the boys resembled him a bit and reverting to denial of any relationship. He also complained bitterly that the furniture in the pictures was unspeakably ugly and inappropriate. Focusing upon the furniture apparently gave him partial relief from his unbearable feelings about his sons.

Alberto no longer assigned to others all blame for his losses. He voiced guilt about unspecified misdeeds, and with more sadness than paranoid anger spoke of having been kicked out of marriage, home, college, and church. Then, as if to deny that these losses increased his present need, he reiterated his wish to leave the Lodge soon, adding that he certainly would not miss the place or anyone in it.

As his self-critical capacity expanded, he accepted more anger in his self-definition. In vivid detail he recalled smashing a window in anger at another boy. He also recalled having beaten his wife, and said defensively, "I'm proud I did it"; moreover, he claimed to have once prevented her from striking their children with an axe.

Anger became openly evident in Alberto's intrahospital relationships with both staff and patients. As his avoidance lessened, he frequently attended staff-patient meetings at Hilltop. At the monthly all-hospital meetings at the Center he sometimes took the floor to declaim on the evils of the place and of the staff.

His surges of anger toward Dr. Hein assumed less dissociated forms than his earlier "just an aside" thrusts. Instead of fearing that he might harm some unidentified person in the Justice Department, he feared destroying his doctor: "Sometimes I think of finding mutilated, cut-up bodies; one might be you. . . . I could put a knife through you. . . . My father was a crazy man; he might put a knife in my hand and cause me to stab someone."." His fear that his father's influence would make him violent was typical during this period.

He still feared that his anger would disrupt vital relationships: "I'm angry, Dr. Hein. I shouldn't be; it would be terrible if I harmed you." He went on to restate earlier grievances against Dr. Hein and to recall his grandmother's warning that doctors were terrible. Quite suddenly he paused and then pleaded, "Please sit over here and hold my hand," while he wept and spoke of the terrible violence of World War II. At the end of this session he asked, "Will you be my friend until I see you again?" as if to make sure that his poorly integrated anger had not destroyed the relationship.

On occasion he made this meaning explicit when he said, "Whenever I feel anger I try to move close to you and to touch you. This makes me feel better. . . . I often think about you between appointments and fear that I might do something to destroy you; you don't seem to realize this danger." Asked how he tried to manage these fears, Alberto said, "I will demonstrate it for you"; he then proceeded to lie on the couch, embraced the pillow, and rubbed his chest against the couch, saying, "I try to get next to you and in that way to shield you." On other occasions, after storming at Dr. Hein he would say, "Please forgive the nasty things I have said about you."

Further documentation of Alberto's fear of the destructive effects of his anger was provided by the following exchange: Dr. Hein asked, "How come you're so antagonistic toward me in public situations like the all-hospital meetings, but you're friendly here in the privacy of my office?" Alberto replied, "I really don't like you, but I have to, or the whole organization would break down into fighting and disorder." Here we can see the link between his struggle to control his anger and his quest for a violence-free world.

Alberto feared being unworthy of friendship. He would say, "I am good; I have never done anything bad. . . . I would like to call you by your first name, but I shouldn't if I have been bad. . . . I remember smashing a car my father gave me even though I didn't want it." Sometimes he told Dr. Hein, "I want to love you, but am afraid you will hate me in return."

The theme of unworthiness was further evident in his saying, "When my father embraced me, he winced." He added, "People like to see a father and son together and they like the father-son concept." Then in a wave of anxiety he lapsed into chanting, "Father, Son . . . Father, Son, and Holy Ghost . . . Easter eggs . . . Easter eggs on toast . . . Father, Son, and Holy Ghost . . . Easter eggs on toast." This was punctuated by eerie laughter.

Alberto's descriptions of his father changed noticeably, although periodically he continued to made such claims as: "My mother didn't want my father present at my birth for fear he would kill me. Later he threatened me with a knife and a gun, and on his death bed he cursed me." Now, however, these claims were interspersed with positive statements: "My father and I loved each other. . . . I want to forgive him. . . . I felt guilty and sad when he died." Alberto wept as he recalled once calling his father "despicable." Depending on which side of his ambivalent feelings toward his father was expressed by Dr. Hein, Alberto would take the other side. If the doctor said, "You must have hated him," Alberto would counter, "No, I loved him"—and vice versa.

Alberto's earlier definition of his mother as goodness incarnate underwent some modification. He did not thank her for the problems caused by the names she had given him, one of which his father detested and refused to use. Another made him the namesake of Saint Gabriel, the messenger of God, and contributed to his feeling that he should somehow save the world. Alberto said that his mother had prohibited him from opposing his father. To become angry was to disobey her. He spoke poignantly of persons not understanding each other and called his family a "tower of Babel." To this he added, "That was what all the integration was about."

When Dr. Hein said, "Your relationship with your mother doesn't seem to have been entirely perfect," Alberto answered unprotestingly, "That's an interesting idea." More frequently, however, he reverted to trying to preserve an all-good image of her. In depicting parental disagreement in his upbringing, he usually exonerated his mother and blamed his father. He also continued to displace criticisms of her onto her cousins, the Wiggers, and sporadically to redefine Dr. Hein as one of them.

In becoming more tolerant of inner badness, Alberto less consistently denied illness and even admitted hearing "voices" in various situations. Once he offered Dr. Hein a choice of several ceramic bowls he had made and was delighted by the doctor's choice. He said, "I hoped you would like that one best; I intended it for you. I wasn't sure whether to give you a bowl, and I heard voices in the back of my head telling me different things, so for a while I didn't know what to do."

He recalled that after his brother had ordered him from the family home, he had heard "voices telling me to go to an ice cream parlor and to do terrible sexual things with the children there." Such an admission was a far cry from his earlier proclaimed total benevolence. He also remembered hearing a voice describe industrialist Henry Kaiser's "good care of his men." In discussing this he realized that it described what he had wanted from his father.

In acknowledging illness, Alberto volunteered a remarkable description of what "schizophrenia is like to me." Demonstrating with gestures he said, "It's like having your arm held behind you, and then a false arm is put in its place from behind and does things you don't want done; it even bats down your good arm and interferes with good things the good arm is trying to do. It is as if the false arm were part of an invisible person behind you." When Dr. Hein commented, "It sounds like something that feels alien to yourself and that intrudes on you," Alberto replied, "Yes, that's just it."

Another time he said, "I'm not crazy, just mixed up." To Dr. Hein's, "Mixed up?" Alberto quickly added, "Not mixed up *about* things, but mixed in *with* things." Typically he was reluctant to have his admissions of illness underlined or pinned down.

He admitted difficulties in maintaining his focus of attention: "What was I talking about? I seem to have switched the subject." Concurrently, he was more able to listen and to tolerate differences of opinion and perspective: "I suppose *you* might think such and such," or, "You as a psychologist might think. . . ." He was quicker to sense accurately when he wasn't being understood and sometimes would say, "I'll try to explain by acting the way those persons behaved."

He was generally more receptive to Dr. Hein's interpretations. Earlier, any attempts to comment on his problems, especially inner ones, had usually been met by storms of protest, epithets like "psychological rot," and vilification of the doctor. This had been the case particularly when Dr. Hein had tried to link Alberto's past with his present experiences, or his quest for world peace with his wish for harmony in his family and in himself. No longer was this the case. This change became evident in Alberto's eager interest in newspaper reports about the ecumenical movement. Dr. Hein suggested that the religious movement seemed to promise harmony for the family of churches of the sort that Alberto had hoped his family might achieve. With fervent tears Alberto replied, "It is so, it is so, it is so," and spoke of the anguish caused by "civil war" and his feeling of being in a "no-man's-land." Another interpretation to which he responded constructively concerned the defensive function of scorn and contempt for others. He answered, "I have contempt for myself; not contempt for my life, but for myself." To comments on his appearing sad and lonely, Alberto would usually abruptly deny such feeling, but then would burst into tears and, literally clinging to Dr. Hein, admit how horribly lonely he felt.

During this phase of treatment Alberto reported fewer dreams and no longer claimed that they were "induced." His dreams were pleasanter, without repugnant sexual imagery, and peopled by persons he recognized. Concurrently he became less certain of various of his redefinitions of others, such as his belief that he had known Dr. Hein somewhere in the past.

Among the indications of greater integration was his increased capacity to structure experience in time.[10] Near the third anniversary of his admission to the Lodge he said incredulously, "Have I really been here almost three years? I have tried to keep track of time by the Christmases, but it has been hard and in these terrible places Christmases are miserable." Earlier his demands for immediate release from the hospital had stressed how little time remained for accomplishing his world-saving mission. Now he seemed to value more positively his time in the hospital. He became a stickler for punctuality, especially regarding his appointments with Dr. Hein.

A sense of being out-of-phase with others was apparent in a note he wrote after Dr. Hein had urged that he work in either the hospital canteen or laundry:

> Dr. Hein:
> Please try to be fair with me.
> My motor is going fifty or sixty miles an hour. These other people's are ten to twenty miles an hour.
> Naturally I will get into a crash under such conditions. Please understand.
>
> Alberto

RÉSUMÉ

In this study of three years of the treatment of a severely schizophrenic man, we observed that in different phases of treatment his efforts to relieve an intense need-fear dilemma took different forms. In the first phase he defined himself as a world savior. Preoccupied with grandiose schemes for unifying the world, he claimed total benevolence and denied illness or need for help. He split his need and fear. He clung to his psychotherapist, fearful of losing him by separation or destruction, and at pains to preserve a good image of him by redefinition. Concurrently he avoided the Third Floor staff and other patients from whom he feared bad influence. Meanwhile he turned to various substitute objects to maintain a sense of object contact.

In the second phase he relinquished a part of his self-definition as world savior and more openly expressed needs, primarily toward

[10] Cf. Chapter XIII on the importance of time structuring in the schizophrenic person's organization of himself.

his therapist but also toward several auxiliary helpers. While continuing to locate much badness in staff members and other patients, he began to fear inner badness, especially as he became more aware of previously unintegrated anger. He regarded anger and criminality as identical and feared that uncontrollable forces might turn him into a criminal. He attempted to exempt Dr. Hein from his anger by redefinition maneuvers.

In the third phase he continued to change, aided by trifluoperazine hydrochloride. Fears of inner badness became more pronounced. He feared that his anger might destroy others, his vital relationships with them, and even the entire world. As he discovered that his relationship with his doctor survived surges of anger, it became more integrated. He modified his all-bad view of his father and became more capable of self-criticism and acknowledgment of illness. He progressed toward recognition that his urge to bring peace, stability, and integration to the outer world derived from his desperate wish for harmony in his inner world and in his family. Greater differentiation of inner and outer realms was accompanied by integration of conflicting aspects of his self which had been shaped by his family's dividedness. As he achieved greater inner unity, his good-bad splitting of his object world lessened, as did his need-fear dilemma.

IX

HARVEY APPLETON

ARTHUR I. GLADSTONE

HARVEY RICHARDS APPLETON was the son of Charles Appleton, a prominent and successful engineer with his own firm. The father's main interest in life has been his work and he had little to do with his children during their formative years. He is rather distant, with a conventional manner of southern affability. The mother, Maryanne Richards Appleton, is talkative, aggressive, and insistent upon having her way. She is tremendously concerned with being socially correct and maintaining the appearance of a happy and successful life, and tried to protect the father from too much interference by the children while they were growing up. Harvey's only sibling is a brother, Clark, 15 months older than he.

Before Harvey was born his mother had expected a girl—she had bought girl's clothing and had decorated the nursery for a girl. Harvey was a frail and docile child. He imitated his brother so assiduously that the family nicknamed him "Me Too." He insisted on doing whatever the brother did and getting whatever the brother got, behavior which was encouraged by the mother. The mother remembers him as being sweet-tempered and not presenting any problems. However, Harvey recalls a fight with his mother when he was five. Driven by anger, he hit her on the knee and thigh. His father came into the room, grabbed Harvey, and struck him across the back so forcefully that Harvey was knocked to the floor unconscious. Harvey claims that it was upon waking up later in bed, that he first felt determined eventually to learn some sort of self-defense.

The mother described Harvey's relationship with his brother as ideal, but the father reported that the two had many fights, which Clark usually won. Harvey remembers feeling very competitive with both his brother and his father.

Harvey told his parents very little about his experiences and activities, in contrast to Clark, who talked much more freely to the parents about such things. When he was 10 or 11, Harvey became very interested in boats and sailing. He bought an old wreck of a boat with his own money, repaired it, and dragged it several miles on a wagon to a lake where he could sail it. This he accomplished almost singlehandedly, with his parents having minimal knowledge of the whole endeavor. Another incident demonstrating Harvey's independence and secretiveness occurred during his freshman year at college, when he got a job as night watchman in order to pay for flying lessons. Not until Harvey completed his lessons and obtained his pilot's license did he tell his parents of his accomplishment.

Harvey did very well in school and received many honors. In high school he was on the track and football teams and in the class play. He was chosen the most popular boy, and in his senior year received the award for the highest achievement in all fields. Despite his popularity, there are no indications that Harvey had any intimate friends with whom he exchanged confidences.

Harvey was very popular with girls, who actively showed their interest in him by phoning him and inviting him to parties. He was rather passive, and repeatedly got involved with aggressive girls who took the lead in developing relationships with him. During his later high school years Harvey was friendly with a girl named Sally, with whom he claims to have had the most pleasant relationship he has ever known. Harvey's mother disapproved of Sally because her family wasn't "proper" enough. After high school Harvey and Sally went to the same college for two years. They talked about being married, but Harvey was eager to go to a military academy and Sally did not want to postpone marriage until he had graduated. This disagreement ended their relationship. Harvey's mother, whose disapproval of Sally undoubtedly contributed to the rift, was instrumental in securing his appointment to the military academy, through the aid of a senator. Commenting on his breaking off with Sally, Harvey said that women aren't interested in waiting, and conveyed his feeling that women are interested only in their own needs and not in his.

Harvey complained that he has always had great difficulty in saying "no" to his parents, especially when both wanted him to do something. His mother is especially interfering and controlling, and Harvey felt it was extremely difficult to get along with her and yet maintain his individuality. (Clark insisted more on what he wanted and waged many stubborn battles with his mother.) The mother pressured her sons to be good. When they were young she kept a chart on which she pasted stars for each child's good behavior. Harvey was also extremely concerned with being good. He considered himself a devout Presbyterian and said he adhered very strictly to the Ten Commandments.

Harvey achieved an excellent academic record at the military academy, and also did well in sports, especially boxing. After graduation he served as an officer for three years. He then resigned his commission in order to study engineering. He has given several reasons for this decision. The idea of leaving the service first occurred to him when an officer unjustly accused him of lying. This idea was strengthened when he developed an interest in engineering after visiting some construction projects. He also thought that perhaps he could earn more money as a civilian. Underlying these various reasons was a growing concern with the fact that the primary purpose of the military is destruction, to which he did not want to devote his life. When Harvey was contemplating resigning his commission, he wrote to his father asking, "How would you like to have an ambitious young man in your engineering firm?"

When Harvey secured his engineering degree, he went to work for his father's firm. He and two other young engineers had wanted to join forces and start their own firm, but both his parents opposed this idea bitterly. They argued that entering his father's well-established business, with a decent salary from the very beginning, was a wonderful opportunity. Harvey did not, at this point, want to enter his father's firm. Nevertheless, he felt that his parents' arguments were reasonable and that he could not oppose them, especially when they both felt so strongly.

Harvey was unhappy with his position in his father's firm. He felt that his father was old-fashioned and that the people in the firm were not congenial. He thought too, that he was a better engineer than his father. Harvey had hoped to move somewhat closer to his father, with whom he had never felt particularly intimate, but felt that he was making no progress with this.

A year after starting to work for his father, Harvey met a girl named Mary Sullivan, whose father had started out a poor man but had become wealthy. Harvey became seriously interested in Mary and invited her home for a week's visit with his parents. But Mary prolonged her visit, and while Harvey's parents would have liked to ask her to leave, they did not feel they could. The father finally left on a business trip and the mother soon followed him, hoping that Mary would leave while they were gone. After six weeks, Mary returned to her home. She told her parents about Harvey and they suggested that he come and marry her right away. Harvey's parents were horrified by this suggestion and astounded that Mary's parents would be willing to have her marry a boy about whom they knew nothing. Harvey's parents had disliked Mary and her background from the beginning, regarding her as coarse and common. They also felt that Mary had pursued Harvey far too aggressively. Nevertheless, they did not openly oppose the marriage, which took place at the end of that summer.

Harvey brought his bride to live in the house his mother had bought them, next door to his parents' home. Harvey's parents kept an unfriendly watch on the marriage. They thought that Mary was not providing a proper home for their son, and that she did not have his meals ready on time or dress neatly for his arrival from work. Harvey's mother told her friends that they should not waste their money giving parties for the couple because the marriage probably would not last. Harvey and Mary soon did have difficulties. Harvey began to suspect, without evidence, that Mary was unfaithful to him.

The next summer Harvey and Mary went to Europe. During the trip Harvey became more suspicious of his wife. He saw peculiarities in the way she danced or how often she excused herself to go to the toilet, which he took as indicating that something "funny" was going on. He was not sure what this was, but thought she might be taking dope or seeing other men. Harvey also felt that his wife was very much like his mother, and was distressed that sometimes she refused to talk with him. On their way back from Europe, Harvey asked Mary for a divorce. She agreed, and when he called his parents from New York to tell them of the impending separation, his father replied that it was the best news he had heard in his whole life. Harvey returned home, and for a time was fearful that Mary's family might try to poison him or kill him.

The divorce became final a few months after the trip to Europe. We do not have much information about Harvey for the next year or so. He engaged in several sexual affairs during that period which apparently aroused considerable conflict for him. He felt strong sexual desire for the women he dated, but felt very guilty about having intercourse with them. He and Mary had been sexually intimate a few times before they were married, but after the divorce he felt that he should not trust any woman who was willing to engage in sexual relations with him outside of marriage.

The following summer, while his parents were in Europe, Harvey frequently talked with his father's secretary, whom he described as an elderly, understanding woman. He confided that he was worried about being oversexed, and described a memory from the age of five, when he had overheard people in the next room talking about his circumcision (which had then been recently performed). Since that time he had felt that there was something wrong with him sexually.

At about this time Harvey noticed in a girl friend's apartment a picture of the Prodigal Son kneeling before his father. To Harvey it looked as though the son were kissing the father's penis. During the following year Harvey increasingly tended to interpret things as having homosexual significance. His former preoccupation with the idea that his wife had been interested in other men, for which he had no evidence, may have been related to this homosexual concern.

The following winter Harvey consulted an internist, complaining of pain in his right shoulder and a slight tic on the right side of his face. The physician found no organic pathology and recommended that Harvey seek psychiatric treatment. He also informed Clark of his findings, saying that Harvey showed delusional thinking and needed hospitalization. Clark told the parents about the doctor's findings and recommendation. They were incredulous, shocked, and very upset. The father made an appointment for Harvey and himself with a psychiatrist, who also recommended that Harvey be hospitalized. Harvey refused and the matter was dropped.

At the beginning of March, Harvey went to a mountain resort for a vacation. While there he met and became friendly with a woman named Sally Champion. Afterwards Sally came to Harvey's home town where she stayed for a while with a friend of her mother's. Sally and Harvey had an affair, and in May she told him that she was pregnant and wanted to marry him. When Harvey made it clear that he didn't want to marry her, Sally's family hired an attorney who put considerable pressure on Harvey and threatened to take him to court. Harvey was afraid to tell his parents about this situation and had no friends in whom he felt he could confide.

Harvey took a weekend trip to see a man named Mike, who had been a classmate at the military academy and was apparently as close a friend as he had. When Harvey arrived he had lunch with Mike, but that evening refused to accompany Mike and his wife to a dinner party, pleading an upset stomach. The following day Harvey continued to refuse to eat and seemed confused. His symptoms included nausea, diarrhea, severe headaches, and a very high fever. He felt that this was the worst experience his body had ever endured. When the physician Mike summoned diagnosed possible meningitis, Mike phoned Harvey's parents, who came, with Harvey's brother, to take Harvey home. During the trip back on a commercial airliner, Harvey refused all food and beverages, telling his parents that he had been afraid to eat or drink anything during the weekend for fear of being poisoned. At home he repeatedly asked his father to pray with him. Harvey asked his father whether he (Harvey) had had any kind of accident or illness as a child which might have caused the confused feelings he was experiencing. He also said or did something which the father interpreted as a homosexual advance, and which shocked him violently.

The following day Harvey was admitted to a sanitarium in his home town. During an evaluation interview held a week or so earlier with Dr. Wallis, a psychiatrist at the sanitarium, Harvey had described an organized ring of homosexuals who were trying to influence him. He believed that the ring included social acquaintances and the bartender at his club, and used an elaborate system of hand signals to communicate. When Dr. Wallis had told Harvey that he needed psychiatric hospitalization, Harvey had become angry and stalked out of the office.

Upon admission to the sanitarium, Harvey was described as "delusional, agitated, somatically preoccupied, and quite impulsive." His preoccupation with sexually significant hand signals continued. For example, he had noticed his father's habit of rubbing his mouth with his hand and wondered whether this had something to do with kissing a penis. He was given 12 electroshock treatments and then placed on chlorpromazine. He also had regular psychotherapeutic interviews with Dr. Wallis, during which he talked about his sexual confusion, and linked it to difficulty in his relationship with his father. After three months he was discharged, but continued to see Dr. Wallis twice a week for psychotherapy. He returned to work in his father's firm, and soon became involved in still another affair with a young woman who pursued him aggressively. Upon growing increasingly tense and anxious, he began to see Dr. Wallis more frequently. He became openly delusional again, convinced that people were trying to communicate with him through various media, such as Christmas candles. He was troubled by guilt feelings, by an impulse to get down on his knees in front of his father, and by increasing homosexual feelings about his father. Harvey began to withdraw from social contacts and was soon rehospitalized. At the sanitarium he was again given large doses of chlorpromazine and continued to receive psychotherapy. During this period Harvey attempted to talk to his father about the hand signals he thought his father was making, and about his own feeling that he had not been a loyal, obedient son. Harvey thought the hand signals meant that his father expected him to "kiss his ass." Harvey's tenseness and delusional thinking persisted and Dr. Wallis recommended that he be transferred to Chestnut Lodge for long-term intensive psychotherapy. Harvey liked Dr. Wallis and felt very let down when Dr. Wallis recommended his transfer.

In this review of Harvey's life before he came to Chestnut Lodge several characteristics deserve comment. One persistent theme is Harvey's docility, submissiveness, and inability to assert himself, especially with his parents and the women with whom he became involved. He repeatedly selected situations and relationships in which he would be dominated, as when he decided to enter the military academy, and later to study his father's profession and join his father's firm. His repeated relationships with aggressive women were undoubtedly not wholly accidental; he was probably not the passive victim of their active interest in him, but more than likely encouraged their attention. This represents a particular aspect of the need-fear dilemma, a need for and fear of being controlled by others. Harvey's concern with following the Ten Commandments further indicates his deeply felt need for control. His excellent record in school demonstrates his ability to function very well when tasks and standards were imposed upon him. We have also seen that he could carry out his own projects when not opposed, and especially when he kept them secret. This suggests a split between Harvey's own desires and his relations with others. Harvey kept his thoughts and feelings to himself. He confided in no one, from early childhood on. This was apparently the only way that Harvey felt he could be independent.

His inability to make an independent decision in the face of opposition is striking. When he decided to go to the military academy despite Sally's opposition, he had the support of his mother. He was unable to oppose his parents' urging that he enter his father's firm. His decision to marry was not independent, since Mary actively promoted the marriage; nor was it openly opposed by Harvey's parents, who did, however, strongly support his decision to be divorced. The first time in Harvey's life that he made an independent decision in the face of strong opposition was when he decided not to marry Sally Champion despite pressure from her, her family, and her lawyer. The visit to Mike was an attempt to secure support. We were not able to establish whether Harvey ever told Mike about his relationship with Sally. The attempt to win Mike's support was interrupted by the onset of Harvey's first psychotic episode.

In addition to his inability to resist strong opposition, there are other indications of his unusual susceptibility to influence by others, first manifested in his childhood "me too" imitation of his brother. Harvey's strong and lasting concern about the officer's unjust accusation indicates the importance of others' opinions to his own self-esteem.

These three aspects of Harvey's behavior—keeping secret his thoughts, feelings, and independent projects; his difficulty in resisting opposition without help; and his susceptibility to influence—are all closely related, and all point to a lack of differentiation in his relationships. He both welcomed and feared relationships with strong individuals, evidence of the longing for support and fear of domination typical of the poorly differentiated person.

Harvey's behavior also manifests a lack of integration, particularly of aggressive and hostile impulses with the rest of his functioning. His mother's memory of him as a sweet-tempered and docile child would indicate that she didn't want to recognize aggressive and hostile impulses in him and presumably either ignored them or tried to eradicate them when they appeared. The father's extreme reaction to Harvey's hitting his mother also tended to inhibit Harvey's open expression of aggression. By the time he reached adulthood Harvey had become extremely mild-mannered and agreeable. His unexpressed aggressive impulses were probably completely unconscious, except as projections, such as his concern about the destructiveness of the military and his fear that Mary's family might kill him.

Harvey's dissociated homosexual impulses may have been related to a childhood fantasy that his father would rescue him from his critical and demanding mother. The theme of turning from a woman to a man (or men) appears several times. Breaking off with Sally in order to go to the military academy is an early instance. Turning to Mike for support in his dispute with Sally Champion is another. After Harvey's first hospitalization he became anxious during the course of an affair with another aggressive young woman, which led to more frequent visits with Dr. Wallis and an increasing awareness of homosexual feelings about his father. Harvey's heterosexual relationships generally made him more aware of homosexual impulses. This is exemplified by his reaction to the picture of the Prodigal Son which he had seen in the apartment of a girl friend, his groundless suspicions that his wife might be intimate with other men, and his homosexual overture to his father following his affair with Sally Champion and the weekend visit to Mike.

Harvey's lack of both differentiation and integration subjected him to especially severe stress when he visited Mike. He feared Sally and her family, and was apprehensive of his parents' reaction were they to learn of his predicament. In his attempt to take a stand he had felt the need for support, which must have had disturbing implications in terms of his own weakness, and consequently aroused homosexual longings which threatened to break into awareness. Perhaps awareness of homosexual feelings toward Mike precipitated Harvey's disorganization. Whether or not this was so, the attempt to escape an aggressive woman and secure the aid of a sympathetic man upset the poorly differentiated and poorly integrated structure of Harvey's personality.

EXPERIENCES AND TREATMENT AT CHESTNUT LODGE

Harvey Appleton was brought to Chestnut Lodge early in 1959 and admitted to Third Floor. He was scheduled for four sessions of therapy per week in the office of Dr. Bart Wimpole, the psychotherapist to whom he was assigned. At the beginning Dr. Wimpole liked Harvey, was interested in working with him, and thought his prognosis good. He tried to let Harvey move at his own pace and bring up whatever topics he wanted to. Harvey expressed concern about his feelings of self-criticism and inadequacy, and indicated his desire to do something about them. He also spoke of his difficulties with women, especially aggressive women. It was his feeling that his recent psychotic episode had to do with his desire to become more independent of his parents, especially his father, combined with his conflicting desire to move closer to his father. However, he now felt that it was impossible to achieve such a relationship with his father and that he had to get out on his own.

Harvey was unhappy about being placed on Third Floor. He complained that the other patients there were odd and quite sick, and expressed the hope that he would soon be able to move to Hilltop. (At that time Hilltop and Third Floor were the only units in which male patients were housed. On the average, the patients at Hilltop were considerably more organized and in better contact than Third Floor patients, but there were exceptions. Hilltop was a more open unit, with easier access to the grounds and more contact between male and female patients.) Dr. Gibson, his administrative physician, also concerned about Harvey's being housed with patients far sicker than he, gave him grounds privileges within two weeks after admission so that he could get away from the ward whenever he wished.

When Harvey arrived at the Lodge he had been receiving 600 mgs./day of chlorpromazine, which Dr. Wimpole and Dr. Gibson agreed to eliminate by cutting down the dosage gradually. He received his last small dose of chlorpromazine one month after admission.

When Harvey discovered that he could not move to Hilltop because there was no space available, he began to express interest in moving out of the hospital. Dr. Wimpole and Dr. Gibson responded cautiously to this idea at first, but when Harvey continued to behave nonpsychotically after chlorpromazine had been eliminated, they agreed that he could become an outpatient. Two months after admission Harvey moved to a room in a house in Rockville.

As an outpatient Harvey had a rather lonely and isolated life. Shortly after he moved out of the hospital his mother paid him a visit. Harvey complained to Dr. Wimpole that his mother had examined the contents of his closet to see if he had enough clothes and had told him he needed a haircut. He was furious at his mother's behavior, feeling that he was old enough to decide such things for himself. According to Dr. Wimpole, it was at about the time of the mother's visit that Harvey began to withdraw from him; he became evasive, and began to make somatic complaints. Before long Harvey became distrustful of Dr. Wimpole and announced that he wanted to stop treatment. He complained that Dr. Wimpole was trying to maneuver him, and he resented questions about his thoughts and activities because he felt that Dr. Wimpole didn't really care about him and was just carrying out an impersonal treatment process.

During this time Harvey met a girl from his home state whom he began to date. Harvey told Dr. Wimpole very little about this girl, except that she was aggressive and wanted to neck, but that he wasn't interested in necking with her. While dating this girl Harvey became anxious and confused. At about the beginning of May, having heard that Harvey was confused, disheveled in appearance, and seemingly depressed, Dr. Gibson asked Harvey to pay him a visit; upon seeing him, he insisted that Harvey move back into the Lodge. He was accommodated at Hilltop where it was felt that he would make a better adjustment than he had on Third Floor.

The day Harvey returned to the Lodge he said at the end of his hour with Dr. Wimpole, "I'm not afraid to die," a statement to which Dr. Wimpole attributed the possibility of suicidal intent. During that hour Harvey also said that he had been thinking about his sexual problems, that he had been a fool, and that he had been angry at Dr. Wimpole but wasn't any longer. He spoke slowly and much of what he said was hard to follow. Nursing staff reported that there were periods when he appeared aimless, sitting or standing and staring into space. He spoke of how depressed he was, saying he had never felt so low in his life.

When Harvey saw Dr. Wimpole again two days later, he was still very depressed. He asked for help and talked confusedly about thoughts which were bothering him. He felt that the world was against him and that he wasn't a member of the human race. He dreamt that people were making fun of him, and reported a dream he had had the night before in which he was all-powerful and people were turning to him to be saved.

Later in May, Harvey refused to see Dr. Wimpole and requested a consultation with the Director of Psychotherapy. Harvey told the Director that he felt very uncomfortable lying down during his therapeutic sessions and that Dr. Wimpole was too rigid in urging him to use the couch. Harvey asserted he had been "shanghaied" into Chestnut Lodge and that it was dishonest of Dr. Wimpole to treat a patient who had been brought to the hospital against his will. Upon the Director's urging, Harvey agreed to see Dr. Wimpole at least a few more times.

Toward the middle of June, Harvey was again depressed, anxious, and frightened. On June 25, Harvey's mother came to Rockville where she was joined on July 4 by Harvey's father. Both remained until July 11, seeing Harvey nearly every day, sometimes for several hours. At first he showed little interest in seeing his mother, had little to say to her, and once or twice refused to see her. Later he showed more interest and became more communicative. At the same time his behavior on the ward improved and he became more active and cheerful. There is no record of what went on between Harvey and his parents during the visit, except that on the last day the father expressed displeasure at the deterioration in Harvey's condition since his previous visit. After his parents left, Harvey became markedly inactive for several days. He was often found lying on the floor, had almost nothing to say, would eat little even when spoon fed, and was at times incontinent. He began to hit people unexpectedly and without apparent reason. This kind of catatonic behavior was repeated at times throughout the summer. One night he carried on a long, disorganized monologue, referring to atomic bombs, the end of the world, and the death of everyone except himself. For a while during this period another patient took a special interest in him, and tried to be helpful by spoon-feeding him at mealtime and putting him to bed at night. Harvey eventually grew tired of this and asked him to stop, but the other patient persisted. Shortly after the middle of August Dr. Wimpole left on his vacation.

In September Harvey began to run away and to resist coming back from walks and outings. In his attempts at running away he did not go very far and was usually located and brought back without difficulty, although occasionally force was used. At times he indicated that he was going to leave, either by saying so directly or by requesting a key or asking to call a taxi. He told a female aide that he wanted to leave the Lodge because people did not like him. He also said he had many problems that had to be cleared up before he left, and that he required a lot of support and had a need to talk. Later in September Harvey's attempts to run away became more frequent.

On September 21 Dr. Wimpole returned from his vacation. Harvey remained mute throughout their first hour, and Dr. Wimpole felt that Harvey did not want to see him. In succeeding hours Dr. Wimpole urged Harvey to cooperate with him, to tell him what was going on, and to have his therapy hours in his own room instead of the living room as they had been. On the evening of September 23 Harvey started to run away and was brought back. Later that night he succeeded in running away and was picked up by the police in the early morning hours of September 24. Later that day he said to a male aide, "You've got to let me out of here; these people are against me." Harvey ignored Dr. Wimpole that afternoon and refused to go to his room for their hour. Dr. Wimpole became annoyed, said that Harvey was making him insist, and told him "I hope you don't make me force you to have the hour, but if necessary I will do that." At supper time Harvey made another attempt to run away. Three men were required to bring him back, and in the course of the struggle Harvey suffered a black eye, a bruised arm, and sore ribs. Harvey apologized afterwards for causing trouble, but said he should not be in a hospital. The following day Dr. Wimpole came for their hour and again expressed annoyance with Harvey. Harvey appeared to be confused, not quite sure who he was or who Dr. Wimpole was. He asked, "Why don't you get the hell out of here?" and threw a cigarette at Dr. Wimpole. Dr. Wimpole stayed, and Harvey finally grabbed him by the shirt and began beating him on the head and chest. Dr. Wimpole was alarmed by the attack and felt that Harvey was filled with murderous rage. He gave orders that Harvey be put in pack for his therapy hours from then on. The next time he saw Harvey he explained the pack by saying, "I have no intention of being the victim of your rage." On the morning of September 30, Harvey packed his clothes and told several staff members that he was going to leave and would kill anyone who tried to stop him. He did not attempt to leave just then, however. Later he said that he and some of the other patients had received orders from the President to blow up Chestnut Lodge, to kill his brother, an aide, and other people whose names he couldn't remember. When Dr. Wimpole came that afternoon, he realized that Harvey was feeling murderous and several times invited him to talk about his rage. Harvey talked instead about such topics as the weather and golf. That night he slept for only an hour and spent most of the night pacing in the hallway. At one point he tried to climb out of a window. The following evening he made two more attempts to leave, once by breaking a window and once by forcing out a screen. The next morning he twice attacked aides suddenly and violently. His talk varied from remarks about his being sick to confused statements about blowing up Chestnut Lodge, an army plot to take over danger areas, and murder. At times he appeared extremely frightened and seemed uncertain whether he should attack staff members before they attacked him. The administrator of Hilltop and Dr. Gibson conferred and decided to move him back to Third Floor.

After Harvey's transfer back to Third Floor there followed a long, difficult period in which there were many events but little real change. After arriving on Third Floor he continued to attack staff members and other patients and made further attempts to escape. Many people became alarmed, with the result that a stringent policy of control was established. Harvey was kept in seclusion most of the time and led a very isolated existence. This period continued for nearly a year and a half, until Dr. Wimpole stopped working with Harvey. The following account covers the more significant events between Dr. Wimpole and Harvey during that year and a half.

When Harvey was transferred back to Third Floor, Dr. Wimpole was very discouraged about him. He felt unable to say anything that would be useful or pleasing to Harvey. Harvey said little to Dr. Wimpole and apparently thought him stupid and dishonest. Dr. Wimpole felt that Harvey had some control over himself and that his behavior was a way of showing that he needed to be firmly restrained. Dr. Wimpole expressed this viewpoint both to Third Floor staff members and to Harvey himself. During an hour Dr. Wimpole conveyed to

Harvey that "he was obviously struggling with some intense anger . . . and that it must be frightening to him to feel this way, but at the same time his hitting people was pushing them away; he was . . . getting the aides less and less interested in helping him." Harvey was largely silent during most of their sessions and Dr. Wimpole continued to urge him to talk, to tell about his troubles, to talk about what made him feel like killing people. At times Dr. Wimpole would try to convey sympathy and reassurance to Harvey.

On October 29 Harvey made a number of complaints and requests. He said he would like to have another doctor because he and Dr. Wimpole didn't understand one another. He objected to being put in pack for the hours and suggested having a third person in the room instead. Then he said he really needed a medical doctor who would give him a prescription. Dr. Wimpole responded to this by asking, "Do you really feel that if there were a drug which would make you feel comfortable that I wouldn't give it to you?"

During the second week of December Harvey hallucinated during the hours, and seemed to be involved in some kind of a war or air raid, making comments like, "Send the bombers. Here come the planes. Red three. . . . They have captured the queen." Dr. Wimpole made interpretive comments like, "Perhaps the danger has to do with explosive feelings of yours," and "Could it be competition with brother and father for mother?" At other times Dr. Wimpole dealt with immediate practical problems, like cleaning up Harvey's room, clipping his toenails, and dealing with Harvey's requests, instead of making analytic interpretations. Dr. Wimpole noted that Harvey responded favorably when something was done for him but became more anxious upon being questioned.

On December 23 Dr. Wimpole said, "I feel ready to take your suggestion and rather than use the pack, have a third person in the room and see how it goes." Starting December 24 this change was made. Dr. Wimpole felt that things went well without the pack, that Harvey was friendlier toward him, and was reintegrating. However, on January 11 and 13 he saw Harvey in pack again because Harvey had been verbally belligerent. Starting January 14 they again met without the pack, but it was reinstituted on January 20 and continued thereafter. On January 26 Dr. Wimpole noted that he "tried to give some direction today on how to go about understanding shifts in his state of feeling." Harvey's response was that Dr. Wimpole was dictating or trying to brainwash him. During the second week of February Dr. Wimpole was ill and did not see Harvey for a week. When he returned he noticed that Harvey would neither speak to him nor look at him and remembered that Harvey had reacted similarly to his previous absences.

On March 22 Dr. Wimpole took a male aide with him when he went to see Harvey for his hour, thinking that this might make Harvey more comfortable. When Harvey responded well to this arrangement, Dr. Wimpole took it as confirming his surmise that Harvey was afraid of him. Consequently, he continued to have an aide join them.

Early in April Dr. Wimpole increased their hours to five a week because he felt that Harvey was very isolated and needed more contact with him. Around this time Dr. Wimpole also asked the personnel to write more detailed nursing notes about Harvey, in the hope that this would induce the nursing staff to pay more attention to Harvey, that it would enable him to keep in better touch with Harvey, and that it might be useful for reading to Harvey. During each session Dr. Wimpole read aloud the nursing notes from the preceding day. Harvey seemed to make an effort to remember the events described. He asked questions about them and often inquired about the date. Then he asked Dr. Wimpole for several magazines and a calendar, which were provided. The extra session, reading the nursing notes, the calendar, and the magazines all seemed to help Harvey become more organized and better able to communicate with Dr. Wimpole. He also became much less assaultive. In June there was a day on which Dr. Wimpole did not come for the hour but Harvey was packed nonetheless because nursing personnel had not been notified. When Dr. Wimpole arrived the next day Harvey did not return his greeting; he kept his eyes closed and looked angry. Dr. Wimpole apologized for having cancelled the hour without informing him and explained that a problem had suddenly arisen that he had had to deal with. Harvey still did not respond, but later in the hour he said, "You know, Bart, they only give me iced tea and some lemon. It's been an awful ordeal." Dr. Wimpole said, "Yes, you really have been going through an awful ordeal for some time now." Harvey said, "I get awfully tired of this room." Dr. Wimpole suggested he might like to go for a walk; this led to Harvey's going for an occasional walk escorted by an aide.

Another conversation which took place that month was less successful. Soon after Dr. Wimpole arrived one day, Harvey asked, "Are you ready to tell me something now?" Dr. Wimpole asked, "Do you have something to tell me?" Harvey said, "You're hurt." Dr. Wimpole asked, "Do you mean that you feel you have been deeply hurt?" Harvey said, "No, I said, 'You're hurt.' " Dr. Wimpole asked, "Could you mean you are afraid that I might be hurt by what you have to say?" Harvey said, "No. Someone else might hurt you." Finally, Dr. Wimpole said, "OK, I'll listen."

In October, Harvey said that Dr. Wimpole didn't know what he was letting himself in for and seemed to imply that if they went on working together one of them would die and that there was something very destructive going on. Following that session Dr. Wimpole felt that Harvey again withdrew from him. Harvey stopped talking, though at times he moved his lips as though he were talking. At this time Dr. Wimpole began to feel that he and Harvey were no longer making any progress and had reached a stalemate. The following January, when Dr. Wimpole was cutting down his case load, he stopped working with Harvey. In their final session, Harvey's last remark was, "You are running off, huh?"

Several months later Harvey described to Dr. Wilson, his new therapist, the feelings he had had while in pack. (Dr. Wilson saw Harvey without the pack, following a discussion about it during their first session.) He wanted to scream; he wanted to move; his body ached all over; he felt completely lost; he couldn't express himself unless he could get into a more comfortable position. (Harvey improved considerably in the course of his therapy with Dr. Wilson. He became an outpatient again, this time more successfully, and was again able to work as an engineer. However, these developments go beyond the data-gathering period of our study. Furthermore, Harvey began to receive trifluoperazine when he began to see Dr. Wilson, so it would be difficult to determine how much of his improvement was due to the drug and how much to the new psychotherapeutic relationship.)

Harvey's relationship with Dr. Gibson, the administrator of Third Floor, began on a very friendly basis. As mentioned earlier, Dr. Gibson was concerned because Harvey seemed much more normal than the other patients on the ward. Dr. Gibson gave Harvey grounds privileges within two weeks, lent him a set of golf clubs, and generally tried to treat him as more his equal than he did the other patients.

During his first few weeks at Chestnut Lodge Harvey at times complained bitterly to the aides but not to Dr. Gibson, except very mildly. This would suggest some fear of Dr. Gibson and fits in with Harvey's pattern of submissiveness to parental and authority figures. Harvey addressed Dr. Gibson by first name only once, but addressed Dr. Wimpole by first name from very early in their relationship, which suggests more respect for or fear of Dr. Gibson. After Harvey moved to Hilltop, Dr. Gibson did not see him until he was transferred back to Third Floor in October. Harvey was then very disturbed and assaultive, and nursing personnel became alarmed and angry. With the aim of helping nursing personnel to feel fairly secure about dealing with Harvey, Dr. Gibson decided to keep him in a seclusion room most of the time, letting him come out only when things were relatively quiet and there was adequate help available. This approach reduced Harvey's attacks on nursing personnel, although it did isolate him, as we have seen. Some staff members felt that Dr. Gibson had a calming effect on Harvey. This is illustrated by an incident which occurred when Harvey was about to be put in pack. Dr. Gibson was in Harvey's room with several aides. Harvey made some comments with a cocky smile which suggested to Dr. Gibson that he was acting like a tough guy and might attack. Dr. Gibson moved quite close, so that Harvey would be less able to hit him hard and also to show that he was not afraid, and took both of Harvey's hands. Harvey then asked if he could lean on Dr. Gibson and put his head on Dr. Gibson's shoulder for a few minutes while Dr. Gibson held him. Dr. Gibson felt that this was an open display of Harvey's desire to be taken care of. However, this incident was exceptional. For the most part, Harvey's relationship with Dr. Gibson was not very intimate and did not seem especially significant for either of them. Dr. Gibson concentrated mainly on practical and medical problems, limiting the time he spent with individual patients.

Our data concerning Harvey's interaction with the nursing personnel are mostly from the period of Harvey's second stay on Third Floor, when he was disorganized and assaultive and spent much of his time in the seclusion room. During this period the questionnaire was given three times, in January, late March, and December of 1960. In March and December Harvey was below average on all five scales of the friendly social approach cluster, although in January he had been close to the average on all five scales. This shows that between January and the end of March Harvey and the staff members withdrew from each other. During January and March, Harvey was above average on all five scales of the problem behavior cluster, but by December he was somewhat below average on "Expression of Negative Feelings by Staff" and "Use of Control Techniques by Staff" in addition to which he showed less "Problem Behavior" and "Noncompliance," though he was still above average on both these scales. Between March and December he increased in "Confused and Unrealistic Communication." To recapitulate, between January and March Harvey's interaction with the nursing staff became even less friendly than it had been, and he was treated even more as a problem patient. Between March and December Harvey became less prominent as a problem patient, but was still not interacting as a friendly and sociable patient (although there had been a slight rise on some of these scales since March). Thus, by the end of this period Harvey did not closely fit either of the most common patient roles and was therefore somewhat neglected. This is undoubtedly related to the decline in clarity of Harvey's communication. By the end of 1960 Harvey's interaction with nursing staff was similar to the mutual discouragement and withdrawal in his relationship with Dr. Wimpole.

Harvey often showed special interest in and preference for female staff members and seems to have evoked greater interest from them than from most of the male staff members. Many of the women regarded him as handsome, attractive, and charming, outstanding not only among the other male patients, but among men in general. One of the women Harvey was interested in was Mrs. Unterlinder, the social worker for Third Floor. On at least one occasion he made sexual overtures to her. On another occasion, when he had been registering many complaints (about the room he was in, about being put in pack, etc.) he asked to see Mrs. Unterlinder and told her that he considered her to be in control. Apparently he wanted her to assume responsibility, since he wasn't getting what he wanted from Dr. Wimpole or Dr. Gibson.

During Harvey's second stay on Third Floor there were few women staff members. Miss Janni, a nurse, worked there for one week shortly after Harvey's return to Third Floor (and thereafter worked on a neighboring unit until she left the Lodge in September 1960). Harvey became interested in her and at times asked Dr. Wimpole to tell her to visit him. He also asked to see Mrs. MacMaster, an older nurse who worked on a neighboring unit. There were at least two student nurses he became fond of; he persistently called each of them "Sally" (though neither was named that), perhaps identifying them with the Sally he had known in high school and college. However, when Harvey was disorganized and assaultive the student nurses were afraid of him and avoided him even more than the male aides did.

Harvey developed an important relationship with one of the male aides, Buck Wheeler. Mr. Wheeler started to work on Third Floor in October 1959, at about the time that Harvey returned to Third Floor. By the fall of 1960, Wheeler found Harvey more interesting to work with and spent more time with him than with any other patient. He made a point of spending some time with Harvey every day; he made certain that he bathed and shaved, encouraged him to come out of his room for a while, and sat with him while they watched TV, etc. At one time, when Harvey was not even sure of his own name, Wheeler had written "Harvey Richards Appleton" in large letters on the wall of his room and encouraged Harvey to trace the letters with his finger, repeat his name aloud, etc. When Dr. Wilson began to work with Harvey, he asked Wheeler to sit in the room during the hours instead of having Harvey in pack.

Let us now review Harvey's experiences and relationships at Chestnut Lodge. At the beginning, both his therapist and his administrative psychiatrist liked him and judged his prognosis to be good. Harvey was eager to benefit from psychotherapy and was able to state some of his problems. But this promising beginning did not lead to the progress hoped for. Harvey's displeasure at being placed among patients who were obviously disturbed helped him get grounds privileges very quickly and to become an outpatient only two months after admission. (Harvey's concern about being among such patients was probably related to his lack of differentiation and the resultant fear that by being with these patients he would become like them and perhaps was already regarded as being like them.) Thus Harvey and the hospital staff collaborated to uphold his claim to be functioning relatively well. However, Harvey again found himself struggling alone to protect his independence from aggressive women. First there was the visit of his critical and overbearing mother, and then the demands fom the girl he was dating. Faced with these pressures, Harvey became confused and depressed and Dr. Gibson insisted that he move back into the hospital. (Thus Harvey got a man to come to his rescue, although not by asking for this directly.)

Now that they had seen him disorganized, the hospital staff members would not honor Harvey's claim to be functioning adequately. Much of the subsequent interaction involved conflict between Harvey's attempts to assert that he was sane and the staff's refusals to confirm that he was. Thus, in asking to be discharged and in trying to terminate his relationship with Dr. Wimpole, Harvey was trying to exercise normal prerogatives and to deny his needs for help and support. Such denial was also expressed by his dream of people turning to him to be saved. Harvey's attempts to run away from the hospital reflected his realization that the staff could no longer be persuaded to treat him as sane; thus his attempts to escape were denials of being crazy and of needing help. They may, at the same time, have represented appeals for help and tests to find out how vigilant and how concerned about him the hospital staff members really were. The attempts to escape probably also reflected a feeling that the hospital was a dangerous place and was responsible for the confusion and discomfort he felt.

In the course of these escape attempts and being brought back to the hospital, Harvey's struggles with staff members became more and more vigorous, which undoubtedly increased his fear and anger. When Dr. Wimpole expressed annoyance at Harvey and ignored his requests that Dr. Wimpole leave, Harvey attacked him. Dr. Wimpole's interpretation of this attack as evidence that Harvey was filled with murderous rage affected their entire subsequent relationship. This conception, that the rage was *in* Harvey, rather than between Harvey and others, implied that the rage would emerge regardless of what others did, and failed to recognize the fact that the rage appeared in the course of increasingly conflictful interaction between Harvey and staff members. The incident in which Harvey put his head on Dr. Gibson's shoulder suggests that Harvey's rage might have been reduced if staff members had been less influenced by the interpretation that the rage was in Harvey, waiting to emerge.

Dr. Wimpole tried to keep his interaction with Harvey mainly verbal and intellectual. Perhaps this was an attempt to apply the psychoanalytic method for the treatment of neurotics, with the patient lying on the couch being encouraged to free associate while the analyst listens and occasionally makes an interpretation. Harvey complied at first, but later complained about having to lie on the couch. He wanted to stop seeing Dr. Wimpole, and asked for drugs. At times Dr. Wimpole varied his approach, and noted that Harvey responded favorably when he was helped in some simple, concrete way but became anxious when questioned. However, Dr. Wimpole continued to strive for a highly verbal interchange. This interfered with the freedom of communication between them, since Dr. Wimpole was urging Harvey toward a kind of communication which was difficult and often impossible for him.

We commented earlier that Harvey was able to function well when tasks and standards were imposed on him, although he also feared control and at times tried to escape from it. During most of the period just described, Harvey's fears of control and attempts to avoid it predominated. In previous situations (school, the military, his father's business), Harvey's accomplishments were respected and he was often highly successful, but at Chestnut Lodge acceptance of control would have meant acceptance of the frightening and humiliating conception of himself as insane. This tremendously increased the fear side of Harvey's need-fear dilemma.

As we pointed out in the chapter on the development of relationship, two principal types of interaction between patients and nursing staff were found: friendly social behavior, and interaction around problems. When he first arrived, Harvey was capable of friendly, social behavior, but he was so successful at this that he found himself out of the hospital. When upon his return the staff tried to persuade him to accept the problem patient role, the result was a prolonged, intense conflict. Could the hospital have provided control and support for Harvey without frightening and humiliating him? Might some other approach have avoided or reduced Harvey's formidable attacks on staff members? It is not possible to answer these questions, but it seems possible that Harvey's problems might have been alleviated had the hospital staff's approach to Harvey been better differentiated and better integrated; that is, had they been better able to discern and respond to what was going on within Harvey, and had they been more aware of the interrelations between their own behavior and his.

X

HENRY HARRASHAW

ARTHUR I. GLADSTONE

HENRY HARRASHAW was the first born of three children, the son of a perfectionistic and authoritarian father who tried to demonstrate to his wife and children that he was always right. He was a physician, and watched carefully over the family's health and physical development. Henry's mother was afraid of doing the wrong thing and willing to be guided by her husband and various published child-care authorities, one of whose books she followed religiously during Henry's infancy. (She remembers standing by the crib with tears streaming down her face because the book advised against picking up a crying infant.) Although outwardly submissive to her husband, and willing to let him do most of the talking and win the arguments, she has maintained a subtle rivalry with him and does not really want to concede that she is in the wrong.

Henry's mother regarded him as a feeding problem almost from birth. He was breast fed until he was six months old and then put on a rigid schedule of feeding from spoon and cup. From the age of about one year to a year and a half, he became more and more of a feeding problem. When his baby brother was born (Henry was then 17 months old) he stopped eating altogether. His parents consulted several physicians, one of whom recommended that instead of his mother, their maid feed Henry. As soon as the maid began to feed Henry, he began to eat. He continued to eat fairly well until the maid left when Henry was about two and a half. He had been fond of her and his eating deteriorated again after she left. During childhood Henry developed many food dislikes, especially for milk.

When Henry was about two, he frequently soiled himself at night. His mother related this to the fact that he shared a room with his younger brother, Carl, who was given a 6 a.m. bottle. When Carl was no longer given an early bottle, Henry's soiling ceased. Mother's preferred discipline to persuade Henry to stop soiling had been to wash him with cold water, telling him that he could not have warm water because he was dirty. At two or three he had severe temper tantrums which she dealt with by throwing cold water on him.

Henry suffered a series of serious illnesses in his early years. He had tonsillitis at nine months and a tonsillectomy at 14 months. At two and a half he had a severe strep throat, and at three he had polio. From infancy throughout his early school years he was sick much of the time with frequent colds, bronchitis, or ear infections. From the beginning the father was concerned about Henry's physical development. Henry's weight, which he charted, was disappointingly low. Both parents were constantly solicitous about Henry's health and worried by his frequent illnesses. Later, in his desire to see Henry develop athletic skills, father prodded and nagged him into one activity or another, but Henry never became proficient in any of them.

Henry and his brother Carl were very jealous of each other and rivalrous almost from the beginning. Once, when Henry was about three and a half, the mother took the boys on a shopping trip and left them in the car for a few minutes. She returned to find Carl screaming —Henry had pulled out almost all his hair by the roots. Mother was so angry that she felt unable to deal with the situation. She said nothing to Henry but drove directly home and turned him over to the maid, saying, "He's yours, you do something about him." The mother's unwillingness to deal with anger is also indicated in her reactions to Henry's temper tantrums. She remembers that Henry could never tolerate being frustrated. When anything was contrary to his wishes, he would have a temper tantrum and throw himself on the floor. She would either put him in bed or try to ignore the tantrum.

Henry's sister Sarah was born when he was three and a half. He was enthusiastic about her from the first and she was his favorite in the family. The relationship between Henry and Sarah was close and important to both of them. When interviewed at the time Henry was admitted to Chestnut Lodge, Sarah reported that she had had an episode similar to Henry's psychosis, though not as serious. She had received no treatment and had recovered spontaneously, but this experience convinced her that it was possible for Henry to recover. Sarah had become emotionally upset at examination time and had experienced some delusional ideas, such as being the counterpart of Jesus Christ and receiving undeserved help from others. She never told her parents about this experience.

Henry was eccentric, shy, and somewhat solitary throughout his childhood and adolescence. He did not get along well with most children. The few friends he did have were usually less privileged than he, or were sick in some way, or came from a lower economic group than his family. (This was his parents' view of the friends.) When Henry was about five years old, a boy named Larry moved into his neighborhood. The two boys became close friends and their friendship continued to the time of Henry's hospitalization. Larry was much larger and something of a bully, and Henry's mother frequently intervened in their disagreements. Henry was slow to show any interest in girls and when he was in high school would frequently go to dances alone. He has never had a close relationship with a girl. He would take a girl out once or twice and then drop her, although he was an attractive boy and girls were sometimes interested in him. This pattern continued into his college years.

We have no information about Henry's sexual education or sexual behavior. His sister reported that she had received very little sexual information from her mother and that the parents obviously felt that the less said about sex, the better.

When Henry was nine or 10, he gained a great deal of weight. He was uncomfortable about this and about the special clothing he had to wear. Perhaps some of Henry's discomfort was related to the fact that his father was thin and his mother was fat. After a year or two Henry lost much of his excess weight. Following this, his parents felt that he often dressed sloppily just to tease them. The mother reported once:

> He always ate sporadically—sparingly some days and voraciously other times. It seemed to have nothing to do with the food offered, but was more a matter of resisting conventions and routine. As he grew older he sometimes talked of the advantages of primitive people who ate only when hungry rather than following a three-meal-a-day schedule.

He also protested regimentation in dress and social life—in fact, he was never as happy as when he went to camp or on fishing trips when such requirements were at a minimum.

Henry's parents sent him to military school for the last two years of high school, expecting that this would give him an advantage when he was drafted. In addition, the father liked the military academy because of its emphasis on athletics. Henry was very unhappy there. Although he told his sister and brother that he hated the school, he did not tell his parents. When he graduated from military school at 18, he enlisted in the Army for 18 months, to avoid being drafted. He wanted very much to be a paratrooper but because he had had polio, he was not considered qualified. At first he was given Signal Corps training, but he finally succeeded in being assigned to the paratroops, a feat of which he was proud. It was his parents' feeling that he wanted to do something dangerous to prove he was not a coward. Henry's father had played football, basketball, and baseball, but Henry had achieved no prowess in any athletic activity and seemed to feel that being a paratrooper compensated for this. Since his mother had never liked flying, his parents were of the opinion that he was showing her that he didn't share her fears. Henry was extremely happy in the paratroops. He completed the entire course of training, including the required number of plane jumps, and then was discharged from the Army.

When he returned home after his Army service, his father greeted him at the railroad station with the remark, "Now that you are back home from the Army, we have to think about your going to college." Henry replied, "Listen, I'm not taking orders from you or anybody else!" Henry's parents did not like the change in him, considering him belligerent, cynical, and unwilling to trust people. There had been three generations of doctors in the father's family, and the parents had assumed that Henry would go into medicine. However, he made no arrangements for entering college, although the parents continually pressured him to do so. They finally took it upon themselves to arrange for him to enter an excellent college in a nearby city although Henry had not said that he wanted to go. His younger brother was entering the same college that fall, and the parents arranged that they would share a room. Although Henry had never openly agreed to go to college, when the fall came he did leave with his brother.

While Henry was at college his visits home were marked by arguments, especially on religious subjects. For example, he asked his mother why she had joined the Episcopal Church. When she did not answer at dinner, he followed her into the kitchen. In this way he would press his attack until the other person got angry. As soon as he received a show of anger, he seemed satisfied and would then be quite pleasant for the remainder of his visit. Before he arrived home his parents would brace each other, "Let's not allow him to get under our hides," but Henry was always able to provoke them.

During his second year of college Henry decided to spend the summer working in Alaska. He had long been interested in travel and in reading about distant places. His father opposed the trip but was unable to dissuade Henry. On his way to Alaska, Henry stopped at a college much further from home and enrolled there for the fall semester. After that summer he returned home for a few days, and then left for the more distant college. The following summer he stayed at school, resisting all suggestions that he return home for a visit. The summer after that one Henry's parents went to visit him, but Henry was annoyed at their having come and their expressions of interest in him.

During Henry's junior and senior years at college, his academic work deteriorated. As his grades in premedical courses were unsatisfactory he began to take social science courses in order to acquire enough credits to graduate. He repeatedly expressed a desire to quit school and join the Coast Guard, a plan which his parents opposed vigorously. He had not accumulated enough credits to earn a degree at the end of his senior year, so he continued to take courses until the end of the following fall quarter.

Soon after he arrived home for that Christmas vacation, he received notification that he had gotten a "D" in a required course and would have to repeat the course or take another. This was very upsetting. He had not expected to return to school, for had he passed all his courses he would have had sufficient credits to graduate. He was determined not to go back to school, declaring that he didn't care whether he got a degree or not and that he was going into the merchant marine as a radio operator. This announcement provoked heated arguments with his father. Both parents insisted that he finish college and get a degree, and said they didn't care what he did after that but they expected that much. They did, however, disapprove strongly of his plan to go into the merchant marine.

Soon after this Henry began to talk, especially to his brother and sister, about economic theories and the possibility of an economy without money. He had been reading Orwell's *1984* and said he was the only one who knew what *1984* was really about. He implied that he had a detailed insight into what Orwell was getting at but he would not communicate it except that it had to do with too much regimentation. Arguments continued about whether he should return to college, and finally he accepted his parents' demand that he do so. After this decision he seemed to relax and became more pleasant. His parents contacted the college and arranged for him to repeat the course he had failed. He had wanted to make the arrangements himself, but they had insisted on ensuring his acceptance. After Henry returned to school, his letters were filled with worry about international politics and foreign affairs. He said little about himself, except that he was studying mind reading and was interested in psychology.

Within a few weeks the Dean of Students called his parents to inform them that Henry was extremely upset. In a state of panic, he had gone to the home of a professor the previous Sunday, declaring that the campus was in an uproar and the war was on. He spoke to the professor about germ warfare and about planes and bombing, and seemed extremely frightened and confused. His parents went immediately to bring him home. Over the next few years Henry was successively admitted to three psychiatric hospitals before he was brought to Chestnut Lodge in June 1955.

Throughout Henry's childhood and adolescence a central issue between Henry and his parents involved the question of control. Henry's parents both had doubts about their own abilities. The father attempted to resolve his doubts by proving to others, especially his family, that he was right about everything, and insisting that they acknowledge his rightness. The mother dealt with her feelings of inadequacy by relying on the advice and help of others, her husband, other physicians, the book on child care, and the nursemaid. Both parents must have seen Henry as a continuous challenge, the father especially concerned about his health and physical development and the mother especially frustrated by his feeding difficulties, his toilet training, and his temper tantrums. Both parents assumed, as many parents do, that there were explicit and detailed norms which should be followed, not only in terms of their son's development but in terms of their behavior toward him. This is exemplified by the father's concern about Henry's weight curve and by the mother's efforts to base her treatment of Henry on authoritative instructions. It is likely that their insistence that Henry's development and treatment follow a prescribed course contributed to the development of the very problems about which they were concerned. Thus the maid had no difficulty in feeding Henry, whereas the mother's approach failed. The mother's attempt to force Henry's eating into a prescribed pattern was the first of many struggles for the control of Henry's behavior.

The fundamental shortcoming in the efforts of Henry's parents to control his behavior was that minimal attention was paid to what was actually going on within Henry. *His* needs, wants, and preferences were disregarded. Thus, the rigid feeding schedule ignored whether or not Henry was actually hungry. This approach leaves a child only two possibilities: submission or rebellion. Any attempt at independent action by the child will either be ignored or treated as rebellion. This hampers the development of self-regulation, the ability to assess and take care of one's own needs so necessary to independence. The child treated in this way is likely to remain dependent upon his parents or parent substitutes to control his behavior and satisfy his needs. Attempts at rebellion are self-defeating because the child has not learned to get along without external control.

Henry's childhood and adolescence fits this pattern. His behavior was characterized by submissiveness and rebelliousness, with little true independence. There is no record of his having achieved any success on his own, whether in work, hobbies, sports, social activities, or personal relationships. Henry's rebellions generally ended in capitulation. The happiest period of Henry's adolescence was the time spent in the paratroops, where he received the external control he needed in a form that did not challenge his manhood; on the contrary, it allowed him to demonstrate his manhood. His plans to join the Coast Guard or the merchant marine were apparently attempts to find another such situation. It may be significant that the Army is predominantly male; going to sea is an even more drastic way of avoiding women. Submitting to control by a woman may have been especially conflictual for Henry.

Henry's submissiveness to his parents made him something of a martyr, thus enabling his parents to maintain their beliefs in their own rationality, maturity, and opinions of what was right. It was Henry who was wrong, bad, and ultimately crazy, not they. Henry's martyrdom also seems to have shielded his brother and sister from the full impact of their parents' attentions, especially their competence-proving, norm-imposing attentions, and therefore allowed Carl and Sarah to grow up somewhat more successfully.

The acute onset of Henry's psychosis was marked by growing concern about control and regimentation, as shown by his interest in money, one of the principal means of social control, and in *1984*, a description of an extremely regimented society in which rebellion is hopeless and leads only to more extreme identity-destroying control. At the time of onset, Henry was completing the last requirement for college graduation, after which, his parents had told him, he could do as he wished. It was also a time when the usual expectation would have been for him to become more independent and self-reliant. Thus Henry's great need for and resentment of control, which he had managed to keep in precarious balance during his college years, threatened him anew with conflict and the necessity to achieve a new balance. Henry's psychosis can be viewed as an all-out rebellion against all systems of control and regulation. Having so little self-regulatory capacity of his own with which to replace external regulation, Henry became extremely primitive and helpless.

This account of Henry's relations with his family has concentrated on the issue of control because of its importance in Henry's psychosis. It is not intended as a complete view of Henry's childhood and adolescence. There were many positive aspects of Henry's upbringing which enabled him to do as well as he did before the onset of his psychosis, and which were instrumental in providing him with the considerable charm and appeal he held for others during his hospitalization.

Over three years elapsed between Henry's psychotic outbreak and his admission to Chestnut Lodge. During that time he was in three hospitals and was subjected to many shock treatments. For most of this period he was confused, withdrawn, and negativistic. He would occasionally improve, but never remained in this improved state for very long.

The admitting physician described his interaction with Henry shortly after Henry's arrival at Chestnut Lodge:

When seen . . . he was found to be a thin, extremely withdrawn man, who was mute upon approach, and who stood or sat motionless for long periods of time. Although when he was first interviewed it was not possible to establish verbal contact with him to which he would respond, later in the day when he was found standing on the porch, he said in a quite friendly, rather wistful way, "The trees are very pretty." He continued to talk about the trees for some time and expressed some wish to go outside and look at the hospital grounds. He explained that the last hospital he had been in was not a very pretty place and that he was glad to be away from there. He gradually began to talk more about himself, stating that he had been in school and had gotten sick and that was why he was in a hospital. He claimed that he was studying to be a doctor and that he had been interested in that and remained interested because there were so many sick people in the world. He indicated that all the time he had spent with sick people had simply furthered his medical ambition. The patient seemed extremely friendly during this exchange but then indicated that he would just like to stand and look at the trees for a while and seemed to feel he had talked enough. I asked him if he was interested in seeing his family, as they had come from their home at the same time he came to the hospital. He said that he was always interested in seeing nice people and indicated that he considered his family nice, thus a visit was arranged for the next day. However, by the next day the patient was again extremely withdrawn and lay quietly and rather rigidly in bed. He indicated that he just wished to remain in bed and rest, evincing no interest in a visit; it was decided not to press him on this point—consequently no visit from his family took place.

Shortly after his arrival at Chestnut Lodge, Henry was assigned to Dr. Mario Zilla for intensive psychotherapy; they worked together for the next four and a half years. During the first few days Henry was catatonic and lay in bed without moving for long periods. He was incontinent and at times smeared or threw feces. He did not eat and had to be tube fed. Before each tube feeding he was put in pack in order to minimize resistance. At times the tube feedings seemed to have considerable sexual meaning for Henry; he would become quite excited and wiggle as if he were masturbating. Sometimes he spoke of the tube as containing "wild sperm." He gave a variety of reasons for not eating: "They want you to eat and food makes people fat. Then you get fat and they do not like you." And, "I don't eat because if I eat I flunk. . . . If I eat I break my promise. . . . If I eat, my head

gets bigger; a tube is close to my brain." At times Henry said that he
was an animal and that animals didn't have the right to eat. At other
times Henry would say that food was poison, or shit, or cruel. As in
childhood, he objected especially to milk, often saying, "Milk is cruel."

After a few months he began to attack staff members, jumping and
striking at them suddenly and unexpectedly, but continued to spend
most of the time lying in bed or on the floor, typically in a fetal position. Over the next four years he gradually improved, with many ups
and downs. He became less withdrawn, talked more and responded
more to other people, started to feed and dress himself, and otherwise
take care of himself. He also became less assaultive.

Dr. Zilla described the beginning of his work with Henry as follows:

The first day I saw him he very soon said he did not want to be bothered
and so I left, telling him I would be back some time later. When I came
back later, he said the same thing and I again left. Later the same day
I came back again and I said, "How is Mr. Harrashaw?" and he just
repeated the same statement, "How is Mr. Harrashaw?" He was being
spoon-fed that same day and he was asking for potatoes. The nurse went
out for potatoes and I remained with him. When I made a gesture of
talking, he made a gesture of silence, that I should stay quiet. I did. Then
he went on commenting on the potatoes, "They look like potatoes; they
are potatoes." I said, "Yes, they are." Then he said, "How can I help
you?" I said, "Let's help each other; let's talk some. Let's hear what you
are thinking." He said, "Well, it is like this. People make me eat. If I do
not eat, a hose is given to me, shots are given to me, pills, medicine.
Then you become fat." Thereupon, he disjointedly mentioned things like
mental disease, and getting rid of mentality. By this time I said, "It sounds
confusing," and he said, "Yes, that's it." I also said, "It sounds like you
are trying to please people," and he responded, "Well, one has to be correct. He has to be correct or right. I rather laugh, not at anybody, not to
myself, but because it has to be correct. They feed me; they chase me;
I do not like it." I said, "Maybe you should do something for yourself,"
to which he replied, "Well, I have gone to school." Then he became
silent. When I was going to leave, he said, "My head is heavy; I do not
like it." I said, "Well, maybe next time we will see if we can do something about it. Maybe we can make some light." I wanted to say, "Maybe
we can make it *lighter*." He said, "Yes, I need that." That was the first
day that I saw him.

The following is a description by Dr. Zilla of what he tried to do in
his hours with Henry. The description was given after they had been

working together for nearly three years, but it seems characteristic of Dr. Zilla's approach throughout their relationship.

> I try to be with him. That's my main effort, to be with him in his world and actually to get him out of his world and into my world. . . . When I come in I say, "Good morning, Henry." I may not say anything more and I sit close to where he is, usually where he can see me. I prefer to sit where he can see me, and always with enough distance to prevent him from jumping on me suddenly when I will not be able to defend myself. This reflects the fear that has remained from the days when he was assaultive. It generally takes him some time, maybe five or 10 minutes, before he will suddenly turn and say, "Good morning, Bob." He will say good morning one way or another. And then I may say "Hi" again. . . . Most of the time I don't say anything until he says something. . . . When he is covered up with his blankets, I let it go for a while. I tell him that I wish he would uncover himself and after some time has elapsed I tell him that I am going to uncover him if he doesn't. . . . Sometimes he uncovers himself; sometimes he does not. . . . I often uncover him and he then stays uncovered, whereupon he may talk or just stare at me.

When Dr. Zilla was asked how he tried to help Henry, he replied:

> I have tried to show him that there are people different than his parents. . . . The history indicates a great deal of his mother's difficulties in dealing with Henry and perhaps his mother's difficulties with Henry's father; this projected into Henry as a consequence, sort of getting Henry into trouble. I think that I very clearly emphasize to him how different I am than possibly his father is. His father is a very systemized, rigid, compulsive guy, which I am not, fortunately, and I can take advantage of that.

A year and a half later Dr. Zilla described his approach in terms of presenting himself to Henry:

> . . . demonstrating to him that I also have a way of life, a way of my own. And so does he. . . . Making myself a person also conveys the idea that, if convenient, he could switch from his own way of life into a better one, taking for granted mine is a better way than his. . . . (My passivity) is in direct contrast or direct opposition with the anxiety of the mother who makes this guy sick, a mother who is pushing her children all the time, or pulling them, satisfying her own needs rather than theirs, and I feel my passivity is just the opposite of that, one of taking my own reality in my own stride and living it, but at the same time letting the patients live their own. Of course, I . . . interrupt their self-destruction and I also interrupt, at times, the delusional, hallucinatory existence. But the whole

system is letting them know there are two ways of living and it's up to them.

Dr. Billings, who supervised the early stages of psychotherapy, encouraged Dr. Zilla in this attitude and formulated its effect in terms of Henry's first incorporating Dr. Zilla and then identifying with him.

At the very beginning of psychotherapy Henry remained motionless for long periods, seeming almost dead. Dr. Zilla felt that he needed physical contact and made a point of touching him gently several times during each hour. Then Henry started to attack Dr. Zilla (and others), so that Dr. Zilla had to defend himself and tried to set limits. Shortly afterwards, Dr. Zilla asked an aide (Gordon Baxter) to be present during their sessions; almost immediately Henry became less assaultive and more talkative. Later there was a period in which Henry and Dr. Zilla did little but sit and look at each other. Dr. Zilla encouraged Henry to stare at him, feeling that Henry was incorporating him visually. Still later Henry became more active and talkative again.

In the beginning Dr. Zilla tried to protect Henry from pressures and coercion, and found himself in conflict with the nursing staff, especially with Sylvia Samuel, who was charge nurse from June 1956 to February 1959. The main issue was whether Henry should be "pushed" into feeding himself, dressing himself, keeping himself clean, etc., or allowed to do as he pleased. Dr. Zilla felt that Henry had already had far too much pressure from his parents. Miss Samuel felt that leaving Henry alone to be apathetic, filthy, and helpless was harmful because it supported his negative self-conception and underestimated his capabilities. Dr. Zilla thought that Miss Samuel was very anxious and that the ward atmosphere became freer and more relaxed after she left. Miss Samuel's opinion of Dr. Zilla is not recorded. Dr. Zilla also disagreed about Henry's treatment with the other charge nurses who were on Third Floor for shorter periods. Dr. Zilla's attitude toward these nurses resembled the extremely critical attitude which Henry's father had toward his wife about the way she handled Henry. Dr. Zilla pointed out that he had not had comparable conflicts with nurses about any of his other patients, which would suggest that Henry helped to bring about this kind of situation. Henry gave the impression that his great potential had been damaged by cruel mistreatment but would blossom forth if he were treated properly. Related to this was the notion, which Dr. Zilla often expressed, that Henry's attacks on others were never entirely unprovoked, but were always preceded by some slighting, pressuring, or cruel act toward Henry by the other person. Despite this belief Dr. Zilla was fearful of and guarded toward Henry for a long time.

Dr. Zilla described a number of specific interactions with Henry, some examples of which have already been given. We find some consistent themes in Dr. Zilla's reports of his conversations with Henry. One theme was that Henry should do something for himself, that he was punishing himself, and that it was up to him to improve his own condition. Dr. Zilla usually did not say *what* Henry should do; the most specific suggestion reported was that he should eat. Another theme was that Henry had (or could have) warm feelings, which pleased Dr. Zilla. Another theme was that Dr. Zilla wanted to help Henry, which required that they talk to each other, especially that Henry tell Dr. Zilla his thoughts. Still another theme was that Dr. Zilla and the hospital would not let Henry die, but that Henry had to remain in the hospital as long as he was sick. These themes suggest that Dr. Zilla resembled Henry's father more than he realized or intended. He pressured Henry to take more responsibility for himself and to behave more reasonably; he described his concern for Henry partly in medical terms: he wanted to keep him from dying and to help him get better. However, Dr. Zilla was undoubtedly far less critical and pressuring than Henry's father had been. Henry himself sometimes thought of Dr. Zilla as his father. For example, in April 1956, Dr. Zilla reported: "Just recently he asked me if I were his father and I told him I could function as such and that at times he may feel that I am his father. In the same hour later on, he said, 'My father is a psychiatrist.'"

Henry became devoted to Dr. Zilla and benefited considerably from their relationship. This was shown by the gradual improvement in Henry's behavior, already mentioned, and by his many demonstrations of affection for the doctor. Two other indications were Henry's response to increased contacts with Dr. Zilla and his reaction to Dr. Zilla's departure. The first was described by Dr. Zilla in July 1959:

I had noticed that every Monday he would be looking more withdrawn than on the previous Friday when I had seen him. So I decided, around a year ago, that since I had the time I was going to see him six times a week, and I did. An interesting thing was that the two extra sessions that I was putting in were at first rather short—20 or 25 minutes—and gradually one of these two "hours" became a full hour and the other one became something like 30 minutes or more, indicating to me that I too was sort of enjoying seeing him these extra hours. During the next four months, the Mondays of withdrawal gradually disappeared. Also, he became able to keep his clothing on, he ate by himself at times (of course, the tube feeding had been given up sometime earlier), and he also was more outgoing and more outspoken.

Dr. Zilla described Henry's reaction to his departure:

Two months ago I told him that I would be leaving the hospital. Very soon after that he asked me if I were going to leave my "little brother." He went on calling me his big brother, father, grandfather, etc. . . . Then he proceeded to talk about having lost his soul and that he had no chance. . . . He asked me why I didn't kill him and later on it was why didn't I eat him. . . . And he said that I had eaten his eyes. I replied, "Do you mean that I don't want to see you?" He said, "Yes, eat me." I suppose he was saying, "Take me with you; take me inside you." . . . Efforts to bring about some insight into his difficulties because of our approaching separation failed. He went on experiencing ups and downs of depression, withdrawal, and staying on the ward; this alternated with periods of coherence and being able to go out with other people. At a moment in late November when I decided it would be useless to continue working with him (which had actually been suggested by several other people and finally accepted by me), he went into a state of bewilderment. He hit himself against the walls and the furniture, hurting himself in many places—his head, his hands, and his feet. He regressed rather dramatically into not being able to eat, staying nude, crawling under the bed, etc. In this bewilderment he even ran a temperature of 104 and at times appeared to be in a dead stupor. It was at this point that Dr. John Cameron took over his therapy.

Henry's relationship to his administrative physician, Dr. Gibson, was minimal. Dr. Gibson was mainly concerned with Henry's medical problems. In discussing his questionnaire responses on Henry, Dr. Gibson said, "Strangely I never seemed to take to him very much even though he was usually the ward's favorite."

As this comment suggests, Henry received a great deal of attention from the ward staff. Staff members reported approaching him more often than any other patient on five of the six administrations of the staff questionnaire (for the nine patients who were on Third Floor on all six occasions). Henry's approach behavior was rated below average on five of the six questionnaire administrations. The ward staff consistently expressed positive feelings toward Henry more frequently than toward the average patient. However, they also tended to express negative feelings toward him somewhat more frequently than average, which suggests that the greater expression of feelings was partly a result of more frequent contact. Henry tended to receive above average questionnaire scores on scales dealing with staff activity, and below average scores on scales dealing with his own activity. The principal exception was Henry's problem behavior, on which he always scored above average, and which became especially great after his separation from Dr. Zilla. The questionnaire, therefore, shows that Henry's relationships with the ward staff were largely passive on his part, except for his problem behavior, while staff members were quite active toward him. Henry's principal problem behaviors were refusal to eat, refusal to keep his clothes on, incontinence of urine and feces, and aggressive behavior (which usually meant hitting or kicking someone unexpectedly). Much staff member activity with Henry consisted of attempts to deal with this problem behavior, to get Henry to eat, to keep his clothes on, etc. However, there was also a great deal of more playful interaction including talking, joking, and horseplay. Henry was often treated as a clown or a pet whose nonsensical remarks were regarded as quite funny. He was often treated as a child, an animal, or even a kind of doll (to be dressed, fed, and dragged from one place to another). Henry showed confusion about just what he was. At various times he spoke of himself as an animal, the Holy Ghost, Jesus, dead, a turd, trash, the Wild Man of Borneo, and many other things. The behavior of staff members showed a corresponding variety and variability in their conceptions of him.

Several of the ward staff were very much interested in Henry and developed close relationships with him. Dr. Zilla reported that there had always been someone especially interested in Henry but that unfortunately these relationships had always ended because the staff member left or was transferred. The first of these relationships was with Susan Rollins, charge nurse of Third Floor when Henry arrived. She was occasionally able to get him to eat when no one else could.

After she left Third Floor Henry was more withdrawn for a while. All of his subsequent close relationships with nursing staff were with men. For a long period Henry showed hostility to women, spoke about hating them, and said he wanted to kill various women. We will describe two of Henry's close relationships with male aides.

Gordon Baxter, a Negro aide, came to work on Third Floor in April 1956, less than a year after Henry's arrival there. Baxter was initially interested because he had heard that Henry had been the only white soldier in a unit of Negro paratroopers. Baxter and Henry frequently talked about the Army. Henry was the first patient who responded well to Baxter, so that Baxter felt he had accomplished something and that he had some ability as an aide. Baxter emphasized physical care and was very direct and outspoken with patients, which seemed to be effective with Henry. In the fall of 1956, when Henry was mute and at times assaultive, Dr. Zilla asked Baxter to sit in on the hours because of his good relationship with Henry. Baxter's presence had an immediate effect, helping Dr. Zilla to feel less fearful of Henry and apparently also helping Henry to be more comfortable. The next day Henry began to talk to Dr. Zilla again. During the following year Henry improved considerably, becoming less assaultive, more willing to eat, more talkative, and more relevant and coherent. Baxter's interest in Henry was largely responsible for two or three sets of systematic observations on Henry, which were mainly planned and executed by nursing personnel. One of these, over a six-week period in the spring of 1957, investigated whether the amount of time nursing personnel spent with Henry was related to the quality of his behavior. Such a relation was not clearly demonstrated, but there were marked gains in Henry's eating, dressing, and sociability during the observation period. In February 1959 Baxter was transferred to the night shift on another ward (so that he could go to college during the day). Following this, Dr. Gibson noted that Henry's behavior began to deteriorate somewhat; he was less active, and was not dressing as well. Although the connection was not noted at the time, it seems likely that Henry's slump was largely due to his separation from Baxter. A contributing factor may have been the departure at the same time of Miss Samuel, the charge nurse.

Another person of great importance to Henry was the aide James Wallace, who arrived on Third Floor a few days after Baxter was transferred elsewhere. Soon after he arrived, Wallace became interested in Henry. By the next questionnaire (April 1959, two months after Wallace came to Third Floor), Wallace reported that he was spending more time with Henry than with any other patient, three or more hours per day. Wallace continued to report spending this much time with Henry on every succeeding questionnaire. (This was the highest answer category for this question.) A dramatic test of Wallace's importance to Henry was provided by the departure of Dr. Zilla, at which Henry became wildly upset, as already mentioned. After Dr. Zilla's departure, Henry's behavior was entirely different and far better on the days when Wallace was on duty. When Wallace was there, Henry was more willing to dress, ate better, and talked more coherently. Wallace attributed his success with Henry largely to his consistency and persistence. For example, he described his efforts to keep Henry from lying on the floor in terms of picking Henry up from the floor over and over again and telling Henry over and over again not to lie on the floor. Other staff members made occasional efforts of this kind, but soon gave up. Wallace said he was interested in Henry because Henry responded to him, paid attention to what he said, took his hand, called him by name (which Wallace said Henry did not do with any other aide). Wallace described his first reaction to Henry as follows:

> When I first came to work here, Henry was on the floor 90 per cent of the time, and undressed most of the time, spitting, and smearing, and everything else. And I just couldn't believe my eyes. I just couldn't understand how any person could ever be that crazy, to apparently hate himself so much to do that to himself—a person must really feel a lot of disgust with his own self to smear feces all over his body, and treat himself the way Henry did. And I don't know whether it was anything personal right away, but I just didn't want to see anybody do that to himself. Maybe that was what made me get started with Henry.

As he came to know Henry, Wallace began to identify with him. Wallace said that he saw himself as being like Henry since both their fathers had tried to push them into doing things they didn't want to do. Wallace felt that he was better off than Henry because he had resisted his father's pressure much more strongly and, unlike Henry, had gotten support from his mother in doing so.

While Henry was recovering from the loss of Dr. Zilla, Wallace began plans to leave, for personal reasons (mainly to get away from the domination of his father). Wallace was concerned about the effect his departure would have on Henry. After Dr. Zilla left, Henry had been telling Wallace such things as: "You're the only buddy I have," "You're the best friend I have." Wallace discussed his approaching departure with Henry several times, giving his reasons for leaving and asking if Henry thought he was wrong. Henry always answered "Yes," which Wallace assumed was an indication of Henry's fondness for him and fear of losing him. When Henry began to show anger, Wallace responded with strong feeling:

> I just came out real angry at him one day because he spit on my pants, and I said, "You're just doing your damnedest to drive me away, aren't you?" He said, "Yeah." I came right out and told him that no matter how much he tried to make me mad—"I won't pat you on the back and tell you you're a sweet lamb when you're spitting at me or throwing food at me,"—I still wasn't going to get disgusted and get up and go and stay away.

After Wallace left the Lodge, Dr. Gibson noted that "Henry did seem to be disturbed by this and was particularly upset when Jimmy (Wallace) came back and visited the ward. When he realized that Jimmy was leaving, and also on this later visit back, he seemed to be deliberately doing everything he could do to give Jimmy a hard time."

For comparison I shall describe Henry's relationship with another aide, Frank Grabble, who also evinced considerable interest in Henry and devoted much time and attention to him but never achieved the emotional importance to Henry or the ability to influence him which Baxter and Wallace had. Grabble came to Third Floor in mid-April 1958. On the relationship questionnaire given the following month, Grabble's responses about Henry emphasized concern with Henry's anger and aggressiveness, as well as the difficulty in managing him. At the same time Baxter's answers emphasized his warm and affectionate attitude toward Henry. Grabble's answers to the next questionnaire (August-September 1958) became more like those of Baxter, emphasizing interest in and friendly feelings toward Henry. By the following questionnaire (January 1959) Grabble seemed to be showing more friendly interest in Henry than did Baxter; this was just before Baxter left Third Floor and may indicate that he and Henry had started to withdraw from each other. In April 1959 Grabble's questionnaire did not show any special interest in Henry, and in June 1959 there were only slight indications of special interest. Meanwhile, Wallace's June 1959 questionnaire showed a considerable amount of special interest in Henry and a great deal of friendly interaction with him. In September 1959 Wallace showed even more special interest in and activity with Henry, while Grabble continued to give very slight indications of any special interest. In January 1960 Grabble's responses were again showing pronounced concern with problems of managing Henry, while Wallace's responses continued to emphasize friendly interaction, though somewhat less strongly and with less variety than in September. (These comments on questionnaire responses are based on the tabulation of extreme responses given about Henry by each aide, that is, the use of a higher or lower answer category than that aide used for any other patient on that administration of the questionnaire. Most of these were at the high extreme. This examination of extreme responses is intended to find how the aide sees the patient's behavior, and his own behavior in relation to the patient, as distinct from his interactions with all the other patients.) This comparison of Grabble's questionnaire answers with those of Baxter and Wallace suggests that Grabble was quite interested in Henry at times, but that at other times he withdrew or became preoccupied with controlling Henry. This supports Wallace's comment about his own consistency toward Henry, as contrasted wtih the more variable interest of other aides.

There is one more important relationship of Henry's to be described —that which he had with Dr. Cameron, who became Henry's psychotherapist when Dr. Zilla left. Dr. Cameron described the beginning of his work with Henry as follows:

> During the first week or so that I saw him . . . he was restless, sleepless, would not eat, and threw himself around to such an extent that he was covered with bruises. He was losing weight rapidly, and was dehydrated. He had minor infections all over his body, and seemed to me in peril of his life. During the early phase, then, my predominant efforts were directed towards simple and immediate physical care, such as seeing that he was bathed while I was present on the ward, insuring that he drank at least some fluids, preferably containing nutrient materials, etc. . . . I also tried to prevent him from hurting himself in any way that I could. This led to the two of us rolling around on the floor a great deal, and he

talked, almost incessantly, after the first two or three days. . . . He referred to himself as a "turd," as "shit," as various sorts of animals; he would occasionally refer to himself as a fruit or as a fruit cake. On one occasion we had been rolling around some on the floor—about 10 days or so after we had started working. . . . He started to talk about this as his "slithering act." I didn't like the slithering act at all because he would try to bash his hands or his head or something against the wall, and I would hold him and in the struggle he was like an octopus with umpteen feet. . . . [Once] when we fell on the floor and I was holding him, he proceeded to slither along the floor in such a way that our combined weights lacerated his skin and I was raising cain and protesting very energetically about this, and he suddenly shook his head, looked at me, and said, "For goodness sake, what on earth am I doing here? You know, I must be cracked." And I said to him, "You know, I don't think you have ever said anything truer. I think what you are doing is quite crazy and quite daft and also extraordinarily cruel." Then all of a sudden it struck me that it was a case of the pot calling the kettle black . . . and I said to him, "You know, there are two of us in this mess and I think I am being rather foolish too." Wtih that I stood up and sat down on the bed and with that this phase, which I call the emergency phase, in retrospect, ended.

Following this he made it clear to me that he was under the control of a cruelly insane machine. This machine controlled not only him but the rest of the family. Only if he remained quite mad could his family survive. Following some "analytic discussion" of this type of influencing machine, the patient, who by now was much more relaxed, began to talk of himself as a martyr. He was a martyr who was sacrificing himself on behalf of his family and he gave me a good many historical examples which purported to support the logic of this position. This concept, based as it is on such a destructive way of life, led to very energetic exchanges of strong feelings between the two of us. However, a point of particular note is that at no time during this period did he make a personal assault on me nor had he done so earlier. He talked a great deal during this time of another almost constant theme—the need for medical treatment. At this point I began to appreciate the importance of his relationship with his father whom he seemed to feel he could only appeal to in the role of clinician. This takes us up to June and July of 1960. As this type of exchange gradually began to fade, there was a marked tendency during hours for us to exchange humorous comments often of an adolescent type, the kind of remark in which the joke is usually so private that only the two people concerned can understand it. There was a good deal of childish tenderness exchanged and I wish to emphasize that I am using the term "childish" in its best and not in its decayed sense. During this period, however, there was in addition much more of a tendency on the part of the patient to subject me to personal attack and it was during this period that for the first time he succeeded in landing a painful blow. . . . On one occasion when I went in he slapped me very hard across the face. Very quickly and spontaneously, without any thought, I slapped back at him and hit him on the bare shoulder. He looked very straight at me and said, "Thank you." I was left quite puzzled by this at the time. Afterwards I noticed that on several occasions when I responded physically, very energetically, to some attack like this, Henry seemed very pleased and he very often ended up by saying, "Thank you." I also detected a quality of surprise in Henry and asked him about it but he would give me no information at all. At about this time, we had a visit from his father . . . which I felt was quite illuminating. . . . Henry struck him, producing a rather nasty laceration inside his mouth. I saw Dr. Harrashaw not very long afterwards and expressed some concern about the injury and the pain that he had received. His response struck me as a rather strange one. Without being too clear as to why, I felt that he was somewhat pleased that Henry had struck him, as though he were perhaps being punished, but when I asked him what he had said to Henry, he told me he had behaved in what he felt was a physician's manner with a sick person; that is, he had regarded the blow as an aspect of Henry's illness. At this point I felt I had some information as to why Henry should say "Thank you." It seemed likely that his reply was a function of the quite different response he got out of me because I'm not so inclined to view a neat right cross as a manifestation of illness; I'm inclined to regard it as painful and respond quickly.

After this we got stuck, and what we got stuck with was a constant repetitious pattern of situations arising in which Henry provoked me, or another staff member, or one of the patients on the ward. . . . For example, if I got fed up with his spitting and he realized that this antagonized me a bit, I could count on his doing a lot of spitting in my presence. . . . If people were particularly concerned about seeing to it that he got fed . . . he would really "cook their goose" over this. Thus he was really engaged in a wide variety of activities which revolved around this one constant theme.

In July I told Henry I was going on vacation at the end of the month, and with this announcement I saw again some of the material that had been so obvious in the separation between him and Mario Zilla. We argued . . . about all of this, and I can recall asking him if he were attempting to create a situation whereby I would feel so worried that my holiday would be spoiled, and could he not find a better technique or a newer technique than that for taking the rise out of me. The last few days before I went on vacation he seemed to me to be in particularly good form and he cordially wished me a lousy time, told me that he thought I was a sonofabitch, and that he was going to be very glad to be rid of me. I think, when I went on vacation, that I was somewhat more comfortable about leaving Henry than I was about leaving some of my other patients.

When we resumed work at the beginning of September, there was a marked change in the quality of our relationship. His attacks on me became more direct, but at the same time there was a curious attempt on his part to place me in the role of the person who, for some obscure reason, was sacrificing himself for him. This quality could even be seen in his tendency to be violent toward me, as my very presence in the room seemed to him to indicate that I was prepared to tolerate a great deal. He talked about "the book," "the book of rules" and "physician's ethics," and I soon grasped that he felt I was following some special code of behavior rather than my natural feelings in my dealings with him. It was at this point that I began to understand something of the nature of Henry's very early relationship with his mother and to appreciate the extreme degree of discomfort through which they both passed. In the Harrashaw family they had followed a textbook on the bringing up of children . . . the child was placed on a strict regime, being lifted only for the purpose of feeding and cleansing and then only at strictly scheduled hours. Apparently the severe discomfort which Mrs. Harrashaw had experienced at this time became a predominant theme in her relationship with Henry, and she tended always to do what was laid down in this book of rules rather than to follow the dictates of her own feelings. As we pursued this further, it became clear that Henry was deathly afraid that if we expressed our natural feelings toward each other, particularly those which belong at the positive end of the spectrum, it could only lead to the death or dissolution of one or both of us.

At the beginning of November 1960, Dr. Harrashaw decided to remove Henry from Chestnut Lodge. He gave as reasons the great financial burden of the cost of treatment and his lack of hope for really substantial improvement in his son. Henry was transferred to a VA hospital near his home at the end of November.

This account of Henry's experiences at Chestnut Lodge confirms and extends the view of his psychosis as a very primitive rebellion against control, a rebellion which failed to achieve independence for Henry. It also sheds light on how Henry's role as a martyr to his family was developed and maintained. This may be seen especially clearly in the contrasting reactions of Dr. Cameron and Dr. Harrashaw to Henry's angry attacks. Dr. Cameron responded with anger while Dr. Harrashaw controlled himself and thought of Henry's anger as a manifestation of illness. The father could not acknowledge his son's anger; instead he disregarded it and explained it away. In so doing he refused to recognize any possible message the anger might have for him, ignoring an aspect of Henry which didn't fit his rigid conception of what his son should be like. The message of the father's behavior was: "I am the wise and benevolent doctor; if you disagree with me or get angry at me, you must be crazy." By ignoring feelings or impulses that he disapproved of, the father presented Henry with only two alternatives: complying, or having his attempts at self-assertion regarded as crazy. By the time Henry became psychotic he was sufficiently alienated from his own impulses so that he, too, often regarded them as crazy (or as wild, animal-like, dirty, trashy, etc.). By this time he had become so habituated to the kind of relationship in which he sacrificed his own independence and self-esteem to bolster the self-esteem of the other that he tended to re-establish this pattern in his relationships in the hospital. This seems to have been the major basis for the tremendous appeal which Henry held for members of the hospital staff. Even fellow patients felt this appeal to the extent that two or three of them participated at times in his care, which was a very unusual occurrence on Third Floor. The essence of the appeal was: "I am so badly off and you are so sensible and understanding and good, surely you will help me." To anyone with a strong desire to prove himself understanding and good this appeal was all but irresistible. But at least for part of the time, Henry was aware that this kind of relationship perpetuated his martyrdom. This led to rebellions against his would-be helpers which drove many of them away, but not those who were most determined. When threatened with separation from one of these helpers, Henry was often overwhelmed with angry feelings, some of which he expressed, but most of which he turned against himself, perhaps to make himself even more pitiable and needful so that his helper would stay with him.

His relationships with hospital personnel differed from one another in some important respects. Dr. Zilla was restrained in responding to Henry's anger, but he did acknowledge it and express displeasure, especially when hostile behavior was directed at him. The freer and more direct nature of Dr. Cameron's and James Wallace's responses apparently had a more beneficial effect on Henry. Dr. Zilla avoided participating in the physical care of Henry, partly because of his opposition to putting pressure on him. Baxter and Wallace were very active and persistent in their physical care of Henry and exerted a great deal of pressure on him to do such things as dressing and feeding himself. Henry benefited from both approaches. In retrospect, the question of whether or not to put pressure on Henry, about which there was so much strong feeling and lengthy discussion, now seems to have been misleading. What probably made the greatest difference to Henry was whether his own feelings and impulses were recognized and responded to. For example, Dr. Zilla's program to increase Henry's therapy hours from four to six times a week was a nonpressuring response, whereas Wallace's persistent efforts to keep Henry from lying on the floor and Dr. Cameron's strenuous efforts to keep Henry from injuring himself were highly pressuring. But all three responses were effective, at least to some degree, because they were, in fact, responses to Henry himself, showing strong interest in Henry's feelings and needs. Responsiveness is crucial both for the learning of interpersonal behavior and the development of relationships. Sensitive responsiveness by another person heightens awareness of one's own behavior and provides feedback about its effects. It also contributes to the ability to differentiate oneself clearly from the other, which is necessary for the development of a highly integrated relationship, the unique interaction which is only possible between two individuals. It was not originally our goal to study responsiveness as an aspect of relationships, but this account of Henry's relationships, in addition to illustrating the need-fear dilemma and separation anxiety, clearly shows its crucial importance.

XI
ROBERT FELDMAN

Robert W. Gibson

Object Relations and the Patient's Dilemma

Robert Feldman was admitted to Chestnut Lodge in April 1953 as a transfer from another mental hospital. He was 27 years old, single, and had never been employed. He was first considered psychiatrically ill in 1943, when he expressed concern about masturbation, withdrew from college, and undertook psychoanalytic treatment on an outpatient basis. He resumed college work and continued psychoanalytic treatment for about two years. At that point his father interrupted the treatment because he felt critical of the doctor. The patient on his own sought orgone therapy from a therapist of the Wilhelm Reich School. Over the next seven months he spent progressively longer periods in an Orgone box, became more disorganized in his thinking, and ultimately was hospitalized.

For the next five years he was treated in various hospitals where his diagnosis was schizophrenic reaction, paranoid type. His thinking was disorganized, he was delusional and hallucinated. He received insulin coma and electroconvulsant therapy. Several times he improved sufficiently to leave the hospital but was never able to maintain himself outside of institutions for more than a few months. Once he made a serious suicidal attempt, cutting his wrist deeply enough to sever several tendons. In all he had about a dozen admissions to eight different institutions before his hospitalization at Chestnut Lodge.

Upon admission to Chestnut Lodge, Robert claimed that he had no emotional problems but considered himself the victim of a lifelong

264

"psychological plot." He accepted hospitalization so long as he was allowed to rest, but he objected strenuously to seeing Dr. Gibson, who in this case was the patient's psychotherapist. He gave various reasons —it was too hot, he had been completely psychoanalyzed already, his previous therapist forbade it, and so forth. Dr. Gibson insisted on regular appointments, indicating that force would be used if necessary. In response Robert became angry and threatening, but after a few appointments was willing to see the psychotherapist for regular appointments and even began to come to his office.

After about a month, Robert became more friendly toward the psychotherapist. He asked if they could walk together during the therapeutic hours. When Dr. Gibson said this might be possible, Robert replied, "That pleases me very much." Later that same day he ran away from the hospital. After about 10 hours the police located him some five miles from the hospital. He was disheveled, wet, and appeared to have been wandering through the woods. He explained that he had run away because the hospital was too dirty and he could not stand the people there.

In succeeding hours he again became more relaxed and friendly toward his psychotherapist. He began to talk more about himself, acknowledging that he did have feelings toward other people and was discouraged about his many past hospitalizations.

Approximately three months after the patient's admission to Chestnut Lodge Dr. Gibson became the Clinical Administrator of Third Floor. This required discontinuing his treatment of the patient, though as ward administrator he continued to see him daily. When Dr. Gibson informed Robert of the change, the patient said simply, "I would rather have you." During the next few hours he was silent and seemed hurt. He became sullen and demanded that he be taken out of the hospital. His behavior became more bizarre and at times assaultive.

For several weeks he repulsed his new therapist but after the therapist insisted on regular appointments, he became less threatening, acknowledged that he was mentally ill, and began to go to the therapist's office for his hours. Over the next two months he complained that the hospital was dirty and engaged in elaborate bathing rituals. He accused his therapist of trying to seduce him and of stealing his semen. His speech became so fragmented that it was virtually unintelligible. He continually tore his clothes and was nude much of the time. He smeared feces and masturbated openly. He regularly assaulted anyone who tried to come near him. This state continued for over a year despite concerted efforts by the staff to engage him in more positive interaction.

This sequence during the first few months of hospitalization at Chestnut Lodge graphically illustrates the patient's difficulty in maintaining relationships. He felt enormously threatened whenever others approached him and saw himself as the victim of a psychological plot. He handled his fear by object avoidance. When the therapist insisted that they meet, he seemed reassured, even expressing some of his longing for a relationship. Experiencing this feeling of need, the patient was exposed to the full impact of the need-fear dilemma. He felt threatened, became frightened, and by withdrawal and regression tried to escape from the conflict of feelings evoked by the relationship. As contact with the therapist continued he became less fearful and less conflicted about his need for support. The premature termination of this therapeutic relationship by Dr. Gibson's change of role may have intensified the patient's dilemma. He spoke directly of feeling need for Dr. Gibson, expressed his anger at the loss, and then showed a marked disorganization. Throughout his hospital course Robert continuously vacillated between these poles of the need-fear dilemma.

EARLY DEVELOPMENT AND THE DEFICIT IN EGO FUNCTIONS

Having briefly sketched the presenting problem, we will go on to a consideration of the patient's background history. The parents' first two children were daughters, four and three years older than Robert. The older one died of diphtheria at three, approximately a year before Robert's birth. The mother was seriously depressed by this death. The patient was conceived in the hope that a new baby might replace the dead child and relieve the mother's depression, which apparently was the case. The mother was pleased with the patient. No particular difficulties were reported in the early years. He was described glowingly as a wonderful child. In her initial account of Robert's infancy and childhood his mother said that he had had serious difficulty with constipation and that she had given him frequent enemas. Later she denied this, presumably out of fear and guilt that her earlier handling might have contributed to his later disturbances. (In adolescence he was pathologically preoccupied with his bowel functions and for a time administered enemas to himself and was sexually excited by fantasies of ripping his mother's anus.)

At the age of six the patient developed asthma that did not respond to treatment. For two years he and his mother went to live in the southwestern United States, some two thousand miles distant from the rest of the family. They shared the same bedroom of a small cottage. Mother had an active social life with many friends, pursued a variety of interests, and felt important in her son's life. For her, the relationship was warm and close; life was rich and rewarding. This period was described by the mother and other members of the family as being the only truly satisfying time in her life.

As to what this period meant to the patient we can only speculate. He characteristically described his mother as a "mother-goddess" who was nagging, neurotic, compulsive, and greedy, and against whom he must always guard himself. Of the Arizona trip he said he was sent away because his father wanted to get rid of him.

To the Chestnut Lodge staff, Robert's mother presented herself as a pathetically insecure woman, seemingly bewildered by life. She was ill at ease and had a knack of antagonizing people. She seemed to have no appreciation of what went on in her interaction with others. For example, she repeatedly referred to an incident in which the patient had struck her. She was convinced that he had been disturbed by a new pair of glasses which created the illusion that the pupils of her eyes were of slightly different size. It seemed totally beyond her comprehension that anything more could be involved.

The patient's father was quietly disdainful of his wife. He had worked his way through college, ultimately becoming a statistician. He was meticulous, highly controlled, and placed great emphasis on intellectual achievement. The patient spoke of his father as a "stupid, fat, unintelligent mathematician who could not turn into a military man." The father had a capacity for wearing people down with persistent, carefully considered, logical arguments. He withdrew from any issue, thus avoiding open disagreements. Of course, he would soon return to the problem with further carefully considered arguments. The net effect, as reported by family members and as experienced by hospital staff, was that people felt themselves under pressure from him, but puzzled as to why they should feel this way about such a quiet, reasonable man.

The father reportedly never spoke to his wife beyond the bare necessities of communication involving factual matters. In interviews with hospital staff he would lead off the discussion with a series of points he wished to take up with the doctor. Having completed his portion of the interview, he would sit back with an indulgent smile while his wife began to speak. She would tell the story of her glasses, mention her latest physical complaint, and ask if it would not help for the patient to read more good books. By his manner and a few comments, the father would convey the message—"Isn't it too bad that two intelligent men such as we have to be bothered by the inane chattering of this stupid person I'm married to?"

Robert's sister openly rebelled against the parents. After finishing college she moved from home, avoided her parents, and allowed no intrusions into her personal life. During the patient's psychotherapy at Chestnut Lodge he described feeling envious and competitive toward his sister. He wished he had been able to break away from the family, become independent, and go out on dates. He said that she had brought out his feelings of hate toward Jews and particularly his parents.

The father exerted a continuous, rational control. He avoided differences of opinion that would allow the patient to see a distinction between "this is what I think" and "this is what my father thinks." The personalities and interactions of the parents were such that it was virtually impossible for the patient to bring together his identifications with them into an integrated identity. To be like his mother was to be the object of his father's scorn. To be like his father was to be a collaborator in the contemptuous destruction of his mother. Having failed to achieve a real separation from either parent, the patient desperately needed object relations for support. At the same time his parents, in their own interaction, were so destructive that all relationships became threatening. Even when the patient was at his highest level of integration he could not tolerate visits by his parents. Such visits—even the anticipation of them—always resulted in severe disorganization.

The childhood sojourn in Arizona had profound consequences for the patient. In the role of sickling then, he perhaps more fully gratified his mother's psychological needs than at any other time of his life. He had his mother to himself and was relieved of the difficulty of dealing with both parents simultaneously. We believe that this may have been a determining factor in the patient's later solution to his conflicts by adopting a role of the sick invalid. We will elaborate on this point later.

THE MANIFEST ILLNESS

No particular difficulties were noted as the patient progressed through puberty and early adolescence. At the age of 17 he entered a college away from home. He was intensely disturbed by masturbation. He had elaborate fantasies of forcibly giving enemas to various people, and gave enemas to himself which he retained for long periods of time, achieving sexual excitement. Because of vague feelings that he experienced toward his roommate he was concerned that he might be a homosexual. There were unconfirmed reports that he was sought after by boys suspected of being homosexuals. Toward the end of his first year at college he wrote a letter to the family physician expressing concern about masturbation. This led to psychiatric referral and the patient's first psychiatric treatment.

Much of the retrospective information concerning this period was contributed by the patient when he was grossly psychotic. He referred to the religious laws governing the conduct of a Jewish boy who was 16 to 18, emphasizing the dangers in violating them. We can surmise that he was undergoing several stresses. He was separated from his parents for the first time. He was faced by the possibility of relationships of greater intimacy. In this situation the patient experienced chaotic sexual feelings. These feelings often included expressions of violence, ripping, and complete destruction. His failures in differentiation and integration made him peculiarly vulnerable to these stresses.

Although the patient's adjustment was precarious he managed to obtain a college degree. His father urged him to attend medical school and made all arrangements for his admission despite Robert's uncertainty as to whether he wanted to study medicine. His father went so far as to literally escort his son to the medical school to register, at which point Robert balked. Despite his father's pleadings, he steadfastly refused to enroll or to offer an explanation for his refusal. Later during his treatment he spoke often of this conflict. At times he denied the whole episode and claimed that he was a full-fledged physician. At other times he reiterated his refusal to let his father force a career on him. From discussions in therapy it became apparent that another factor had been his conflict over taking a step toward adult responsibility and independence from his family, a step he simultaneously desired and feared. His disorganization in the face of this conflict adumbrated later decompensations that occurred each time he seemed on the verge of making forward steps in his treatment. He fought against the control and direction of his father, yet any move toward independence made him acutely conscious of his need.

Following his refusal to enter medical school, Robert had become increasingly isolated, spending long hours alone in his Orgone box in the basement of his home and communicating less and less with his family. His behavior became so bizarre that the family arranged for hospitalization. At this point the patient wrote a note: "I am entering a stage in which I may withdraw completely for awhile. It may take the form of paralysis or insanity. I expect this and know what it signifies. My need to die comes when I have nothing to think about."

Once hospitalized, much of the patient's behavior was in response to what was done to him—total push, insulin coma, electroshock, and the like. His belief that life was one big "psychological plot" contained the kernel of truth so often found in delusional systems.

OBJECT AVOIDANCE

The patient's initial reaction to hospitalization at Chestnut Lodge has already been described—including his regressive withdrawal and disorganization following what he probably interpreted as abandonment by Dr. Gibson. He remained in this state for approximately 15 months. Since the ataractic drugs were not yet commonly used, his treatment consisted primarily of manifold attempts to establish some kind of human relationship in which he would feel less apprehensive and more secure. He rebuffed most efforts to approach him, often by violent assaults. The best results were achieved when the patient was placed in a cold-wet-sheet pack for two hours every day, during which his psychotherapist saw him for therapy sessions and members of the nursing staff sat with the patient. They bathed, shaved, and spoon-fed him, generally dispensing the kind of nursing care that would be applicable for a small child or infant. The therapist often participated in this nursing care. The patient relaxed at these times and his speech became somewhat more coherent. His relatively favorable response to this regimen suggests that he felt most comfortable in the role of the sick, helpless person receiving simple physical contact and nursing care. This response may partly have been determined by the patient's earlier experience when he developed asthma.

A turning point came when the patient was given Reserpine in small oral dosages, gradually increased to a maximum of four mgms. per day. Within a few weeks his communication became clearer. He began to dress and behave more appropriately. He showed a greater interest in his surroundings. He was able to leave the hospital ward and attend various activities.

The exact manner in which the ataractics influence behavior is unknown, but in this patient they may have diminished drives. His psychomotor activity was decreased, assaultiveness lessened, sexual behavior diminished, as a result of which the task of the ego was sim-plified, permitting him to handle these drives without being over-whelmed.

Under the impact of psychological stress, the patient's ego functions could still break down into a state of psychotic disorganization. Even while he was receiving Reserpine, a visit by the patient's parents re-sulted in a two-day period of behavior fully as disturbed as it was during the patient's most psychotic condition. Over a period of years, he gradually became less disrupted by these visits. The change did not seem to come through any changes in medication. Many therapeutic hours were spent in discussions of the patient's relationship to his parents and presumably this had some effect.

Following the initiation of his treatment with Reserpine, Robert showed a gradual decrease in psychotic symptoms but at no time was he completely free of delusions and hallucinations. He never regressed to the degree he had during the early phases of hospitalization. Even when such regressive behavior occurred, the therapist often was able to maintain some contact with him. For example, when he began to masturbate in the therapist's presence, the therapist asked if he felt anxious and was attempting to relieve such feelings by masturbating. When Robert agreed the therapist asked if he would like to be alone for a short time until he had finished. He feared the patient might feel embarrassed by what was occurring and wanted to afford him this privacy. When the therapist did return the patient looked around for something with which to clean himself, and the therapist got some Kleenex for him. The therapist saw the patient's behavior as a defense against anxiety and made distinct efforts to be noncondemning and supportive.

Vulnerability and the Struggle for Autonomy

After several months, with no change in medication, there was a gradual shift in the clinical picture. He insisted that a precipitation of feces from an odor in the men's room had formed a coating on his tongue. Superficial reassurance seemed to relieve him a bit but the complaint persisted and ultimately he made vigorous efforts to cleanse his tongue with a commercial cleaning fluid. Over a period of several years similar complaints recurred. At times Robert became preoccupied with bathing, trying to cleanse himself from noxious substances he believed had settled in his hair. On another occasion he said that microscopic particles of feces had settled into his mattress as a result of the incontinence of a patient on another part of the ward.

The therapist handled this complaint first by a factual explanation that a deviation of the nasal septum might have caused excessive breathing through the mouth and given the illusion of bad taste. He then reminded the patient that when he was disturbed he had actually eaten feces. He made further references to the first time the patient had made such complaints when he had attended a movie. Thus the therapist made clarifying comments at several levels. He gave a rational explanation for the patient's symptoms or complaints, directing his attention to underlying impulses against which the complaints might be a defense, while also outlining some continuity to the complaints by recalling their onset.

Along with fears of contamination the patient sometimes became preoccupied with the desire to acquire good, healthy substances for his body. He wanted ever-increasing amounts of vitamins, purchasing them from the local drug store. He was especially persistent in his desire for fresh air. At one time he tried to enlist the aid of various hospital authorities in his campaign to keep all the windows open in the dead of winter, going all the way to the State Commissioner of Mental Health. This particular interest on the part of the patient seemed especially significant in the light of his childhood history of asthma and the crucial importance of fresh air to him.

On several occasions this constellation of fear of noxious substances from without and the desire for the health-giving substances came up in a setting in which Robert was developing some attachment toward another patient—usually a roommate. For example, on one occasion the patient developed a friendly relationship with his roommate. They often attended activities together within the hospital and shared in their outings. There was no evidence of any overt sexual contact between the patient and the roommate, although the relationship was obviously a close one. This roommate had mild diabetes which occasionally required small doses of insulin. Robert began to complain that his roommate smelled of insulin. His complaints had a teasing quality yet he persisted in threats of violence, eventually forcing a shift of rooms.

It is of interest to recall that the patient's initial obvious psychiatric difficulty occurred in college when he was for the first time in a situation of potential intimacy with a roommate. We explain this as follows: early life experiences interfered with the process of differentiation, among the results of which were gross distortions of body image and indistinctness of self-other boundaries. On one occasion he protested "my body is bigger than the room, too big for the hospital—I am this place—I am you—when I knew I was coming here I bought this place —what else can I do?" His failure to achieve clear boundaries left him with a feeling of particular vulnerability to influences of the external world. As he moved toward a relationship of some intimacy these boundaries became even less distinct. His fears were expressed in terms of his delusional ideas about noxious substances. He took steps to interrupt the relationship with its frightening prospect of intimacy, establishing points of disagreement and conflict with significant others as if to strengthen his self-other boundaries.

At times he said his brain was crumbling from the effect of smoking stale cigarettes. A similar complaint was that his head had become misshapen and lost its structure. At other times he spoke of a crumbling process in his knees. In more lucid moments he spoke of being unable to stand on his own two feet. His enthusiasm for vitamins was partially expressed in the hope of counteracting his sense of body weakness. Some of his delusional complaints about the dissolution of his body were a means of describing his awareness of the disintegration of ego functions.

THE ISSUE OF CONTROL

The patient's conflicting expressions of need and fear were shown by his great concern that people were trying to control him. He regularly objected to medications on this basis. At times his complaints were directed toward his parents, their selection of clothes, and so forth. In these situations, the patient was more interested in the argument than its outcome. For example, he would insist that his therapist take him home, and then immediately demand a change of doctors. In the course of a single appointment he would say, "Stay with me—no, I don't want to see you anymore—yes, I do want to—no, I want to leave the hospital." Frequently he shifted the focus of these disputes to some remote person in a position of authority. A voluminous correspondence accumulated between the patient, the Medical Director, and the Commissioner of Mental Health.

As might be expected, these complaints occurred in the therapeutic relationship in a variety of ways. The patient often tried to place himself in the position of the helpless victim of his therapist. He accused the therapist of stealing his underwear, stealing his semen, and forcing him to masturbate. At other times he insisted that he was in complete control of the situation and would not be dominated. During early phases of treatment the therapist allowed the patient some latitude about appointments, indicating that he did not have to spend the full time if it were too anxiety provoking. At other points the therapist indicated that he could understand Robert's wish to strike him but emphasized that he would not permit this. Frequently the therapist emphatically told the patient that neither of them controlled the other. In other situations he did everything possible to make his comments nonauthoritative, allowing for a difference of opinion. At times the therapist underscored his own involvement in the situation by threatening retaliation if the patient should attack him.

While the patient's complaints were ostensibly geared to gain more freedom, they invariably were couched in such a way as to prompt greater restriction. He did this so many times and in so many settings that it is difficult to escape the conclusion that he knew full well what would eventually happen. For example, he was informed that repeated requests for action by the Commissioner of Mental Health could result in a court commitment. He came perilously close to this, at all times protesting that he simply wanted greater freedom. On another occasion he told his therapist that he needed no further help from the hospital and would insist on leaving. Later that day the patient did, in fact, run away. He went directly to the police station where he gave an obviously psychotic account of how he was being persecuted at the hospital. This, of course, led to his prompt return by the police. He made no protests about this and indicated that he was pleased and relieved to be back in a closed ward.

We would interpret this as an indication of the patient's fear of object relations. Being overwhelmed and controlled was threatening, but even more frightening was the recognition of his inability to control himself. He found a partially workable compromise in his various campaigns against the authorities. First of all, the disputes were usually carried on with people at some distance and not the people upon whom he was immediately dependent in the day-to-day activities. Second, by carrying on such a campaign, he could deny the inordinate need that he had for external controls. Third, the clashes with the authorities always resulted in tangible reminders that they would, if pushed hard enough, exert control over the patient.

At times he tried to resolve the need-fear dilemma by clinging to his therapist. He asked him to be his father, expressed concern about appointments, and literally tried to embrace him. He sometimes defended against his sense of victimization and terrible vulnerability by attempts to reverse the doctor-patient roles. He referred to himself as a doctor and claimed superiority over his therapist. He made extravagant claims to being a five-star general, a famous scientist, and a great athlete.

The preponderance of historical data indicates that the conflict over control had its origin during the patient's anal phase of psychosexual development. Throughout that time the patient's mother was preoccupied with his physical health, particularly focused on bowel movements. Enemas were a prominent part of her regime of dealing with him. During adolescence the patient himself took over this ritual of the enema as a method of achieving erotic stimulation. During his psychosis he again showed great preoccupation with his bowel functions and at times was coprophagic. Intermittently he was able to defend against this with extensive cleansing rituals. Clearly, control was a crucial issue for the patient. He could not allow the intrusion of any foreign substances or influences that might contaminate him. He had to guard against the release of all of his own body substances and was in constant dread that he would become physically depleted.

It is of interest that in several situations with the head nurse he was able to put her into the role of benevolent controller. He had his greatest success on a weight-reducing diet when he turned over all decisions about his eating to this particular nurse. He would plead and cajole with her in an effort to get her to increase the amount of his food. He would try to make her an accomplice to outwit the diet, but with obvious pleasure would accept the final limitation that she set. Occasionally he tried to bring this under his own control by writing out lists of instructions himself.

CLINICAL COURSE

Over a period of some five years, the patient followed roughly the following course. There was gradual diminution in psychotic symptoms. As his capacity to function effectively increased he found himself in situations requiring greater involvement, closeness, and responsiveness to the expectation that he assume a more adult role involving a greater degree of independent action. At this point (and it is important to note that there was no change in medication) the constellation of complaints centering about fears of noxious substances, desires for health-giving substances, and fears of body deterioration occurred. We explain these symptoms as having their origins in the patient's failure to achieve a sufficient degree of differentiation and integration. On the one hand the symptom complex can be viewed as an indication of his ego deficit. On the other hand, it also served to remove the patient from the threatening situation and was a return to the role of the sick invalid that had afforded him comfort and relief in childhood.

During the summer of 1959, in his seventh year at Chestnut Lodge,

Robert achieved a level at which he could operate the hospital switch-board and do other jobs of some difficulty. In the fall of 1959 the patient made a visit home for several days. His father reported no delusional ideas or other psychotic behavior. Robert saw many family members and even visited an old college friend. For the first time he acknowledged that the hospital had been helpful and he talked of getting a job. The family thought that Robert was now on the road to recovery and would soon be able to be gainfully employed. He objected to returning to the hospital, but on the scheduled day he was up early with his bag packed ready to go. This visit home was followed by renewed pressures from the family that he obtain regular work outside the hospital.

At this point his father arranged interviews preliminary to job training with a large corporation. This was done in a manner virtually identical to the arrangements for Robert to enter medical school. Consequently, he ran away from the hospital to a place near his parents' home and ultimately was picked up by them. At that point he was argumentative and truculent with his father. The family, having gradually lost patience over the years, arranged for his admission to a state institution.

FINDINGS OF THE RELATIONSHIP QUESTIONNAIRE

During the last year of the patient's hospitalization, data were collected from the ward personnel through the use of our questionnaire on relationships and it is interesting to compare findings from the questionnaire with clinical observations.

Clinical observations indicated that during the summer of 1959 the patient functioned more capably than at any other time during his hospital stay. Early in 1960 the clinical impression was that he was on a plateau with some danger that he might falter and regress.

Questionnaire findings as indicated in Figure 1 agreed with the clinical estimate that his best level of function in relationships was in early and mid-1959. For the subsequent period—the fall of 1959 and early 1960—the questionnaire reports differed from clinical impressions in showing a distinct decline rather than a leveling-off of the quality of the patient's relationships. According to the questionnaire reports, he approached the ward staff less, the frequency and clarity of his communication diminished, and he expressed fewer positive feelings, while his problem behavior and expression of negative feelings increased in frequency. Concurrently staff members spoke less and expressed fewer positive feelings to him. Thus it becomes clear that a deterioration of his relationships with the hospital staff were an important part of the context for his running away from the hospital. In

FIGURE 1A. Questionnaire Scores for Robert Feldman:
Patient's Behavior Toward Ward Staff

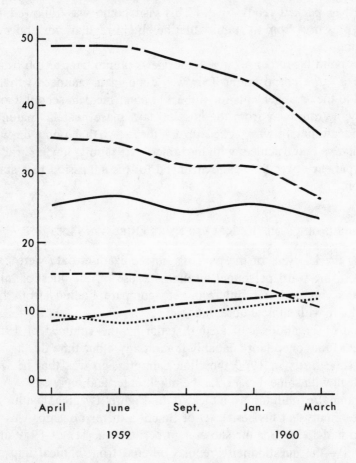

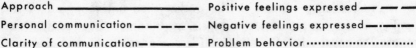

FIGURE 1B. Questionnaire Scores for Robert Feldman:
Nursing Staff's Behavior Toward Patient

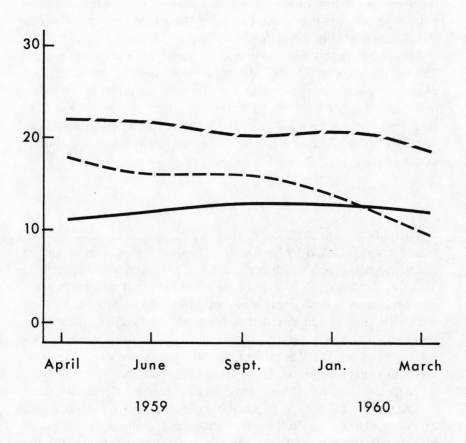

Approach ───────────
Personal communication ─ ─ ─ ─ ─ ─ ─
Positive feelings expressed ── ── ── ── ── ──

this instance the questionnaire appears to have been a more sensitive instrument than ordinary clinical observations.

This is an example of the potential usefulness of such a questionnaire. The changes that occurred were too subtle to be recognized in the course of the usual clinical observations. Combining the question-naire reports formed a cumulative picture in which the changes in the patient's behavior stood out more sharply than in each individual staff member's impression of him. The quantitative nature of the question-naire reports made it possible to identify small changes unnoticed in global impressionistic evaluations.

Unfortunately this discovery was not made until after the patient had left the hospital, because of a lag between collection and analysis of questionnaire data, and because at that time the direct applicability of the questionnaire findings to current treatment efforts was not real-ized. Had this not been the case, the treatment staff might have been alerted to a need for modifications in the plan of treatment and clinical administration.

DISCUSSION

The patient's early life experiences interfered with his differentia-tion. He was intended by his family to replace his dead sister and to relieve the depression which her death had precipitated in his mother. This was further reinforced when he spent his ninth and tenth years with his mother in the Southwest in connection with his asthma. Though not by design, he again was used by the mother to handle her desperate needs. His father was subtly but tenaciously controlling, never allow-ing any open conflict. The patient had little opportunity to make clear distinctions between his needs and those of his parents.

In addition to the problems posed by each parent individually, there was particular difficulty in relating to them as a unit. To identify with his mother meant ridicule by his father; to identify with his father meant collaboration with the father's scorn and contempt for the mother. The patient's sister was not exposed to the full impact of this but even so could only achieve some sense of identity by rebellion and severance of the ties with the family.

In college the patient was exposed to the impact of more intimate and mature relationships. The inability of his ego to function in a dif-ferentiated fashion made him peculiarly vulnerable to the feelings raised by these relationships and he was engulfed by chaotic sexual feelings. In addition, his entrance into college demanded more inde-pendent and complex activities than his poorly integrated ego could handle. The patient dealt with these conflicts by object avoidance. This pattern of events was in many ways recapitulated early in his stay at Chestnut Lodge. As he began to establish a relationship with his first psychotherapist he had a brief period of disorganization, much as he had at the onset of his illness. Many times throughout his stay at Chestnut Lodge, the same conflict was reexperienced with the second psychotherapist.

Most of the time the patient was at the mercy of two conflicting forces. He was drawn toward more intimate relationships and more mature functioning. At the same time he was threatened by the fear of being overwhelmed by another person and exposure of his own lack of integration. Although there was considerable fluctuation he seemed driven toward a compromise solution. In this compromise the patient assumed the role of a sick invalid, which he had first known as an asthmatic child. At that time the patient had temporarily escaped a conflictual situation. When he developed asthma he was able to have an exclusive relationship with his mother in which she functioned far more effectively than when with the whole family. He was no longer confronted by the disruptive interaction of his parents that made identification almost impossible. In adulthood during his psychotic state, assumption of a similar role of sick invalid permitted a feeling of closeness while still maintaining a low level of performance. Although the patient showed significant improvement, he was unable to achieve sufficient ego differentiation and integration to solve his need-fear dilemma. When even this compromise solution of sick invalid was cut off, he ran away, disrupting treatment.

In a follow-up some three years later it was learned that the patient had been continuously hospitalized. Despite the use of various ataractic drugs there had been a steady regression. He had finally settled into what appeared to be a fixed psychotic condition.

XII

SEPARATION ANXIETY AND LACK OF OBJECT CONSTANCY: FACTORS IN THE NEED-FEAR DILEMMA[1]

Donald L. Burnham

IN PREVIOUS CHAPTERS we have developed the thesis that the personality structure of the potentially schizophrenic person is easily disorganized and lacks autonomy. This renders him inordinately dependent upon and vulnerable to the influence of others. We have designated this predicament as the object need-fear dilemma. In this chapter we shall discuss in detail two key factors in this dilemma, separation anxiety and lack of object constancy.

Separation anxiety refers to the signal of danger and reaction of distress upon isolation or separation from a needed person. This concept has been used mainly to describe the reactions of children upon separation from their mothers, as in the writings of Spitz (1950), Bowlby (1960), Benjamin (1963), and others. Our concern in this chapter, however, is with its significance in the schizophrenic person's difficulties in relationships. At first glance many schizophrenic persons might be assumed to be relatively devoid of this type of anxiety. They are withdrawn, self-absorbed, and narcissistic, with little apparent

[1] Modified versions of this chapter were read at the Annual Meeting, American Psychoanalytic Association, May 2, 1964, Los Angeles, California, and published in the Archives of General Psychiatry, October 1965.

interest in object relations. However, this façade of indifference to others frequently conceals and defends against deep and pervasive anxiety of which separation anxiety is a large part. It is a major factor in their difficulty in establishing and maintaining satisfactory relationships.

Among the reasons why separation anxiety is such a crucial issue for the schizophrenic person are his lack of autonomy and lack of object constancy. His lack of autonomy renders him what Fenichel (1945) aptly termed an "object addict." Without stable built-in capacities for self-regulation and adaptation he has an inordinate need for other persons as sources of help, protection, and direction.

As we explained in Chapter II, the schizophrenic person's lack of object constancy is part of an inability to form reliable reality constructs. Object constancy, as described by Piaget (1954), Hartmann (1953), and others (Angyal, 1958), refers to a person's capacity to construct mental representations of himself and his objects which remain relatively constant regardless of his wishes, fears, or state of drive tension, and regardless of the actual presence or absence of the object. This capacity is extremely important in enabling a person to endure separation from others, and to function with relative autonomy. Since object constancy is both an index and a determinant of total personality structure, a person without it is prey to discontinuity of experience and disruption of personality organization whenever he is separated from needed objects. To him separation from the object signals impending disorganization of his tenuous internal structure. It is this which makes separation so terrifying for the schizophrenic person, epecially when he fails, as he frequently does, to distinguish between brief temporary separation and utter abandonment.

We shall return to the topic of object constancy, but let us first describe a few of the schizophrenic person's manifestations of separation anxiety and his defenses against it. Although we shall speak mostly of these as they are apparent in the patient's relationship with his psychotherapist, they are by no means confined to this special relationship. The doctor-patient relationship does, of course, provide an excellent context in which to observe separation anxiety and defenses against it. The patient is likely to wish the doctor to gratify his intense need for objects, not only as sources of reliable strength, regulation and protection, but, indeed, as sustenance for the very structure of his personality. A hospital such as Chestnut Lodge helps to foster this wish by assigning a personal psychotherapist to each patient and by defining the doctor as the major therapeutic agent in the overall treatment program. The doctor-patient relationship contains repeated separation experiences, such as the intervals between scheduled appointments, especially the weekend intervals. Moreover, the doctor usually divides his time among several patients and performs other hospital duties as well.

The reaction of a schizophrenic patient to these separations is determined by the state of his personality organization, the phase of his illness, and the stage of his relationship with his therapist. A seriously disorganized patient, just beginning a therapeutic relationship, may show little awareness of the presence or absence of the therapist and may not even recognize him as the same person from one time to another. A better organized patient may be perfectly clear regarding the presence or absence of the therapist, but if he has not established a basic modicum of trust, he may deny that separation from the therapist has any meaning. He may protest that he has no wish for contact with the doctor or may state that the less frequent and shorter their meetings the better. In contrast, the patient whose doctor has assumed definite positive significance for him may show marked reactions to separation. Separation of a weekend or longer may provoke flagrant disorganization. Separations may be anticipated with conscious dread by the patient, with such statements as, "What's going to happen to me over the weekend? . . . I may be dead by Monday . . . I'll probably never see you again."

Patients may speak poignantly of their sense of passive helplessness and vulnerability when separated from their major source of strength, direction, and organization. For example, prior to a weekend one patient said, "I don't know what to do. What should I do? I can't decide." This complaint may be accompanied by references to himself as a toy, puppet, or slave, with the implication that he can be picked up or discarded according to another person's whim. One woman who regularly showed massive psychotic disorganization whenever her therapist went on vacation spoke of herself as a doll and even moved like a mechanical toy. While disorganized she frequently hallucinated the voice of her therapist or of God giving her constant directions. Hallucinations of the therapist's voice or face often indicated a wish for his continuous presence. Another patient, while protesting in her therapy sessions that she wished to leave the therapist and the hospital, misperceived figures on television as her therapist sending messages to her and watching her. Later this patient became an outpatient and was managing an isolated existence in an apartment hotel. As her loneliness increased, a recrudescence of psychosis was ushered in by hallucinations of voices of passersby outside the hotel taunting her with the question, "Are you still having 'hours' with your doctor?"

Another psychotic form which the wish for the doctor's continuous presence may take is the delusion that the doctor has appointed observers to send him continuous reports on the patient's whereabouts and behavior. A less comforting delusion is the conviction that the absent doctor is dead and can never be seen again. The connection of this belief with the patient's rage toward the presumed deserter will be discussed in a later section.

Sometimes a patient who has been seemingly indifferent to his therapist will show a massive reaction to separation. Henry Harrashaw, the catatonic man described in Chapter X, when told that his doctor was leaving the hospital to take a position in another country, became wildly disturbed, tore off his clothing, refused to feed himself, hurled himself about the room, and writhed on the floor. He referred to his therapist and himself as "big and small brother," and asked point-blank, "How can big brother leave me?" Becoming even more upset he said, "I have lost my soul . . . I have no chance . . . Why don't you kill me?" and then, "Eat me." Upon the doctor's actual departure the patient became frenzied, but did respond favorably to the presence of one aide. In apparent efforts to assure the constancy of the aide, the patient repeatedly reached out to touch and stroke the aide and even tried to lick him with his tongue. The truly life or death nature of this man's separation crisis was a measure of the risk in taking at face value a schizophrenic patient's apparent indifference to others, and in underestimating his need for them.

Many of the schizophrenic patient's body feelings appear related to separation anxiety. These feelings include a sense of emptiness, of something missing, and fears of the destruction of body parts. Szasz (1957a) wrote cogently of the connection between feared damage to body parts and object loss. The fear of decapitation may express feared loss of a person needed as an auxiliary ego to perform the functions of thought and judgment which the patient feels incapable of performing himself. Occasionally he voices the link between separation and feared body damage in terms of what hospital staff may do to him in the absence of his protective therapist. He may ask pleadingly, "What will they do to me while you are gone? Will they torture me? Poison me? Give me shock treatments?"

Patients frequently manifest keen sensitivity even to momentary separation, such as the slightest evidence that the therapist is distracted or inattentive. A brief glance out the window, a shift in his chair, or a deep breath by the doctor may suffice to disturb the patient to whom minor indications of separation signal the threat of abandonment. Even deeply confused patients may be extremely alert to the approach of the end of an "hour." One man who otherwise seemed grossly confused showed remarkable time consciousness with an uncannily accurate judgment of when only five minutes remained in the therapy hour. He occasionally sandwiched into his disorganized jumble of obscure talk comments such as "Dr. Brown is a clock watcher," or "The ten minutes is more important." He often requested a cigarette, coffee, or other token gifts as the end of the hour approached. Many months later, when he became better organized, he was able to tell his therapist how threatened he felt between therapy sessions. He said, "It is as if everything were going to collapse. You don't seem to understand how important you are to me."

DEFENSES AGAINST SEPARATION ANXIETY

The schizophrenic patient's attempts to defend himself against separation anxiety are many and varied. They include both object clinging and object avoidance, as well as a number of perceptual and cognitive distortions.

Clinging may consist of literal embraces or of insistence upon shaking hands at the end of each therapy session. The patient also may seek to prolong the session by obscure talk which is difficult to bring to any logical conclusion. He may request a token gift, partly as a delaying maneuver and partly as a symbolic substitute for the doctor.

Some patients show a phobic avoidance of words customarily associated with separation. One woman was greatly upset if even a casual passerby said good-by, and would insist that the magic undoing phrase "not good-by" be uttered. If this was not immediately forthcoming she would become increasingly frantic and would pursue the other person screaming, "Say 'not good-by,' say it, say it!"

A man whose family had been deeply involved in rituals designed to affirm family solidarity would regularly insist that his therapist join him in singing a song at the conclusion of a therapy session.

Sometimes a patient may openly and unabashedly voice his wish for an inseparable relationship, for instance in such direct requests as "Take me home with you," or "Let me go with you on your vacation." Occasionally a patient will startle his therapist with the ultimate request, "Please adopt me as your child." Somewhat less direct expression of this wish may be contained in questions about the doctor's extrahospital life and his family or in offers to tutor or baby-sit for his children. One patient quite routinely ended therapy sessions prior to a weekend with the superficially friendly remark, "Give my regards to your wife." Not surprisingly, on other occasions this patient vented extreme rage at the doctor's forsaking him in favor of family life.

More frequent than clinging, however, are various forms of avoidance in which wishes for attachment and inseparability are denied rather than acknowledged. Avoidance may take the form of seeming passive indifference or of an active, hostile, "I hate people" attitude. The patient may incessantly reiterate requests, demands, and threats to leave the hospital. Often the link between this behavior and the threat of separation is directly apparent. One woman attempted to elope from the hospital whenever she experienced an increased feeling of attachment to her therapist and a correspondingly increased fear of losing him. Frequently she assaulted him toward the end of therapy sessions, shouting that he need not return for another session since she would be gone. Once when he unconsciously attempted to smooth his departure by offering to light her cigarette, she viciously kicked him. The overwhelming importance of separation to this patient was graphically manifest in her creating for the hospital art show a totem pole-like figure, eight feet high, which she titled "The God of Separation."

Many of the defenses of patients against separation anxiety contain efforts to transform the separation experience from passive victimization to active mastery, the motivational pattern so beautifully described by Freud (1920) in terms of a child's fascination with repeatedly throwing a spool of thread away from himself and then drawing it back in an effort to master separation fear. He offered a similar explanation for the allure of games of peek-a-boo and hide-and-seek in which a person disappears, then reappears, or is found again. The same urge to achieve active mastery over separation anxiety which the child shows in his play is manifest variously by the schizophrenic patient. Consider, for instance, the patient who assaults the doctor at the end of the therapy session, or who runs away from the hospital just before the therapist's vacation, or who insists on being the one to terminate each session. A special form of transforming passivity into activity consists of role reversal. Assuming the doctor's role, the patient may say, "That's all the time I can spare you today. Come back again if you need more help, etc." One man first asked at the end of an hour if he could please stay just five minutes more. At the end of the five minutes overtime he got up and, in a rather pathetic pose of mastery, said, "You can have the office now. In fact, I'm willing to rent it to you for a penny a day."

On other occasions the same patient evidenced more openly his deep sense of helpless vulnerability to separation anxiety. At the end of a therapy hour he attempted to prolong the contact by asking his doctor if they could go for a ride. The doctor explained that this was impossible, but that perhaps they could take a ride when they met again after the weekend. The patient then muttered repetitively, "Did they pass a law? . . . Did they pass a law? . . ." finally adding, "Did they pass a law that I must see you on Monday?" On the occasion of still another separation before a weekend the patient said, "O.K., I'll see you Monday. I am lost," as his gaze remained fixed on the departing doctor.

The effort to reverse helplessness into active mastery may result in multiple layers and condensations of clinging and avoidance, as illustrated in the following incident: A paranoid woman who stoutly denied illness and any need for treatment began to develop an attachment to her therapist, at which point she refused to meet with him for treatment sessions. After honoring this refusal for several weeks, the therapist decided to insist that they meet for a full hour in a locked room. The patient accepted this arrangement with surprisingly little protest and, in fact, seemed relieved that her strike had been broken. At the end of the hour, however, she refused to let the doctor leave and began screaming to the ward staff outside, "Let me out of here!" thus simultaneously prolonging the session, denying any wish to do so, and attempting to be the person who did the leaving.

Another means of denying and attenuating separation anxiety consists of various perceptual and cognitive distortions. We mentioned previously the hallucination of the voice or face of a comforting, guiding, or protecting person. Misperceiving persons in the here and now as persons actually distant in time and place partly functions to relieve the pain of loss and separation. One man said, "They have all my former associates here." A variation of this type of misperception is the delusion that lost significant objects have been transformed into plants, animals, and furniture and are constantly available (Searles, 1960).

A different form of denial is manifest in the effort to erase all memory of the lost person, with a blank "Who's that? Never heard of him" look, should the name of the lost person be mentioned. Sometimes the denial is not so complete. For example, a patient who had become strongly attached to an aide acknowledged disappointment when the aide left the hospital to enter a nurses training school. However, he denied the purpose of the aide's leaving with the remark, "Mr. White should not have left; I know that he is not going to a nursing school." Another form of denial occurs through amnesia whereby there is denial of one's own past and even of one's own identity. A patient may say, "I am not Mr. Blake; I was never married and never lived in New York," thus excluding from his consciousness any feelings of loss and separation.

Denial may assume such widespread proportions that nothing seems real. One patient said, "It's all a stage production. Everyone is acting and using stage names." Another claimed, "The people here are only pseudo-people, made of papier-maché."

This man's subsequent reaction to a most unfortunate separation experience during his hospitalization merits special mention. For over a year after his admission to the hospital he had maintained a formidable stance of hateful, scornful disinterest in relationships; he would snarl, "Get away from me," at all who approached him and would assault any who persisted. Finally, by dint of great persistence, one nurse was able to penetrate his defensive barrier and became sufficiently accepted by him to a point where they could enjoy talks and pleasure trips outside the hospital for a restaurant meal or a movie. Unfortunately, other circumstances necessitated her subsequent transfer to another ward. When, a week or so later, she came to visit the original ward, he gave her a quick angry glance and turned away, growling, "You're dead. You don't exist."

Turning to other types of perceptual-cognitive distortion, reduplicative phenomena—a special type of misperception in which persons and places are perceived as doubles of the real thing—are clearly related to problems of separation and loss. One man, whose mother's death had been a major precipitant of his psychosis, was unable to believe that she was dead. He said, "She married again, has another name, and is living in South America." The reversal of passivity into activity was apparent in his attributing to her an active choice of a second life instead of her actual helplessness to avert death. He showed the same pattern in his own behavior; when fearful of rejection by his therapist, he protested loudly that he wished to change doctors. During a final therapy session prior to a separation necessitated by his doctor's traveling to the West Coast, this patient suddenly said, "There are two Washingtons. This one is not on the East Coast. I have never been on the East Coast." In the same hour he reiterated his conviction that his mother was not dead but was leading a double life somewhere. Here we have clear evidence of reduplication of persons and places serving to defend against separation anxiety.

OBJECT INCONSTANCY, AMBIVALENCE, AND SEPARATION ANXIETY

Reduplication is related to what we earlier referred to as lack of object constancy, or a lack of stability and continuity of a person's symbolic representations of self and others. Lack of object constancy is, in turn, closely related to ambivalence or lack of integration of conflicting affects. As a concrete example of this connection between ambivalence and lack of object constancy, one might say, "I feel so differently about Joe Green at different times that there seem to be two of him." A schizophrenic patient is likely to experience this phenomenon very literally. He may perceive his therapist as startlingly changed from one appointment to the next or even within the course of a single "hour," or as a total stranger whom he has never seen before.

The schizophrenic person suffers severe and literal object inconstancy because he is so poorly integrated. This applies to his need and fear, his love and hate, and his "good" and "bad" object images or object symbols. He may strive to preserve a constant symbolic representation of an all-good object, but can maintain this only so long as he can avoid feelings of disappointment, hurt, and anger toward the good object. If these mechanisms fail and give way to a sudden increment of hostility toward the needed object, the good object symbol may disintegrate. This renders him peculiarly vulnerable to separation anxiety, since separation arouses the very feelings which deprive him of a constant object symbol.

Benjamin (1963) has observed that the advent of separation anxiety in infants around the age of one year appears to be correlated with their developing the capacity for object-directed aggression. Hoedemaker (1955, 1958) and Pious (1949, 1961), writing of the psychotherapy of schizophrenic patients, have stressed the importance of the patient's developing an image of the therapist which is sufficiently stable to survive separation and surges of rage. Suttie (1952) went so far as to say that hate and separation anxiety are virtually synonymous.

To document further the triad of ambivalence, object inconstancy, and separation anxiety, there follow excerpts from reports by two different therapists of individual therapy sessions with paranoid schizophrenic men.

The first reports an interchange at the end of a therapy hour. The patient was reluctant to start back to the ward, but when the therapist insisted that he must, the patient said, "I don't like you either, *Jim* (not the therapist's name), but I've got to work with you." The actual Jim had been a business associate of the patient's dead father, and the therapist somewhat resembled him physically. The patient had intermittently misperceived his therapist as Jim. On this occasion it seemed clearly to fit into the following sequence: forced separation—anger—disintegration of the inconstant image of the therapist—misperception of the therapist.

The second excerpt, from another therapist's report about another patient,[2] is as follows:

Today the patient came in and as we shook hands, he said, "I feel schizophrenic about shaking hands," and then laughed. I asked him what he meant by schizophrenic and he explained that he was not sure whether he wanted to shake hands with me this morning. He said he had just used the toilet and after washing his hands he had smelled them but was uncertain whether they were clean. He then said, "The soap here is dirty. In fact, everything here is miserable." He followed shortly with a statement that he was unable to figure me out. He seemed to be trying to say that he was uncertain of me and had mixed feelings about me. When I tried to follow this through, he digressed, but after a bit I was able to bring him back to the topic of his uncertainty about me. He said that at times he is very frightened of me and thinks I am an evil person, whereas at other times he thinks I am a person he can trust. He said that this trust is more permanent while he is in the office with me. When he leaves the office, he even thinks I am another person, someone he knew elsewhere in the past. He went on to say that he has similar mixed feelings about Dr. Gibson, his administrative physician. He says that Dr. Gibson must bear him ill will because he keeps him in these terrible surroundings. He added, "It seems to me that Dr. Gibson is almost two people. At times he seems very handsome. At other times his face is ugly and I think he really must be another person."

For this patient the act of shaking hands at the beginning and end of each therapy session was but one of many efforts to cope with severe separation anxiety. One day he arrived late for his appointment. He explained that he had been busy with several projects of great interest to himself. The therapist commented that to a certain extent these projects appeared to serve the purpose of avoiding the therapy hour and the relationship between the two of them. The patient first exclaimed, "Oh, you mean it's an escape?" but then promptly denied any such motive. Soon, however, he mentioned that he used to shake hands when he took leave of his favorite teacher in the eighth grade. He further explained, "I have trouble leaving people; I cannot even think about leaving them." Significantly, this therapy hour immediately preceded a weekend separation from his therapist.

Frequently this man tried to deny object attachment and separation anxiety. For instance, he would end a therapy session by asking,

2 This was Alberto, the subject of Chapter VIII.

"When am I going to be let out of here?" Once when his doctor answered that he probably should stay in the hospital for a considerable length of time, he retorted, "Doctor, you are crazy!" When told that his guardian had arranged for him to stay at the hospital at least another year, he protested that this was the last thing he wanted. At other times, however, he openly acknowledged his doctor's importance to him and how much he feared separation. He described himself as feeling frightened and threatened while not with the doctor. Once he said he felt as helpless as a newborn infant whose life could be snuffed out by others. On another occasion, while reporting his difficulty in conducting a minor transaction in a store outside the hospital, he said plaintively, "Doctor, don't you realize how difficult it was for me?—you don't think your strength goes out to me when I'm out there, do you?"

In other features of his behavior this patient afforded still further evidence of how his ambivalence contributed to his object inconstancy and separation anxiety. He desperately feared that his rage, if uncontrolled, would destroy the person vital to his existence. In one therapy session he hurled hatred and contempt toward his doctor, who commented that these feelings must be very disturbing to him. The patient replied, "Yes, you're the only thing I have." In another therapy hour the therapist informed him that he would be unable to keep their next appointment. The following significant sequence ensued: The patient expressed first fear that others might harm him during the therapist's absence, and then anger at the therapist's "untrustworthiness and stupidity"; then he switched to avowing friendly feelings and esteem for the therapist, in addition to concern that he might harm the doctor. Here we see the elements of the fateful sequence: impending separation arouses anger toward his good indispensable object who is threatening to turn into a hated deserter; then, fearing the possible destructive effects of his anger, he hastily attempts to restitute the good object image.[3]

Other instances of this pattern were frequent. For example, whenever he experienced a momentary flash of anger or voiced some criticism of the therapist, he would literally move toward the doctor,

[3] Cf. Benjamin's observation (1963) of the apparent close association between heightened separation anxiety and the capacity for object-directed aggression.

perhaps sit on the floor near him or touch his clothing, as if thereby magically neutralizing his fear of destroying the vital relationship.

Indications of a sharp tone in the doctor's voice often prompted similar moves to make sure that the doctor was still there and still touchable. One incident which seemed to contain this sequence in capsule form occurred as follows: The patient asked, "You do understand, don't you?" When the doctor answered, "No, I don't," the patient said, "Oh, I'll have to hug you for that!" The force of the hug indicated that despite the effort to deny destructive rage a modicum of it still gained expression.

The quest for object constancy is an enormously important motive for schizophrenic patients and takes various forms, both realistic and autistic. One woman hallucinated God's voice and said that it afforded her greater comfort than did her less constant image of her therapist. When she was assigned a new administrative physician she persisted in calling him by the name of the previous administrator. In another instance, a young man, much troubled by object loss and separation, was greatly preoccupied with the notion that objects photographed in a certain way might be preserved forever.

Some patients approach the problem of object inconstancy and separation anxiety by attempting not only to avoid actual contact with the doctor but also to shut out any image or thought of him. One woman who for months had striven to maintain a façade of self-sufficiency finally acknowledged to her doctor, "You've gotten under my skin; I hate you for it. You don't bother me so much when you are here. It's when you are not here and I can't get you out of my mind that I hate you most. I was sure I could get along without you and take care of myself. I feel that by letting you become important I have lost my strength and have lost part of myself." Another patient said, "I don't even want to know your name and I certainly don't want to think of you as my doctor. That would mean I might lose you."

On the other hand, patients may prefer their image of the doctor over his actual presence, saying, for instance, "I can be more certain of my picture of you than I can of you. I can talk to you more easily when I'm not with you." This would appear to be a variant of eidetic imagery in persons who are fixated midway between the poles of narcissism and object-relatedness, and for whom a vivid image is in some ways more satisfying than the actual object in the real world.

A further consideration is that these patients are beset by inability to reconcile and integrate conflicting feelings toward their objects. They may attain a pseudoconstancy of the object image by systematically excluding badness from the image. Such a purified image can be more readily maintained in the absence of actual object contacts which inevitably arouse some bad feelings which would spoil the good image. One woman told her doctor, "I know that my image of you will never leave me, but you as a person might leave me. When I think of you as a real person, I get sick." Significantly, this patient also frequently fantasied that by suicide she could be reunited with her dead and idealized mother.

This notion of eternal union through death is frequent in the quest for constancy and inseparability. It is an apparent motive in many joint suicides and murder-suicide pacts. These tragedies also reflect the rage reaction to separation and the wish, once and for all, to possess the hateful deserter by killing him; to wit, reports of a murderer's saying, "I couldn't stand to have her leave me." A horrifying instance of this occurred a few years ago when a youth placed a bomb in his mother's luggage just before she boarded an airliner. In confessing to having caused the mass tragedy which ensued, he said, "I decided that she would never leave me again."

The mental images of dead persons may be cherished as defenses against separation anxiety. One young woman with severe separation anxiety clung to an image of her grandfather, who, she was convinced, was the only person who had ever loved her; she vividly recalled that as a child she had pleaded with him at his deathbed not to leave her. Years later a boyfriend kissed her goodnight one evening, and as he turned to leave, she suddenly perceived him as changed into an old man.

Some deeply disturbed and isolated patients give the impression of attempting to preserve the images of lost objects by uttering their names in repetitive and stereotyped fashion. The more isolated the patient's current existence, the more desperate seems his effort to revive and cling to old images which continuously threaten to disintegrate.

The quest for object constancy is not limited to attempts to consolidate the images of specific persons but may extend to a wish to fix the whole environment so that it will not change. One patient said he felt safer in his doctor's office since it and the doctor went together. He was quite upset by a change to another office and even by changes in the furniture arrangement. Another man was much preoccupied with talking of the geography of his home town as well as that of the area surrounding the hospital and pointing out similarities between the two. Listeners were extremely bored by his insistent repetitiousness. However, it was possible to discern that he needed desperately somehow to establish a constancy of his environment. It was noteworthy that his listeners felt as though they were being clung to as he talked to them.

Such efforts to fix the total environment appear to derive in part from the schizophrenic person's mode of perceiving, which is global and poorly differentiated. Figure-ground distinctions are fuzzy and objects are imbedded in their contexts. An example of undifferentiated perception was provided by a woman with severe object inconstancy and separation anxiety who ran away from the hospital one afternoon. When she returned in the evening, she was so startled to see a different shift of nurses on duty that at first she thought she was in an entirely different hospital. This is the type of undifferentiated percept which prompts the wish to make constant the total gestalt. Werner (1957) reports observations of similar modes of perceiving in young children.

Another example of this wish was provided by a man whose life contained a series of tragic losses. He reacted with rage to any changes made in the physical environment, such as remodeling buildings or altering the landscape in any way. For many months after an old inn in the neighboring town was razed to make way for a modern shopping center he periodically vented feelings of outrage at what he considered wanton destruction. During periods of excitement he sometimes walked to the hospital dump from which he resurrected discarded articles and carried them back to his room. In the course of one walk to the dump he picked up many pebbles along the way. At the dump he was angered by the sight of things which he did not think should be thrown away and muttered something about the Smithsonian Institution. His therapist, who had accompanied him on this walk, commented, "One function of the Smithsonian Institution is to preserve the past, isn't it?" Glancing at the pebbles clutched in his hand, he abruptly shouted, "Yes, and I'm going to find the philosopher's stone and bring my mother back to life!"

Substitute Objects and Separation Anxiety

The patient referred to above richly illustrated another important attempted remedy for his object need-fear dilemma, with its associated separation anxiety and object inconstancy. This "remedy" was the use of substitute objects. In clinging possessively to the discarded objects which he had salvaged, he clearly treated them as substitutes for persons of whom he felt utterly bereft. He assembled bundles of rags and odd bits of junk which he carried with him and which he tenaciously hoarded in his room. At times he indicated their substitutive significance in so many words. For instance, he tore from magazines and displayed on the wall of his room pictures of persons whom he misperceived as long-lost relatives and friends. This assemblage of supposed images of friends was strongly suggestive of the funeral customs of some early peoples who, with their dead, buried clay effigies of servants, friends, and fellow-villagers to accompany them in the other world. Perhaps the most revealing and most poignant of this patient's efforts to provide himself with substitute objects was his perceiving in the wood-grain pattern of a wall panel an image of the teddy bear which was his childhood companion. Here is clearly shown the close correspondence between the schizophrenic patient's use of substitute objects and the transitional objects which a child may employ to make the transition from his primary object relationship with his mother to a less continuous and more dispersed set of object relationships. Transitional objects assist the child in developing confidence in his capacity to endure separations from his primary object (Winnicott, 1953). We are familiar with the importance which a favorite toy or blanket may assume in this process. A famous example is Linus and his security blanket in the comic strip, *Peanuts*.

Another illustration from the popular arts of the significance of a substitute object in the effort to master separation anxiety is contained in the lyrics of the following song (Black, 1925):

I'm gonna buy a paper doll that I can call my own,
A doll that other fellas cannot steal;
And then those flirty, flirty guys
With their flirty, flirty eyes
Will have to flirt with dollies that are real.

When I come home at night she will be waiting,
She'll be the truest doll in all the world.
I'd rather have a paper doll that I can call my own
Than have a fickle-minded real-live girl.

One woman, who partly coped with separation anxiety by surrounding herself with arts-and-crafts creations of her own, literally tried to recreate her lost object world. She attempted to make whole bodies and replacements for body parts by knitting a prodigious number of objects of varying sizes and shapes. The art instructor, commenting on the extent of her urge for complete self-sufficiency, noted that she even wanted to make the paper and drawing materials before she began a picture. The obverse of her striving for independence was revealed in her statement that if she moved to an off-hospital-grounds apartment she would need pipes connecting it with various parts of the hospital. This concrete image portrayed vividly the depth of her need for supplies from others which she struggled to deny as she attempted to create her own world of substitute objects.

Live animals frequently serve as substitute objects for schizophrenic patients. One hebephrenic man spent hours on end talking to various members of a herd of steers on the hospital grounds. Another, during a phase of withdrawal from the hospital staff, talked at length to various pet dogs at the hospital recreation center. This man also utilized as substitute objects a variety of autistic projects, such as the ambition to found a network of monasteries which would bring peaceful order to the world. He spent many hours writing to a wide range of persons, in lieu of actual contacts with proximate persons. He well illustrated Fenichel's observation (1945) that philosophical or religious causes may have substitutive and restitutive meaning for schizophrenic persons who have lost effective contact with the world of actual persons.

Clearly, most substitute objects have a highly narcissistic quality. This was apparent in the activities of a woman who filled her hospital room with an assemblage of substitute objects, including live guinea pigs, the pelts of guinea pig predecessors who had died, and numerous personal arts-and-crafts creations. At various times she had a roommate who felt crowded out of the room. One staff member made the cogent observation that to walk into her room was like going inside her.

However, not all substitute objects employed as a defense against separation anxiety are so narcissistic. Some may show a direct link with the needed person. For example, patients often wish to take something from the doctor's office to keep during absences from him. One schizophrenic man insisted on carrying a book with him whenever he left a therapy session. In a subsequent phase of therapy his therapist, with good effect, offered him a drawer in the office desk in which he could deposit various writings for safekeeping. Another man, after a car ride with his doctor, deliberately left his gloves in the glove compartment of the doctor's car, thus not only hinting, "Let's go for a ride again," but also attempting to maintain a proxy connection with the doctor during separations. Another patient gave his therapist a sheaf of personal letters to hold while he was on a trip away from the hospital for several days. After another separation the same patient was especially eager that the doctor give him cigarettes as a means of re-establishing contact. This patient also spent much time between appointments writing voluminous notes which he expected somehow, without his explicit request, to reach his doctor. He would ask at subsequent appointments, "Did you receive the documents?"

Sometimes a gift to the doctor is employed as a substitutive bridge during separation. Occasionally a gift may be offered to the doctor's family rather than to the doctor himself, partly to deny jealousy and hatred of persons who come between himself and the doctor. Occasionally this underlying motivation is revealed by the gift being something of doubtful desirability, such as slightly wilted flowers or fruit verging on overripeness.

Paradoxically enough, destruction of a substitute object is another form of attempted mastery of separation anxiety. The object destroyed may be an article of personal clothing or any item which is at hand and breakable. Certain patients seem compelled to break or destroy something just after being separated from a needed person. In addition to its meaning as an expression of rage, this behavior seems to contain the urge to assert some form of mastery over something in the environment as if to counterbalance a sense of being the helpless prey of environmental forces; in other words, it is another variant of the theme of attempted reversal of passive victimization into active mastery. A further possible meaning is the destruction in effigy of the hated deserter.

Patients may follow a fixed pattern of alternately acquiring and discarding substitute objects. One chronically ill woman repeatedly purchased new pairs of shoes, only to discard them within a day or two. The shoes seemed to serve as substitute objects which temporarily assuaged her separation anxiety, only to have guilt arise over her intense clinging possessiveness as well as probable fear that the object would become bad. It is likely that this fear was increased by the shoes, having also assumed phallic significance. Her contradictory behavior toward the shoes was paralleled by alternating approach and avoidance in her few tenuous actual object relationships.

Another deeply disturbed woman, prey to severe separation anxiety, dramatically illustrated the pattern of need-fear and passivity-activity alternation in relation to a stuffed toy animal, which was a combination of magic helper, constant object, and projected narcissistic self. Throughout most of a therapy hour she clung to this toy as she lay huddled on her bed shivering with fear. Suddenly, in an apparent surge of striving for active independence, she flung the toy across the room. Almost immediately she was seized with remorse and fear at this bold act of independence. She then swung to the opposite extreme of passive helplessness, and pleaded with her therapist to return the toy to her. She indicated that she herself felt utterly incapable of retrieving this most important substitute object. In this dramatic sequence we see a vivid illustration of inability to achieve a mid-ground between active, assertive independence and passive helplessness.

Later, while living outside the hospital and being visited by her mother, the same patient in a fit of upset enacted the same sequence with more obvious aggression in her declaration of independence from the substitute object. This time she literally tore the toy to shreds. She was abruptly dismayed by what she had done and begged her mother to restore the toy by sewing the fragments together. The fact that her mother stayed up much of the night to fill this importunate request indicated the intensity of the symbiotic mother-daughter entanglement, which the dependent-independent struggle with the toy no doubt symbolized.

Still another example of inconstancy of a substitute object was provided by a woman whose therapist had sent her a post card picturing the mountain cabin where he was vacationing. Upon his return the patient reported as follows:

At first your card gave me great comfort. I even took it to bed with me and felt literally warmed by it. After a while, though, it occurred to me that in sending a picture of a lonely mountain scene you only intended to mirror and to mock my acute loneliness. Next I thought that you actually had been in New York City. That made me furious, and I tore up the card.

We shall conclude this section by reporting a most touching and explicit comment on separation anxiety. A young woman, severely traumatized by the death of her mother, was assigned a substitute therapist during the vacation of her regular therapist. The substitute therapist, in turn, was due to depart on vacation. The patient sent him a card through the hospital mail with the caption, "Would have bought you a going-away present but the store was closed." Also on the card was a picture of the only available going-away gift, a pathetic bedraggled girl to whose blouse was attached a baggage tag inscribed with the single word, "Me."

Psychotherapeutic Technique and Separation Anxiety

Separation anxiety, like other psychological problems, should be treated in psychotherapy as an element in a total personality configuration rather than as a separate entity. Nonetheless, it merits at least brief discussion as a specific and often crucial factor in the psychotherapy of schizophrenic patients.

A major goal, especially in the early stage of psychotherapy, is to build a relationship in which the patient comes to trust the doctor as a reliable object. In this context object constancy will replace inconstancy, and the patient will be able to span intervals between actual contacts with his needed objects without being so vulnerable to separation anxiety. Accordingly, whatever facilitates object constancy will assist in overcoming vulnerability to separation anxiety. The patient will achieve full object constancy only as he becomes able to integrate deeply conflicting feelings toward his objects. Progress toward this ultimate goal can be facilitated by the doctor's skillful handling of various phases of his relationship with the patient.

In early phases of the doctor-patient relationship consistency in the formal arrangements for psychotherapy is likely to be important. A definite schedule of regular contacts is no small factor. The therapist may attempt to promote regularity and eventual constancy by scheduling the therapy sessions at the same time each day, meeting in the same place, keeping furniture arrangement the same, and giving the same initial greeting to the patient. At the end of each session he may make a special point of confirming the time and place of their next meeting. With some patients in early stages of building a relationship, several brief meetings a day every day of the week may more effectively promote constancy than less frequent contacts. For such a patient it is a major milestone when he truly recognizes his doctor as the same person with whom he shared the immediately preceding therapy session.

At somewhat later stages of therapy a therapist may attempt, in a sense, to inoculate the patient against separation anxiety by repeated brief separations followed by reunion during the course of a given therapy session. In absenting himself from the room he tells the patient he will return in a few minutes. It has been found that in selected cases this technique of separations and reunion in miniature appears to serve as a useful model for building confidence in the reliability and predictability of the therapist's behavior on a larger scale.

The therapist's own behavior also constitutes an important model for the patient, who will introject qualities of solid reliability as he perceives them in the doctor. A calm, firm, and assured manner is important in this regard. Obviously this must be genuine, not pretended. False assurance makes for an unreliable model, as do glib reassurances and advice offered the patient. The model function of the therapist who demonstrates how he handles conflicts, uncertainties, and troublesome affects has been emphasized by various authors, including Hoedemaker (1955, 1958) and Szasz (1957b).

The therapist's model function is salient in his manner of handling major separation from the patient. In general, a matter-of-fact calm trust in the patient's internal resources is in order, in contrast to an attitude which conveys an uncomfortable, guilt-tinged, fearful concern that the patient may be adversely affected by the separation.

The therapist may vary his manner of announcing an impeding separation according to the particular patient. To a patient who is in a stage of vigorously denying the therapist's importance to him it may be best to say something like, "I don't suppose it is of any special concern to you, but I am going to be away for two weeks starting next Tuesday." In most instances it is well to give some advance notice of a forthcoming separation. Of course, a clear, definite statement of the date that the therapist expects to return is in order.

Many therapists make a point of communicating with their patients by note or post card during absences of more than a few days. Some deliberately provide the patient with some type of substitute object, such as a book, during their absences.

Whether or not to arrange for a substitute therapist during the regular doctor's absence is debatable. It usually is helpful to give the patient a simple reminder that others will be available in the event that he feels a need to talk with them. The explicit provision of a replacement therapist is too likely to connote to the patient that he is expected to be greatly upset by the separation. This creates the risk of his either fulfilling the expectation or of his recoiling with protest, withdrawal, and denial that he has any significant relationship with the doctor.

This is not to underestimate the importance of the availability of multiple sources of support to the patient in his struggle against separation anxiety. Especially in early stages of treatment he may experience multiple sources as distinctly safer than one, not entirely certain, source. Support from multiple objects and the overall milieu is, of course, part of what an active treatment hospital is designed to provide. It is part of the rationale of treatment approaches which provide the patient with multiple therapists or with an administrative physician as well as a therapist.[4]

Multiple objects, on the other hand, may be used defensively by the patient to diffuse and split his ambivalent feelings. Splitting may afford him temporary relief and pseudoconstancy, but genuine constancy can be achieved only when he succeeds in containing rather than diffusing, and in integrating rather than splitting his divided feelings toward his doctor.

To achieve integration the patient must experience, clarify, and pull together the full range of his feelings toward the doctor, including the extremes of need and fear. Usually many layers of denial of the therapist's significance must be overcome first. In the course of repeatedly testing the therapist's reliability, the patient must work through

---

[4] These and similar issues are further discussed in Chapter XV, Strategies of Clinical Administration and the Need-Fear Dilemma.

waves of intense rage at what he considers the doctor's unreliability. Hopefully, he will discover that his rage neither destroys the doctor nor causes the latter to retaliate with rage or withdrawal of needed support. As this occurs, the patient will have less need to repress and split off his fearful anger. Similarly, discovery that his intense needs are tolerable to both himself and the doctor will facilitate integration and object constancy.

A further concomitant of object constancy, and perhaps the most important guarantee against separation anxiety, is a solid capacity for autonomy. This develops as the therapist assists the patient to overcome his fears of active self-regulation and to gain confidence in his capacities to think, decide, and act upon his own initiative. Growing confidence in the reliability of his internal structures will relieve his need-fear of external influence and regulation. To the degree that these goals are achieved, separation anxiety will cease to be a problem for the patient.

BIBLIOGRAPHY

Angyal, A. (1958), *Foundations for a Science of Personality*. Cambridge: Harvard University Press.

Benjamin, J. D. (1963), Further Comments on Some Developmental Aspects of Anxiety. Presented before a joint meeting of the Washington Psychiatric Society and the Washington Psychoanalytic Society.

Black, J. S. (1925), *Paper Doll*. Copyright by Edward B. Marks Music Corporation, New York. Used by permission.

Bowlby, J. (1960), Separation Anxiety. *Internat. J. Psycho-Anal., 41*:89-113.

Fenichel, O. (1945), *The Psychoanalytic Theory of Neurosis*. New York: Norton.

Freud, S. (1920), Beyond the Pleasure Principle. *Standard Edition, 18*. London: Hogarth Press, 1955.

Hartmann, H. (1953), Contribution to the Metapsychology of Schizophrenia. *The Psychoanalytic Study of the Child, 8*:177-198. New York: International Universities Press.

Hoedemaker, E. D. (1955), The Therapeutic Process in the Treatment of Schizophrenia. *J. Amer. Psychiat. Assn., 3*:89-109.

———— (1958), Preanalytic Preparation for the Therapeutic Process in Schizophrenia. *Psychiat., 21*:285-291.

Piaget, J. (1954), *The Construction of Reality in the Child*. New York: Basic Books.

Pious, W. L. (1949), Pathogenic Process in Schizophrenia. *Bull. Menninger Clin., 13*:152-159.

———— (1961), A Hypothesis About the Nature of Schizophrenic Behavior. In: *Psychotherapy of the Psychoses*, ed. A. Burton. New York: Basic Books.

Searles, H. (1960), *The Nonhuman Environment in Normal Development and in Schizophrenia*. New York: International Universities Press.

Spitz, R. A. (1950), Anxiety in Infancy: A Study of Its Manifestations in the First Year of Life. *Internat. J. Psycho-Anal., 31*:138-143.

Suttie, I. D. (1952), *The Origins of Love and Hate*. New York: Julian Press.

Szasz, T. (1957a), The Psychology of Bodily Feelings in Schizophrenia. *Psychosom. Med., 19*:11-16.

———— (1957b), A Contribution to the Psychology of Schizophrenia. *A.M.A. Arch. Neurol. and Psychiat., 77*:420-436.

Werner, H. (1957), *Comparative Psychology of Mental Development*. New York: International Universities Press.

Winnicott, D. W. (1953), Transitional Objects and Transitional Phenomena: A Study of the First Not-me Possession. *Internat. J. Psycho-Anal., 34*:89-97.

XIII

TIME IN PERSONALITY AND SOCIAL STRUCTURE: AN ASPECT OF THE HOSPITAL CAREERS OF SCHIZOPHRENIC PATIENTS

Donald L. Burnham

WE HAVE EMPHASIZED that the personality structure of the potentially schizophrenic person is vulnerable to disorganization as a result of faulty differentiation and integration. Accordingly he is inordinately dependent upon and susceptible to the influence of external structure, whether within particular object relationships or within broader social contexts. In studying the hospital careers of schizophrenic patients our principal concern is to determine how the hospital social structure may affect the personality structure of the individual patient, whether favorably or adversely. Common to both of these structures is the element or dimension of time. It is not only an index of organization-disorganization, but a powerful organizing factor as well. In this chapter we shall discuss time organization first in personality structure, then in social structure, and finally in the interplay between individual and social structure within the mental hospital.

TIME AND PERSONALITY STRUCTURE

Time and timing are important in the processes of differentiation and integration. They are important in each of the previously described major aspects of differentiation: (1) clear, stable self-other separation; (2) specialized, discrete adaptive skills and internal resources which make possible the transition from heteronomy to autonomy; and (3) a differentiated reality and object world construct.

Separateness and Time

Crucial in the development of self-other separateness as well as the ability to tolerate separation are repeated sequences in which the significant object is alternately present and absent. The nature of the synchronization of child's needs and mother's ministrations is a major determinant of the child's capacity to endure delay and frustrating time intervals between satisfactions. This involves, of course, his general capacity to tolerate frustration and separation from comforting and gratifying objects. On these capacities, in turn, rests his ability to make the transition from passive, dependent heteronomy to active, independent autonomy. His success or failure in making this transition will be reflected partly in his attitude toward time, particularly in his attitude toward time intervals between satisfying object contacts. The poorly differentiated person lacks inner resources with which to traverse confidently, easily, and pleasurably the time gaps between object contacts. Accordingly, he fears separations and any expanse of free or empty time (Balint, 1959). To defend against this fear he clings to and tries to fuse with objects in an attempt to keep his time as full as possible.

The urge for continuous contact and availability of supplies also is apparent in myths in which unchanging time, eternal youth, and inexhaustible food are equivalent. Myths featuring the disappearance and reappearance of the moon also contain assuagement of anxiety over separation and loss (Bergler and Roheim, 1946). The need-fear dilemma and fundamental ambivalence toward time and suppliers are further reflected in the mythical personification of time as both a bountiful supplier and a relentless destroyer.

Autonomy and Time

Autonomous functioning based upon differentiated inner resources is variously associated with the organization of behavior in time. An important correlate of autonomy is the ability to direct and aim behavior toward future goals. Purposiveness and intentionality involve abilities for planning, foresight, and active choice of a course of action. This is in contrast to behavior more tied to the immediate moment and to the direct peremptory discharge of impulses. The ability to delay and to aim behavior has even been referred to as the capacity to bind time.

The poorly differentiated person is unable effectively to bind time. At its extremes this inability is manifest either as zig-zagging impulsiveness, distractibility, and stimulus slavery, or as paralyzed inactivity and unresponsiveness to stimuli. Active purposiveness, in contrast to passive helplessness, assists a person in unifying his experience over time (Sturt, 1925). In general, activity tends to correlate positively with strong internal structure whereas passivity is related to structural weakness, although probably what is most desirable is a flexible capacity to employ both active and passive modes of adaptation.

The person who lacks autonomous control and active purposiveness is likely to fear the future and whatever uncertain, unpredictable, and unfamiliar situations it may bring. Concomitantly he fears loss of his precarious sense of personal control.

Reality Constructs and Time

Time is a major coordinate of the reality constructs which a person forms as he organizes his experiences into patterns of meaning. It is significant that the analogy of a flowing stream is employed to refer to both consciousness and time. In the development of the ability to form reality constructs in place of a chaotic flux of events, temporal sequences and basic rhythms are important. Consider, for instance, such sequences as rest-activity, hunger-satiety, sleep-wakefulness, light-darkness, and the presence-absence of significant objects. In learning that certain events follow other events the infant develops the ability to recall those in the past and to anticipate future ones.

With these emergent abilities he begins to form schemata for perception, cognition, and memory, according to which he selects, focuses, and otherwise gives form to his experience. Important in this process is his ordering of mental events into temporal sequences. Furthermore, his consideration of the simultaneity, sequence, and duration of events contributes heavily to his attribution of cause and effect in his structuring of reality.

The adequacy of a reality construct may be judged in terms of its coherence, continuity, and constancy; each of these interrelated qualities is associated with time-ordering of experience.

The qualities of coherence, continuity, and constancy are especially relevant to a person's object world construct. They are implicit in the ability to recognize one's self or another person from one time to the next. Without this ability one's experience of objects, including one's self as an object, is disconnected, discontinuous and inconstant.

A person's sense of identity rests upon the coherence, continuity, and constancy of his experience of himself. A strong sense of identity requires the ability to pull together into a coherent whole one's conceptions of past, present, and future selves. A coherent organization of memory contributes heavily to a person's sense of individuality. As Meyerhoff (1960) wrote, "I know who I am by virtue of the records and relations constituting the memory which I call my own, and which differs from the memory structure of others."

The coherence of one's experience of others is equally important. It is the basis for object constancy and the ability to recognize others after intervals of separation from them, as well as to call up a stable mental representation of them in their absence. These abilities are importantly related to a sense of basic trust in the reliability of objects.

Time is not only a backdrop for placement of objects in a reality construct, but may itself constitute a point of anchorage and orientation in reality. Frequently when a person awakens from sleep, anesthesia, or intoxication, his first orienting move is to ask, "What time is it?" For some years, the American Federation for the Blind provided watches with raised hands and numerals to blinded war veterans. It had been discovered that being able to tell time enormously facilitated their adjustment to a sightless existence (Brooks, 1956).

An important index of reorganization from psychotic disintegration is improvement in the patient's ability not only to orient himself in time but to connect successive moments and days into a coherent, continuous structure. This is correlated with his gaining a greater degree of object constancy, so that he truly recognizes persons rather than experiencing a series of kaleidoscopically disconnected percepts. Greater continuity and ability to bind time also may be manifest in his capacity to sustain a conversation, whereas previously he perhaps could not hold in focus even a single question long enough to respond to it.

Several other evidences of the importance of time as a mode of reality anchorage can be cited. For example, the tenuously organized person may attempt to maintain a sense of control of himself and his surroundings by compulsive timekeeping. He desperately fears losing track of time. For him this would be tantamount to losing himself, his mind, his body parts, and vital object relationships. One patient who sought to avert disorganization by obsessive timekeeping said, "I must never forget myself for a single moment. I watch the clock and keep busy or else I won't know who I am" (Dooley, 1941). Here we see timekeeping functioning as a means of clinging to an aspect of external structure.

Another patient's imminent psychotic break with reality was heralded by a dream that his watch had stopped (Sharpe, quoted in Yates, 1935). Disordered experiencing of time as inordinately slow or fast or as leaping discontinuously is likely to be associated with faulty reality structuring. This may be coupled with omnipotent fantasies of ability to stop, speed up, or control time as well as to manipulate other aspects of reality. These fantasies are a desperate defense against experiencing time and reality as unpredictable and utterly beyond one's control (Scott, 1947).

SOCIAL STRUCTURE AND TIME

Time is a major factor in social organization. It is both an index and a means of integration, coordination, and articulation of persons with each other, from the primal mother-child relationship to the most complex of social networks. Psychosocial development requires the child's learning to order his behavior in time so that it will articulate with the behavior of others. Early synchronization of the infant's needs with the mother's ministrations is the basis for later coordination of social interaction in time. Successful synchronization is important in the development of object constancy and generally reliable object world constructs. Put more concretely, repeated well-synchronized interactions with another person lead to reliable anticipations regarding that person. Failing this, the result is object inconstancy and a host of problems in the time-structuring of behavior. These include difficulty in tolerating intervals of delay, frustration, or separation, along with feelings that satisfactions come too late or are insufficient when they do come.

The development of role-taking skills is importantly related to time-structuring. Role expectations usually specify time schedules for the performance of prescribed actions. Promptness-dilatoriness is a major dimension of role performance and reflects the nature of early child-parent relationships. Conscientious role performance is likely to correlate with punctuality, a strong sense of duty, and a striving to adhere to strict parental standards. Conversely, flouting of role expectations is linked to tardiness and defiance of parents and their surrogates.

The degree to which a person's social roles contain a demand for precise timing of behavior is one measure of the quality of his articulation with the social structure. Emphasis on punctuality varies with how directly and immediately others depend upon his properly executing his role. Contrast, for instance, the precision of behavioral timing demanded in the role of an airport control tower operator with that in the role of a Bowery drifter.

Social disarticulation or desocialization frequently is designated in terms of behavioral timing. The poorly socialized person is said to be "off beat" or "out of step." This is especially likely to occur at times of role transition. Teenagers and elderly persons, for instance, are susceptible to being judged, and judging others, as "out of step" with the times and with society at large.

Lack of a satisfactory role fit may also be manifest in a person's attitudes toward time. The social "outsider" is likely to rebel against his society's attitudes, such as the attitude of our culture that time is a commodity or equivalent to money. The "outsider" may scorn and flout the high societal valuation of punctuality and strict adherence to planned social commitments. He may pursue a course of living-for-the-moment in opposition to the maxim that he should plan for the future. Or he may show restless impatience for change and newness while opposing efforts to conserve the past.

Active rebellion against the time structure of society is, however, by no means as pernicious an index of social disarticulation as passive indifference to time and to coordinating one's behavior with that of others. When, out of fear or despair, a person has retreated from or failed to venture into social interaction, he lacks a major motivation for a time-organized reality structure. In other words, if he has come

to feel that he and others matter little to each other, time likewise
matters little to him. Loss of time structure and perspective makes successful interaction with others even less likely. Such a vicious spiral
is a characteristic predicament for the schizophrenic person whose
desocialization has led to his hospitalization. This prompts our concern with the effect of the time structure of the mental hospital as it
relates to this predicament.

Disturbances of Time Structure in the Mental Hospital

Transition to the role of hospital patient is, in some ways, more
likely to compound than to alleviate the schizophrenic person's difficulties in organizing himself in time. There are several reasons for
this. One is that the traditional hospital purpose of providing sanctuary
and moratorium (or "time out") from the outside world, though helpful in many respects, may have detrimental effects. The hospital is
designed to insulate the patient from burdensome, confusing social
demands and commitments; the role of patient is defined accordingly,
including exemption from usual demands that his behavior be timed
to coordinate with that of others. However, he may be provided with
too much exemption, as a result of which insulation may turn into
isolation. This danger is drastic if the functioning of the hospital requires little or no active contribution from the patient and he is assigned an almost exclusively passive role. Consequently, the patient is
left with virtually nothing which he *must* do tomorrow, or the next day,
or the next; it matters little whether he gets up or stays in bed. Clearly,
such role structuring is likely to erode rather than sustain the patient's
time perspective and total personality organization.

Further blurring of time structure may result from a relative lack
of conventional time markers in the mental hospital. Of course, certain fundamental rhythms such as day-night and the sequence of
seasons are nearly inescapable. However, other markers are not so
readily available. Hospital procedure may deprive patients of watches,
along with other personal possessions. Patients may lack ready access
to clocks, newspapers, periodicals, and radios. Time-marking events
such as holidays and birthdays often pass unobserved. Mail and visits
from friends or relatives are sporadic or totally missing. Those time
markers which are available, such as meals, doctors' rounds, and

changes of nursing shifts, tend to be geared more to staff than to patient organization. In not affording the patient sufficient distinction of one day from another, time structure may be insidiously undermined.

Similar effects have been observed in other situations of social isolation, such as TB sanatoria, prison camps, and polar expeditions. Here unvarying days replicate each other in monotonous succession, which brings about a general atmosphere of timelessness. Thomas Mann's *Magic Mountain* (1927) classically depicts this. Descriptions of brainwashing and concentration-camp experiences also attest to the disorganizing effect of being deprived of time markers and normal social interaction (Bettelheim, 1960). Moreover, prisoners, shipwreck victims, and lost explorers have reported that keeping track of time assisted them in maintaining their personality organization.

Within the mental hospital, some patients, of course, suffer grossly impaired ability to orient themselves in time and place. Significantly, they frequently attempt to reorganize themselves by repeatedly asking others for the time and date, sometimes within a span of minutes. An excellent fictional account of some of the distortions of time perception to which a patient may be prey is contained in *One Flew Over the Cuckoo's Nest* (Kesey, 1962).

All patients, regardless of their degrees of illness or confusion, share certain major preoccupations involving time passage and time perspective. They are concerned with how their personal destinies will be affected by entry into the role and career of patient. Assumption of the patient role means an indeterminate separation from other roles in family and society at large. The patient is beset by fear and uncertainty as to whether he can regain these roles and whether temporary separation will stretch into permanent loss. In various forms he asks or tries to avoid asking himself the fearsome questions of how long he will be a patient and what will become of his present predicament.

The better organized patient may seek answers by asking staff members directly how long he will be in the hospital, or by trying to ascertain the average patient career timetable. Frequently one of the first questions asked by a new patient is, "How long do people usually stay here?" The lack of definite answers is not likely to reassure him as to his personal future. Much patient-staff interaction may take the form of bargaining over the timetable of progress toward discharge. Markers of progress such as privilege status become major points of issue in the bargaining process.

In attempting to master uncertainty of future events the patient may devote much effort to structuring time. As noted by Roth (1963), "One way to structure uncertainty is to structure the time period through which uncertain events occur." This may involve constructing schedules, timetables, and time limits, devices also common in everyday life outside the hospital. A person is aided in tolerating uncertainty, anxiety and discomfort if he anticipates a definite end to these unpleasant states. Similarly, anticipation of a future vacation break or event of special pleasure helps to endure present discomfort and difficulty. A study of penitentiary prisoners revealed that fantasies of escape, though not necessarily accompanied by actual escape plans, tended to improve the morale of prisoners, assisting them to do "easier time" and to make a more effective adaptation to the social system of the prison (Farber, 1944). Still another technique of mastering uncertainty is to split up blocks of time, thus making long indefinite stretches of time psychologically more manageable. This may entail obsessively keeping track of small time intervals.

These techniques of active mastery are unavailable to the patient who is less well organized. He may be unable even to formulate for himself questions about his personal future, let alone ask and bargain with others about them. Nonetheless, his concern with these problems is likely to be otherwise manifest in his behavior. This may be observed in reactions of urgent activity, passive despair, and denial, each of which is significantly related to problems of time-structuring.

In the reaction of urgent activity the patient seems desperately driven to accomplish simultaneously many tasks of heroic magnitude. The desperate urgency is tied to a belief that by his actions he must somehow hold together both himself and the world. He feels that if his imperative message or plan of reorganization does not reach the world immediately, a global catastrophe will ensue. To the person driven by these beliefs the meaning of deadlines is literal in the extreme. He may spend all day and far into the night working in a fashion incomprehensible to others but imperative to himself in order to prevent engulfment by death and destruction. One patient ceaselessly busied herself studying and writing on the subject of unbalancing of the brain presumably caused by gravitation. When asked by a physician visitor to the hospital, "Are you a patient, or do you work here?" she burst into tears, a rare loss of control for her, and replied, "You have no idea how desperately hard I work!" If, as is usually the case, the definition of the tasks deemed so essential and urgent is clouded by ambivalence and conflict, the dreadful urgency is all the more ominous. For such patients, time is precious and not a moment is to be lost.

At the other extreme in reacting to uncertainty of his personal future is the patient who appears to have lost all sense of urgency and to have sunk into an abyss of despair. For him time is oppressively heavy; the future is devoid of all hopes, aspirations, or goals; each day is an eternity; the only thing time can bring is a crushing burden of further misery. Death may beckon as his only release, his only way out. In despair, activity is supplanted by all-pervasive passivity. There is no sense of self-initiated movement through time, only a sense of drifting aimlessly and resignedly.

The patient may resort to various defenses against being overwhelmed by uncertainty, passive helplessness, and despair concerning his personal future. Most common of these is denial in one form or another.

One is the denial of the reality of his current situation. He may insist that he is not in a hospital, not ill, and certainly not a patient.

Another line of denial consists of recourse to unrealistic active mastery attempts, many of which entail verbal magic designed to provide a *sense* of mastery over present and future events. For instance, Dan, the subject of Chapter VII, immediately and challengingly on entering the hospital announced that he would be leaving in less than six months. Subsequently he made frequent announcements of one or another deadline for his departure. Such a prediction to the Third Floor staff often followed a therapy session in which he had more openly than usual revealed fears and doubts about his future. Although his announced departure dates were unrealistic and unconfirmed by hospital staff, they nonetheless seemed to afford him sufficient temporary relief from fear of permanent entrapment to facilitate his organizing himself more effectively in general.

On occasion, however, his defenses weakened and he was abruptly engulfed by feelings of inadequacy over what he considered a cowardly failure to live up to his progress timetable. On the approach of one Halloween he said to an activities worker, "So you're having a Halloween party. You know, this is my third Halloween here. I guess I'll come to the party wearing a black coat with a yellow stripe painted down the back."

Glen, the patient described in Chapter VI, attempted even more unrealistic magical verbal mastery over the future. He gained a measure of relief from his fear of unexpected personal catastrophe by predicting dire happenings to *others* at precisely designed future times. The predicted victims usually were persons who in actuality held some power over Glen's future. His predictions simply reversed the positions of victim and master. For instance, he would predict that at exactly 12:32 a.m. on March 25, Dr. Gibson, his administrative physician, would be hanged. After a judge had denied him a writ of habeas corpus, Glen predicted that the judge would be arrested and sentenced to jail on a particular date. Repeatedly he made generalized prophecies of doom; for instance, that on midnight of a particular day lightning would strike the local court house. Clearly, many of Glen's predictions were designed to deny his dread of sudden loss of control of poorly integrated impulses to violence. Just as clearly, the relief afforded by his prophecies was spurious, tenuous, fleeting, and liable to abrupt collapse.

Still another frequently observed form of defensive denial is a drifting into obliviousness to the passage of time, thereby abandoning the effort to maintain time perspective. Awareness of the passage of time may be pleasant or painful according to a person's past experiences and future outlook. If his past contains a preponderance of failure, his awareness of time passing will be linked more to painful memories of separations and losses than to pleasant anticipations of future opportunities. This is especially true of the mental hospital patient; anything which reminds him of lost relationships and roles is acutely painful. Further pain results from his regarding time spent in the hospital as time lost. He can partly dull this pain by blunting his awareness of time passage.

A patient may show little awareness of the day or month, and perhaps even less of the year, a more damning marker of time lost forever. He may try to ignore or deny time-marking events, such as birthdays, holidays, or changes of seasons. Efforts by hospital staff to mark the event, for instance, by presenting him with a birthday cake may be met with blank indifference or a sudden outburst of rage.

Several examples of time passage denial will further illustrate this frequent defense. One was manifest by a middle-aged woman who had been hospitalized for several years, during which she had only rarely seen her husband and children. At a hospital Christmas party she stood apart from a group of carolers; suddenly she shouted, "You fools, wake up to reality! It's the middle of March, not Christmas!" Similarly, she denied all other reminders of her long and painful separation from her family. She once told her therapist, "I have never lived. I was born here. I need to be born again."

Another woman, who had been hospitalized for nearly 12 years, remarked, "I have been here nine years; we don't call it 10 years." She also employed the defense of presenting herself as a child, though in actuality her own children were nearing adulthood. She would say, "I've been naughty and should be punished; sometimes I feel only five years old." She also played a childlike role by appealing in various ways for advice, direction, and controls from others.

Another woman for several years maintained a double identity; she made extremely unrealistic efforts to look and act according to her preferred self, much younger than her actual self.

Denial of evidences of physical aging is frequent. Glen tried to overlook the fact that his hair was thinning and that he had lost several teeth. At the same time he dressed in inappropriately youthful clothing. Another patient was greatly disturbed by extraction of a tooth, because this loss rendered less possible her fantasied rebirth or rejuvenation. Still another patient, edentulous though only in his midforties, customarily denied time passage, but one day lamented, "It's all over. I can't win. False teeth and baldness lose." He was extremely distressed when reading glasses were prescribed for him. Once as he admired several student nurses, he said, "They are all so young." Then he quickly added, "I never look in the mirror; that way I don't realize how old I am." Shortly thereafter he noticed another patient riding a bicycle and commented, "There goes Smith on his bicycle, letting his childhood win," thus indicating that he feared childishness as well as aging.

This man further denied separation from his past by a form of *déjà vu;* he misperceived present persons as past friends, saying, "They have all of my past associates here." Another patient misperceived trees and animals on the hospital grounds as members of her family from whom she actually had been long separated. Still another patient, who had been hospitalized several years, mitigated her sense of separation by keeping her watch set at the time in the zone in which her distant home was located.

Shared Denial of Time Structure in the Mental Hospital

The defensive efforts of individual patients are not the only source of blurred time structure in the mental hospital. The entire hospital community—patients and staff—may join in a near-conspiracy to ignore time passage and to blur time perspective. Concrete indications of time passage, such as evidences of physical aging, are overlooked. Persons middle-aged or older are called boys and girls; patients are given diminutive nicknames. There is even pseudoscientific speculation that schizophrenia is associated with metabolic changes which cause patients to appear younger than their actual ages.

Values pertaining to patient career timetables may be reversed. Instead of the greatest credit going to persons who progress rapidly toward discharge from the hospital, prestige may be attached to lengthy stay. Long-stay patients may form almost an aristocracy which receives special favors from the staff and looks down upon new arrivals, be they patients or staff members. At a meeting of the whole hospital community a patient said, "Now, take patients like Joe Jones —he's a lifer here and deserves special consideration." Usually such an explicit and public comment upon a patient's career timetable is taboo.

The hospital community may develop a general atmosphere of "timelessness." This is a feature of what has been termed "hospitalitis." An aimless, meaningless attitude pervades. The ultimate goal of leaving the hospital is lost sight of. Victims of "hospitalitis" seem unconcerned about using time productively; they seem content to drift aimlessly or even to waste time deliberately. In some hospitals the perspective is one of unbroken and unmoving barrenness. In others comfortable physical surroundings may mitigate this impression, but the scene is essentially that of a drifting "never-never land" running on "daylight wasting time," with nothing achieving completion and nothing seeming really to matter. The phrase "a succession of drowsy Sunday afternoons" has been used by some observers. Others have referred to a quality of endless waiting.[1]

Some patients may effect a day-night reversal, spending the day in bed and arising only at night. It has been suggested that this may arise from a wish to avoid comparison with persons who are working during the day (Kubie, 1962). Day-night reversal may also be part of an attempt to assume the role of a rebel against society which in many ways is preferable to the role of patient, since it affords a partial, though spurious, sense of active choice as opposed to passive helplessness.

Hospitals in which psychotherapy is the principal mode of treatment may inadvertently contribute an added element of timelessness. At least in certain phases psychotherapy entails blurring the distinctions between a person's past, present, and future. Unconscious mental events, a focus of attention in psychotherapy, are traditionally described as timeless. There also is the dictum, not without some merit, that psychotherapy cannot be planned according to a definite schedule but should unfold spontaneously. Furthermore, the psychotherapist treating chronically psychotic patients needs nearly boundless patience, hope, and perseverance, each of which involves a quality of timelessness. He is ill-advised to look for quick results and must work on a long-range, open-ended timetable. These considerations, however, if applied too literally and extremely, erode rather than bolster time structure in the hospital.

STRENGTHENING TIME STRUCTURE IN THE MENTAL HOSPITAL

We begin our discussion of this topic by reiterating that time structure is more than an indicator of individual and social organization. Since it also contributes heavily to establishing and maintaining organization, it merits consideration as a potentially therapeutic element of the hospital milieu. We do not intend to suggest that strengthened time structure alone could bring about major personality reorganization. We do suggest, however, that it may *assist* reorganization of the schizo-

---

[1] Timelessness is but one feature of hospital life which may contribute to chronicity. Fortunately, the factors in hospital organization which foster chronicity are receiving increasing study (Cumming and Cumming, 1956; Brody and Fishman, 1960; Sommer, 1959; Sommer and Witney, 1961; Talbot, Miller and White, 1964).

phrenic person in view of his special sensitivity to influence by external structure, of which time is an important dimension. We turn now to consider specific ways of strengthening time structure.

Time Markers and Predictability

Obviously, it is important to provide conventional and readily accessible time markers, such as watches, clocks, and calendars. In addition, the hospital program should not only mark holidays but also provide ready means of clearly distinguishing one day of the week from another.

Anything the staff does which makes even minor events more predictable for the patient will contribute to relieving his uncertainty of the future and to strengthening both his time structure and general organization. The staff may foster predictability by giving the patient advance schedules, announcements, and descriptions of future events. Increased predictability, in turn, will bring a greater degree of personal control, continuity, and stability.

Scheduling of events may be carried so far as to organize a formal schedule for each patient. This is part of the rationale for variants of the "total push" technique (Myerson, 1939). Such treatment strategies require decisions as to the proportions of control and permissiveness desirable for patients at different stages of illness. These decisions cannot be made categorically. They involve the manner and tone with which the hospital staff attempts to promote the patient's constructive activity and organization of his time. The ultimate goal is not to impose rigid external regulation but to encourage self-regulation. Rather than issuing orders to the patient, it is important to provide him with incentives and opportunities for meaningful activity. We would further emphasize that it is not activity as such which strengthens organization but activity of specific types, particularly those which promote organization over time.

Patient Activity and Time Structure

Here we are concerned with activities which will facilitate continuity, coherence, and constancy of experience in place of fragmentation and inconstancy.

Shortness of attention span and difficulty in maintaining a major set typically handicap many schizophrenic patients. In psychotherapy the therapist may attempt to overcome these problems by speaking concisely and addressing himself to what the patient has just said or done. Especially with a patient whose stream of consciousness is fragmented the therapist cannot expect to communicate successfully by referring to something the patient said 10 minutes or sometimes even one minute before.

In considering further how to counteract the patient's discontinuity, it is important to encourage him toward activities which he has a reasonable chance of completing in a relatively short time. As an initial step, the opportunity to complete a task, no matter how small, has great value in overcoming a sense of incompleteness. At this stage activities should have a clear beginning and a clear ending. Later, activities which carry over from day to day and from week to week will assist continuity. At either stage it is of little help to engage a patient in an activity beyond his capacities; this would only add another failure to an already crushing accumulation of them.

Coherence in place of fragmentation may also be facilitated by staff efforts to reduce discontinuities of approach to the patient. This is not to say that staff responses to the patient should be absolutely standardized, even if this were possible; rather it is to recommend that a reasonable consistency of approach be established between one shift and the next, or one day and the next. Obviously this requires clear communication between staff members about patients. There are other ways in which good staff-staff communication will promote the patient's integration. For instance, a patient may during the day encounter an event so upsetting that he is unable to discuss it with anyone at the time. His only recourse is to isolate and repress rather than integrate the experience. However, if evening shift staff members are alerted by the day staff, they may be able to assist the patient to discuss and integrate the experience after his acute upset has subsided. Cumulative integration leads to continuity and coherence, whereas cumulative repression leads to fragmentation.

In attempting to facilitate object constancy in the patient's flow of experience, regularity and reliability are important. This applies to both psychotherapy and hospital activities in general. Some therapists schedule the patient's therapy hours at the same time each day, as well as keeping constant the place, the arrangement of furniture, the form of greeting the patient, and so forth. The purpose is to promote stability and reliability of the doctor-patient relationship, with the ultimate goal of constancy of the patient's definition of the doctor. With severely fragmented patients, either multiple contacts or prolonged single sessions in the course of a day, and even into the night, may assist the patient to greater continuity and constancy over time. The same applies to the patient's contacts with other staff members in various other activities.

Regularity, however, should not prevail to the point of utter monotony. Variety has its place too. In fact, as we indicated earlier, unrelieved sameness of experience from one day to the next is likely to erode rather than to strengthen time structure and overall organization. This is witnessed in the techniques of brainwashing which deliberately employ monotony in conjunction with isolation to deprive the victim of customary and necessary stimulus nutriment for his personality structure.

We shall continue our discussion of activity and time structure from the vantage point of the role opportunities available to the patient.

Patient Role and Time Structure

In a previous section we emphasized that time structure is an important index and means of articulating and coordinating the actions of individuals within social systems. Its importance varies according to how directly others depend upon the individual's role performance —in other words, the degree to which his actions in the role are positively valued and socially necessary. All too frequently, in the role of patient he is expected to be a handicapped, passive recipient of shelter and care, unable to assume responsibility for himself. This definition of the patient role subverts his organization of time and of himself.

Clearly the patient should have other or differently defined roles open to him (see Chapter XIV). Redefining patients' roles involves, among other things, the distinction between play and work. Play is an activity which a person doesn't have to do, which others do not depend upon having performed by a certain time, and which is not rewarded by pay; the obverse of these qualifications applies to work. Furthermore, work is an important element of an adult identity; even very young children are aware of it as a badge of adulthood. Accordingly, a hospital patient role which provides only play-type and socially unnecessary activities tends to disqualify the patient from adult social reality. The same applies to make-work as opposed to real work. In contrast, the patient who is expected to perform work which the hospital needs done by a specific time is thereby articulated to a time-structured social reality. To illustrate how personally significant this can be, we recall a patient who, in reorganizing himself out of a long period of disorganization and desocialization, wanted very much to find an active contributing role in the world. He remarked tellingly, "One of the best ways to keep track of time is by pay days—provided you have a job."

It also is important that roles available to the patient contain opportunities for self-determination at as many levels as possible. One level should encourage his participation in choosing and planning the activities composing his daily schedule. The act of planning itself facilitates time structuring and strengthened personal organization. Planning involves anticipating future events and preparing for them; it is closely linked with active autonomy as opposed to passive heteronomy.

Another level of self-determination is provided by opportunities for some voice in regulating the hospital organization. This need not, and in many respects cannot, be total patient government of the hospital; it should, however, at the very least, include seriously seeking the patient's opinion regarding possible decisions as well as informing him in advance about major changes. Participation in the processes of planning and decision-making will counteract his becoming a passively drifting nonentity, to whom events just happen unpredictably, unaccountably, and timelessly.

Progress Markers

These represent another aspect of hospital organization bearing directly upon the patient's structuring of himself in time. We previously discussed the fear and uncertainty regarding his personal future which beset each patient upon entering a mental hospital. To the degree that gross disorganization, blank despair, and massive denial do not interfere, he will seek to establish a career timetable for himself and find markers for gauging his progress on this timetable. Such markers may or may not be readily available, depending upon how the hospital is organized.

The patient may be hesitant about directly asking the question, "How am I doing?" Or he may ask those persons least equipped to provide him with a reliable answer, such as the least experienced aide on the ward. In asking, "When may I leave this place?" he frequently demands an unqualified answer which is impossible for any of the staff to provide. He is intolerant of any answer which begins, "It all depends." To him this is evasion, of which he has already had a surfeit. Furthermore, he may be able to approach this question only in the absolute terms of permanent incarceration versus immediate and total release. In addition, the question is loaded with such latent thoughts as, "Am I hopeless . . . has my family abandoned me completely . . . will I ever be wanted back in society at large . . . will I be put to death?"

As to how to provide progress markers which will relieve this indeterminate and extremely bifurcated view of the future, one thing is clear: the staff should be alert to the patient's need for explicit designation and recognition of progress. These can be accorded him within the system of determining privileges and responsibilities and should be as distinct as possible even when they represent only small increments of progress. The staff should also have in mind the probability that when the patient bargains over such matters as privilege status, he is at some level attempting to relieve uncertainty about progress and his personal future.

The need for clear progress markers is a strong argument for organizing separate sections of the hospital for patients of differing degrees of illness, so that a patient graduates from one to another as he improves. There are, however, objections to such a system. One is that it may be important for a patient to remain in the same section throughout his hospital stay in order to achieve greater continuity and constancy of his relationships. Another is that a graded ward system risks the danger that certain wards will become labeled as repositories for the incurable, such euphemisms as "continued treatment service" notwithstanding. It is conceivable that some patients might benefit most from one system and others from another or that a combination of the two would be most effective. In any event, the patient's need for explicit recognition of progress should not be overlooked or minimized. Such informal rites of passage as a party for a patient who is leaving the hospital may help. Communications or visits from former patients who have successfully returned to the outside world are sometimes surprisingly effective in enhancing time perspective and promoting more optimism among the patients who are still in the hospital.

SUMMARY

Time is an important dimension of both personality and social structure. It is not only an index of organization but a powerful organizing factor as well.

In individual personality, time organization plays a part in the various aspects of differentiation, including attainment of separateness, autonomy, and ability to form reliable reality constructs. This is reflected in the coherence and constancy of cognitive organization over time and in the ability to aim behavior toward future goals while delaying immediate action. It is further reflected in attitudes toward time, especially attitudes toward intervals between satisfying object contacts. Time also is an important mode of reality anchorage.

In social organization, time is both an index and a means of coordinating and integrating the activities of individuals. Weakened time structure and perspective is one measure of social disarticulation. This may be manifest as active rebellion or passive indifference toward conventional time organization.

Time is an important aspect of mental hospital organization as it affects the personality structure of the schizophrenic patient who is peculiarly dependent upon and vulnerable to the social structure of his surroundings. Certain features of hospital life such as a timeless atmosphere and exemption from active, contributing social role demands may erode rather than strengthen the patient's organization of himself in time.

Patients vary in their reactions to the problem of fearsome uncertainty of their personal futures. These reactions may include attempts to establish a patient career timetable, frantically urgent activity, passive despair, various forms of denial, and unrealistic efforts to assert mastery over future events. Denial of and obliviousness to the passage of time may result in a near-conspiracy by the whole hospital community to ignore many of the significances of time.

Possible means of strengthening time structure in the mental hospital are advanced. These include provisions of adequate time markers and attempts to render events more predictable for the patient and

326 SCHIZOPHRENIA AND THE NEED-FEAR DILEMMA

thereby more controllable by him. Patient activities should be structured so as to facilitate continuity, coherence, and constancy. Regularity, reliability, and reduction of discontinuities are important in this regard. Modifications in roles available to patients should provide opportunities for choice, planning, and as much self-determination as possible. Provision and alert use of progress markers are still another means of strengthening the patient's time structure and overall organization.

BIBLIOGRAPHY

Balint, E. (1959), Distance in Space and Time. In: *Thrills and Regression,* by M. Balint. New York: International Universities Press.

Bergler, E. & Roheim, G. (1946), Psychology of Time Perception. *Psychoanal. Quart., 15*:190-206.

Bettelheim, B. (1960), *The Informed Heart.* Glencoe, Ill.: Free Press.

Brody, E. & Fishman, M. (1960), Therapeutic Response and Length of Hospitalization of Psychiatrically Ill Veterans. *Arch. Gen. Psychiat., 2*:174-181.

Brooks, V. W. (1956), *Helen Keller: Sketch for a Portrait.* New York: Dutton.

Cumming, J. & Cumming, E. (1956), Affective Symbolism, Social Norms, and Mental Illness. *Psychiat., 19*:77-85.

Dooley, L. (1941), The Concept of Time in Defence of Ego Integrity. *Psychiat., 4*:13-24.

Farber, M. L. (1944), Suffering and Time Perspective of the Prisoner. In: *Authority and Frustration,* by Kurt Lewin, et al. University of Iowa Studies in Child Welfare, *20*:153-227.

Kesey, K. (1962), *One Flew Over the Cuckoo's Nest.* New York: Viking Press.

Kubie, L. S. (1962), personal communication.

Mann, T. (1927), *The Magic Mountain.* New York: Knopf.

Meyerhoff, H. (1960), *Time in Literature.* Berkeley: University of California Press.

Myerson, A. (1939), Theory and Principles of the "Total Push" Method in the Treatment of Chronic Schizophrenia. *Amer. J. Psychiat., 95*:1197-1204.

Roth, J. A. (1963), *Timetables.* Indianapolis: Bobbs-Merrill.

Scott, W. C. M. (1947), Some Psycho-dynamic Aspects of Disturbed Perception of Time. *Brit. J. Med. Psychol., 21*:111-120.

Sharpe, E. F., quoted in Yates, S. (1935), Some Aspects of Time Difficulties and Their Relation to Music. *Internat. J. Psycho-Anal., 16*:341-354.

Sommer, R. (1959), Patients Who Grow Old in a Mental Hospital. *Geriatrics, 14*:581-590.

——— & Witney, G. (1961), The Chain of Chronicity. *Amer. J. Psychiat., 118*:111-117.

Sturt, M. (1925), *The Psychology of Time.* New York: Harcourt, Brace.

Talbot, E.; Miller, S. C.; & White, R. B. (1964), Some Antitherapeutic Side Effects of Hospitalization and Psychotherapy. *Psychiat., 27*:170-176.

XIV

IDENTITY DEFINITION AND ROLE DEMAND IN THE HOSPITAL CAREERS OF SCHIZOPHRENIC PATIENTS

Donald L. Burnham

THIS CHAPTER,[1] like the preceding one, explores the effect of the hospital social structure upon the weak, easily disorganized personality structure of the schizophrenic patient. As we have emphasized, he is peculiarly dependent upon and susceptible to the influence of external structure. In this chapter we shall view this problem in terms of identity definition and role demand. These constitute a sector in which personality and social structures impinge crucially and may, or may not, mesh.

In Chapter VI we described how Glen began his career at Chestnut Lodge by presenting his professional card, engraved with his name and the words, "Concert Pianist and Horse Trainer." Although not all patients make such a clear and dramatic effort to define and assert their identities, identity definition is certain to be a central concern throughout their hospital careers. This task may be rendered more, or

[1] Much of the stimulus for this study arose from joint meetings between the authors and their colleagues, Drs. Stuart C. Miller, Eugene Talbot, and Robert B. White, whose hospital community studies at the Austen Riggs Center, Stockbridge, Massachusetts, have most usefully applied the role concept.

A slightly different version of this chapter has been published in *Psychiatry*, Supplement to No. 2, 24:96-122, 1961.

less difficult by the role demands exerted by the hospital social structure.

Before proceeding, let us briefly define our use of the terms *identity* and *role*. We use *identity*, in the sense most cogently developed by Erikson (1959), to refer to a person's organized and enduring conception of himself and his place in the social scheme of things. By *patient role* we refer to the place which *others*—in particular, the hospital staff—assign him, and the behavior and attitudes which they expect him to manifest by virtue of his status as a patient. Thus identity definition refers to the patient's side of the interaction, and role expectations and demands to the staff's side. We shall present the thesis that conflict between these two aspects of the interaction may drastically affect the patient's hospital course, and that serious lack of fit between the two may disrupt his total ego organization.

To describe how this identity definition-role demand conflict may arise, we shall discuss each side in turn. Identity definition is a lifetime task for everyone and progresses through various phases and developmental crises. The clarity and stability of a person's identity is an index of the stability of his total personality organization and the nature of his adaptedness to his environment. If he has severe id-ego-superego conflicts, his identity will be correspondingly unclear and unstable. Likewise, if he has failed to establish a satisfactory fit between himself and his environment, his identity will be precarious. The usual candidate for the role of mental hospital patient is in precisely this predicament. He lacks a clear, stable answer to the question, "Who am I?" Furthermore, his conception of self is usually incongruent with his conception of what others expect him to be.

Already uncertain as to who he is, hospitalization confronts him with a new crisis. Now he must formulate answers to the questions, "Who am I in *this* situation?" and "What is expected of me *here?*" He is likely to approach these questions with a mixture of fear, disappointment, discouragement, and faint flickerings of hope. He may be prepared to sink into abject submission, to fight bitterly, or to remain aloofly detached. He may anticipate help or he may dread imprisonment, subjugation, and destruction. Previous experiences with doctors and hospitals may prompt a compound of trust and mistrust, of magical hopes and deep pessimism. He also brings to the situation a blend of incapacities and capacities, with intact islands of good or superior function amidst disabled functions. He will manifest an uneven array of problems and a variety of individualistic attempted solutions.

Strongly coloring his self-definition in this new situation will be his preconception of what it means to be a patient in a mental hospital. Very probably he will picture himself as an outcast from society, removed from his previous roles as wage earner, student, and family member, and other significant places in the social structure. To a large extent he finds himself relegated to the role of full-time patient. The full-time, total quality of the patient role is strongly implied in the word *career*. Some hospital admission procedures strip him of his accustomed identity props, such as his wallet, articles of clothing, photographs of cherished persons, and other personal belongings (Goffman, 1957). He is in unfamiliar surroundings amid unfamiliar persons—a difficult situation at best, and a most formidable one for a person already uncertain as to who he is. His image of a mental hospital patient may be shadowed by the horrible specter of incurable insanity, and at the least will carry connotations of weakness, inferiority, failure, and worthlessness—the very traits which he desperately wishes not to feature his identity. This obviously does not render his task of defining who he is in the hospital situation any easier or pleasanter.

On the other hand, the staff's conception of the role of patient, which affects the role opportunities they offer him and the role expectations and demands they implicitly and explicitly exert upon him, may be shaped by three sets of factors: (1) the definition of the role of patient held by the society and culture at large; (2) the ideology and operating principles of the particular hospital; and (3) the attitudes and preconceptions of individual staff members.

In society at large the role of mental patient derives much of its definition from the general role of patient or ill person, which includes the following features: sickness, limitation of self-sufficiency, need for help, and exemption not only from responsibility for one's difficulties but also, temporarily, from many social responsibilities such as work (Parsons, 1951). The temporary exemption is for the duration of the illness and is expected to terminate with the end of the illness. This definition places the occupant of the role in a distinctly dependent, passive, recipient position. He is to be ministered to by others while temporarily excused from an active contributing role. The mental patient, even more than the general patient, also is expected to be extensively regulated and controlled by others.

In further shaping the role of patient, the therapeutic philosophy of the particular hospital often includes several areas of potential uncertainty and conflict such as the proportion in which the hospital should provide sanctuary or social demand (White, Miller and Polansky, 1955; Polansky, White and Miller, 1957; Talbot, Miller and White, 1960). When the total hospital community is used as a therapeutic agent, the goal is to afford both sanctuary from intolerable environmental pressures and social opportunities which will help the patient to gain strengths and abilities facilitating his return to extrahospital society. There should be sufficient opportunity for his exercise of intact areas of ego function so that disuse atrophy is avoided. He also needs opportunities to try out and consolidate new behavior patterns as well as to develop greater self-awareness. If the goal of sanctuary is dominant in a hospital's ideology, the patient role tends even more toward that of a handicapped, passive recipient of shelter and care. The goal of social opportunities and demands tends to produce a more active role with greater social responsibilities. We have deliberately drawn these images somewhat extremely in order to emphasize areas of potential conflict in the role demands which confront the patient.

Another area of potential uncertainty and conflict concerns the type and extent of controls to be exerted on the patient. Should he be relieved of social demands, or should his behavior be subject to controls and sanctions similar to those in general society? He needs opportunity for self-expression which stops short of chaotic impulse discharge, and, at the same time, social control which stops short of exacting rigid conformity. In pursuit of these goals there may be wide variations in the degree of self-control expected of the patient (White, Miller and Polansky, 1955).

Among the factors influencing staff conceptions of the patient role, nursing tradition and training contribute heavily. In the role of nurse, one cares for persons who are unable to care for themselves. In studies at Chestnut Lodge, confirmation of the strength of this tradition was provided by the charge nurse of Third Floor. When, as a guide to her staff, she wrote a summary of the case history and major problems of each patient, these summaries contained a strikingly conspicuous emphasis on the patient's *needs,* which the staff was to try to *fill.* Further confirmation was obtained from descriptions by staff members of several categories of persons, including patients, staff members, and outside friends. The descriptions of patients contrasted noticeably with those of other persons in an absence of adjectives denoting qualities of helpfulness and assistance to others. These findings suggest that the person in the role of patient was expected to receive help but not to give any (Burnham, 1959).

Still further clarification of the usual patient role was afforded by observations on a trip made by some of the staff and patients to a summer cottage (Gibson and George, 1959). There the distinctions between staff and patient roles were blurred, and patients were expected to contribute actively to the general comfort and daily tasks of the group. This contrasted sharply with the role of passive recipient of care which prevailed in the usual ward situation.

Thus, the composite staff conception of the patient role involves the expectation that he will manifest considerable helplessness, disability, and incapacity for self-regulation, and that he will need help from and regulation by others. This view carries connotations that the patient is different, inferior, and dependent, and at least partially lacks responsibility for himself.

There is likely to be disagreement regarding the extent of his exemption from responsibility, and the extent to which he is expected to contribute actively instead of being passively dependent. From one responsibility the patient is never exempt—the responsibility to try to help himself and to make his illness and his occupancy of the patient role temporary. This contradicts somewhat the predominant expectation of passivity, for the patient is expected to be passive but not too passive.

Another strong staff expectation is that the patient acknowledge that he is ill and needs treatment, and therefore should appreciate and cooperate with the staff's efforts to help him. In other words, he should accept the role of patient. This is doubly important to the staff members because the patient's acceptance of his role tends to confirm and strengthen their reciprocal roles as helpful persons, whereas his refusal weakens their staff roles. To quote the old adage, "Doctors need patients in order to be doctors." Loeb (1957) has written, "Socially, the patient gets along in the hospital just as long as he accepts this (very subordinate and dependent) role and does not complicate the already established confusion of how the staff get along with one another."

As further illustration of the possible conflict and lack of fit between what the patient tries to be and what the staff expects him to be, we shall present four case histories.

Case 1

Joe was 26 years old when admitted to Chestnut Lodge. In the previous year and a half he had been hospitalized several times because of disorganized behavior, threatened and actual violence toward his parents, and persecutory delusions. He had received treatment with electric shock, insulin, and chlorpromazine. His personal history contained much conflict and uncertainty regarding identity and social role. His immigrant parents were economically and socially ambitious, and held strong and conflicting career ambitions for Joe, their only child. Joe, himself, after failing to carry out successive urges to become a physician, a musician, an Army general, a businessman, and a man-about-town, suffered acute awareness of his inability to establish a satisfactory identity and career.

Initial efforts at identity definition: Of relevance to Joe's uncertainties of identity and role was the fact that he was brought to the Lodge by two deputy sheriffs rather than by hospital attendants. He himself had told his girl friend that he was going to another part of the country for a job rather than that he was going to a hospital. Upon admission, despite his history of severe illness, Joe seemed relatively nonpsychotic. His speech, although rather limited and stereotyped, was quite coherent. He stood rigidly and presented himself with an air of superiority, evoking such adjectives as arrogant, snotty, contemptuous, supercilious, and sarcastic. He contended that he was a person of unusual intelligence, perfect insight, and so far above the understanding of the average person that he didn't care whether others in this setting liked him or not.

Protests against the role of patient: Prominent in his presentation of himself was the repetitive protest that he was not sick and should not be a patient at the Lodge. He complained that he did not belong on a ward with such sick patients. As a matter of fact, at that time he *was* better organized than most of them, and at least one observer commented that Joe might become a leader among the patients. He asked repeatedly what procedures were required to obtain his release. From the outset he indicated that he would refuse to participate in any activities provided by the hospital program. The ward administrative physician observed in his admission note that Joe probably would have a difficult time at the Lodge because of his resistance to fitting into the program offered by the staff. A student nurse described Joe's refusal of her invitation to watch a TV program by saying, "He acted as if he were too good to watch TV. He says he's not sick and doesn't want to be around sick patients."

He also was keenly conscious of a role distinction between staff and patients, which he protested, saying, "I consider myself as healthy as anyone who works here." He questioned an aide regarding the legal technicalities of his hospitalization. When the aide said he didn't know about these matters, Joe replied scornfully, "What? And you are a psychiatric aide?" At times he attempted to impress the staff with his technical knowledge of psychiatry and psychology. Occasionally he challenged the staff to find anything wrong with him. He might say, "I feel perfectly well. If I thought I needed therapy, I should gladly seek it. Do you see anything wrong with me?"

Joe's refusals of the role of patient were neither completely constant nor fully successful. There were occasional breaks and contradictions in his major effort to establish the identity of well person. In talking to his therapist he occasionally switched from protesting his wellness to a direct statement that he regarded himself as very sick, and he once labeled himself as a paranoid. In one fleeting acknowledgment of sickness he said, "I know I need some kind of help but part of me resists it very strongly. I fear that if I enter into treatment, I may have another hysterical convulsion." By this he apparently referred to an earlier episode of feeling unable to control his hands, to walk, or to talk. He strongly feared losing control, even of functions ordinarily almost automatic.

Every now and then his challenges to the ward staff to prove he needed hospitalization shaded into a supplication, *"Please* tell me I am not crazy." In a fearful, imploring tone he asked about his psychological test results and wanted to know what observations had warranted his commitment. Once in rapid sequence he contradicted his assertion that he was completely well by saying that he belonged in a state hospital.

In another brief interval he dropped his protest against patienthood and told his therapist that he felt futile and discouraged by his inability to find an occupation. He described his failures to become a physician or a musician, and how his dream of becoming a "social charmer" was now ruined by his hospitalization. He added that his major problem was indecisiveness, especially an inability to make up his mind as to what he wanted to be. Each tentative choice was immediately followed by a wave of fear and uncertainty. He then appended a brief, somewhat vague reference to domination by his parents. Thus the centrality of problems of identity, role, and parental expectations was apparent in Joe's own thinking about himself. It should be emphasized that during his first month these were but fleeting breaks in his nearly continuous protests that he was not a patient.

Initial staff responses: Most of the staff responded to Joe's denials of the patient role by trying to convince him that he belonged in a hospital. His therapist's primary goal early in treatment was to persuade Joe that he needed help and should accept hospitalization and psychotherapy—in short, that he should accept the role of patient. The charge nurse said that the floor staff members were frustrated in their efforts to break through Joe's apparent front and were becoming quite angry at him.

In addition to these rebuffs to his effort to assert an identity other than that of patient, Joe suffered still another when his mother visited. He pleaded with her to secure his release. Only with great difficulty did she bring herself to definitely refuse him. Following this Joe told an aide, "All right, if she says I must stay, I'll stay, but I'll just exist."

Phase of running away: After the first two weeks Joe's protests took the form of attempts to run away and strenuous resistance to returning to the ward following any outside activity. His first effort to run away occurred when he was out for a walk with a student nurse and saw a group of other student nurses together with their dates leaving in cars. They waved and gave an apparently casual invitation to join them on a party. Thereupon Joe said, "I'd like to be free and having a ball. I'm not sick, I'm cutting out," and turned and ran. Once he said he wanted to fight in order to make people understand what he wanted to do. On another occasion he said he would get out in one of two ways—either by running away or by making everyone dislike him so much that he would be discharged.

His behavior did manage to fulfill part of this prophecy insofar as he became the object of considerable dislike. The staff's distaste was manifest in depersonalizing references to him as an "escorting problem" and "an escape risk."[2] Soon Joe became the major ward problem; at least one ward conference was held about him, at which the problem of his running away superseded all other interest in him. The staff percept of Joe as the ward management problem virtually obscured all other possible percepts of him. A variety of opinions was offered as to Joe's motives and purposes—that he was just plain nasty, teasing, game-playing, testing, or trying to get attention. The staff questioned whether Joe really intended to get away. His occasional expressions of puzzlement, uncertainty, and indecision were cited. Once he had stated that he didn't know what caused the impulse to run off, as if it were due to outside forces beyond his control. Opinion formed in the conference that Joe's indecisiveness and lack of autonomous self-control required that decisions be made for him. It was decided to provide a context of firm control and regulation by restricting him to the ward for several weeks. In one sense, this policy might be viewed as an attempt to force Joe into the role of patient whether he liked it or not.

Phase of withdrawal: Approximately concurrent with this policy decision,

2 It often has seemed to us that such references exemplify a dangerous tendency in hospital staff discussions. Similarly, in a general hospital one may hear references to the depersonalized "interesting case of agranulocytopenia in Bed 5," or to the "lung tumor in Room 10," or even to "Number 10."

several changes were noted in his overt behavior.[3] He became increasingly withdrawn and intermittently evidenced presumably autistic processes, such as standing alone in deep preoccupation, occasionally bursting into unaccountable laughter, and staring silently and intently at others, giving no sign of his purpose. In contrast to earlier descriptions of him as talkative, intelligent, and pleasant, he now was reported to be disinterested, silent, and depressed. In his therapy sessions he was nearly mute. He also shifted from predominantly verbal protests to frequent physical struggles with the ward staff.

During this period, which comprised Joe's second month at the Lodge, he evidenced some disorganized thinking and confusion. Once as he restlessly paced the hall he asked what day of the week it was. At times he stared with a blank frown of incomprehension. His efforts to gain freedom became more magical and less well organized. He insisted that undesignated authorities had given orders for his release several days previously. He became unclear in his definition of the roles of various staff members. For instance, he asked an assistant housekeeper to arrange for his release, whereas previously he had limited these requests to persons with clear authority roles such as the administrator and charge nurse. Concomitantly his definition of his own intentions became less clear. Once after returning on his own from a runaway effort, he repeated with incredulous puzzlement, "Why did I come back? Did I actually come back willingly?"

Phase of identity diffusion: The beginning of Joe's third month at the Lodge marked the dramatic disintegration and diffusion of his identity. He began calling himself by the names of other patients on the ward, answering when they were addressed, insisting that their pills were for him, and refusing to answer to the name of Joe. He moved some of his clothing into another room, as if to establish his possession of the room and the identity of the occupant. Similarly, he claimed that the possessions of the other patient were his and that others had been attempting to steal them. If other patients contested his claim to a new identity, he regarded them as usurpers. After repeated, unsuccessful efforts to move his clothing to another room, he began insisting that the clothing was not his.

Joe seemed to claim the identities of patients whom previously he had envied for various reasons—the title of professor, a famous family name, or athletic prowess—and whom earlier he had tried to befriend. Apparently his wish to partake of their admired qualities by association with them now became a magical effort to expropriate their identities in entirety.

This phase of identity diffusion predominated during the next two months. His assertions of a different identity came to be routinely expected by the staff. Nursing notes contained comments such as, "Usual business

[3] Actually, slight evidences of beginning withdrawal had been noted for several weeks, so that it would not be accurate to say his withdrawal followed the conference decision in strict sequence.

of 'I'm not Joe,' " or, "Same old thing—the clothes were not his. He was not Joe. He was Bill today." Such stereotyped percepts of Joe probably served to further depersonalize him (Searles, 1959).

Phase of greater disorganization: During this phase Joe paced the ward ceaselessly, and his talk and other actions became fragmented. His identity further diffused in increasingly magical and grandiose fashion. He referred to himself—he had actually been classified 4F in the draft—as a general, an admiral, or a high government official of one or another department, or as a big businessman, or leader of a criminal mob. He issued orders, insisted that his chauffeured limousine was waiting outside for him, and demanded to make phone calls to a host of prominent persons. He spoke of assembling a large expensive wardrobe for a trip to Europe and invited the charge nurse to accompany him to Paris. He suggested archly to several aides that if they strung along with him, he could lead them to millions of dollars worth of loot. At times he was concerned with taking care of "his boys," making sure that they were prepared for the "big deal" soon to be pulled off.[4] Other grandiose magical identities at which Joe grasped fleetingly were those of airplane pilot, inventor of nitroglycerine, lawyer, gigolo, famous educator, and FBI or secret-service agent. He demanded his files and security papers, spoke of appointments at the Pentagon, and threatened military reprisals if his orders were not carried out immediately.

Throughout this period of increasingly psychotic and frantic denials of reality, the themes of identity and role obviously were paramount concerns. Several nursing notes made explicit comments to this effect, such as, "He seems very preoccupied with a career and makes frequent references to wanting to get established in a career." During this period he resumed smoking, which he had not done since a few days after admission. Joe's protests that he was not a patient became even more magical and fantastic. He claimed that he was an exceedingly brilliant man who had already been released from the hospital, or that he was bound only by military law, not civil law.

Occasionally his grandiosity crumbled and he voiced the belief that he was in jail facing trial for murder.[5] He misperceived his therapist as an FBI agent whose purpose was to trap and convict him.

A few times he asserted that he was a psychiatrist, and in this capacity declared himself fully competent, mentally well, and ready to leave. This form of role reversal was noted by both his therapist and administrator. He told his therapist that he was a very busy man who could grant only a few minutes. On other occasions he attempted to cast the therapist and himself as psychiatric colleagues conducting a lofty, professional discussion. He

---

[4] This constituted a significant reversal of his delusional fear of persecution by gangsters during the onset of his overt illness.

[5] His hospitalization had been precipitated, during the overt onset of his illness, by his threat to murder his mother.

carried the process even further by putting the therapist in the role of patient, saying, "Well, now, tell me what is on your mind. Do you like women? Are you afraid of women?" Similarly, he pointedly referred to the administrative physician as "Mr." and said he had arranged for him to be put away in a lunatic asylum. In better organized moments he questioned the administrative physician's role competency, asking, "What would you do if you had to leave here and *earn* a living?"

Another denial of patienthood was to insist that he was not at a hospital, but at a rest home. His therapist noted his magical avoidance of speaking the words "Chestnut Lodge" and "Rockville," as if hoping thereby to deny the identity of hospital patient.

Concurrent with these efforts to deny patienthood, to reverse the roles, and to assert grandiose identities, was a further blurring of his discrimination between various categories of persons. Whereas all his earlier physical struggles had been with staff members over the issue of conformity to hospital restrictions, he now fought other patients as well and began to ask them to release him from the hospital. Such desperate supplication was in conspicuous contrast to his earlier scorn and contempt for other patients. His conception of who was who often seemed to melt and blur into a kaleidoscopic disarray of fused, split, and rejoined images of himself and others. Sometimes he endowed *others* with magical, grandiose attributes and spoke of being in the presence of famous, powerful personages.

The fragility and defensive inadequacy of these magical, fragmentary identification processes were clearly indicated by the emergence of talk of suicide. He requested a gun with which to kill himself and asked whether the casket and cremators were ready. A wish to be mutilated or killed became apparent in his fights with staff and patients.

Visits from his parents seemed to accentuate his disturbance. There were clear indications of a strong linkage between his grandiosity, his failure to meet his parents' career expectations, and his suicidal urges. Following one visit he showed an almost frenzied outburst of excitement and grandiose fragmentation. He paced ceaselessly, furiously smoking cigarettes and drinking coffee. He shouted orders and boasted of owning 12 big businesses, of having seduced numerous women, including one who he said was a bastard daughter of Eleanor Roosevelt, of being a high government official and an Army general. He threatened to court martial the aides if they did not comply immediately with his commands. Simultaneously with this authoritarian pose he voiced concern about how various figures of authority viewed him. He asked what the Medical Director of the hospital had said when he first saw him and what President Eisenhower had said upon hearing about him. He denied that the Lodge was a hospital, but four days later, in what seemed an attitude of hopeless resignation, said he wished to stay the rest of his life. At the same time a wish-fear of death was evident in his talking of suicide and a suspicion that his food had been poisoned.

338 SCHIZOPHRENIA AND THE NEED-FEAR DILEMMA

The oedipal nature of his grandiose assertions was especially clear in a statement that Princess Grace was actually his lawful wife, that her children were his, and that he intended to fly to Monaco to bring them back to him. While substituting Rainier for Laius, his fear and shame in connection with his father were expressed in projected form when he told an aide that it would be a favor to the aide's father if the aide were electrocuted. At the same time, the wish for protection by a strong father figure seemed to be contained in his statement that his commanding officer had told him that eating dandelions would protect him from poisoned food. Thus he seemed simultaneously to wish to usurp his father's place, to fear death at the father's behest, and to wish protection from a strong father.

A dramatic incident which further indicated a link between Joe's enormous concern over his identity and the parental social ambitions which he was expected to fill was observed by his therapist in a joint interview with Joe and his mother. Immediately after saying, "Joe, you should consider yourself fortunate to be in such a famous hospital," his mother turned to the therapist and asked, "Is Mr. Templeton [son of an internationally renowned family] still a patient on the same ward as Joe?" Thereupon Joe launched into a string of incoherent, fantastic assertions as to his own fame and extraordinary accomplishments.

Later phases: Gradually Joe settled, for the most part, into a stereotyped pattern of behavior and interaction with the ward staff. He paced about the ward, either in self-absorbed silence or accosting others to make a fragmentary, fantastic, and usually highly cryptic statement or inquiry, then drifting away without awaiting, and apparently not expecting, any response. The staff, in turn, came to take him for granted, paying little serious attention to what he attempted to say. There were occasional revivals of mutual interest and responsiveness, but these usually were short-lived and the interaction gradually reverted to a monotonous routine. In time Joe's ineffectual efforts to accost others diminished, and he often wandered about alone in an aimless, morose manner, usually clutching a book from which he read in scattered, perseverative fashion.

Joe's clinging to a book had developed as he had become more disorganized. He also clung to clothing, to repeated words, and to writings obsessively copied from books, apparently without regard for their meaning. This behavior seemed to be a desperate effort to retain contact with part of the real world in the face of increasingly tenuous contact with persons. He clung so tenaciously to clothing that he was exceedingly reluctant to allow the aides to take any of it for laundering; when the aides attempted to change his clothing, he often clung to a book. In flashes of grandiosity he boasted of obtaining a million-dollar wardrobe and a whole library—in effect, he was assuring himself of a superabundance of substitute objects. When he repetitively voiced the names of certain persons, usually women, it seemed that he was attempting to evoke an image of a protective person to which he could cling. This behavior had the quality of the recitation of a magic formula or prayer designed to invoke a guardian or tutelary deity.

Clinging to substitute objects, especially books, was also a means of clutching at the vestiges of his identity. He wrote his name in any book he picked up, regardless of whom it actually belonged to. He also asked to go to a library to look up who he was. This idea was double-edged: he grandiosely expected to find himself listed in *Who's Who*, frantically grasping for anything which might clarify and solidify his identity. In the midst of his mechanical copying he often interpolated the words "Who am I?" Frequently he mechanically recited his name and identifying data such as height, weight, home address, names of his mother and father, and the number of his driver's license. By clinging to identity remnants he seemed to try to retain a grasp of who he was in the face of the threat of utter personality dissolution. Often such declarations immediately frayed out into wild, grandiose claims that he was the world's greatest scholar, soldier, statesman, or other form of great man. He seemed able only momentarily to hold constant his self-definition.

Supplementary role efforts: The pattern of events seems to fit the following formulation: Joe and the staff were unable to find a reasonable fit between what he wanted to be and what the staff wanted him to be, each rejecting much of the other's initial definition of the situation. Joe reacted by phases of withdrawal and physical struggles while repeatedly protesting that he was not a patient; then he underwent identity diffusion.

If this formulation is correct, the question arises whether some better identity-role fit might have been found. Could the patient-role have been modified or could other roles have been offered so that he was not limited to that of patient? There is some evidence on this point.

On Joe's first day at Chestnut Lodge, an aide, acting on the administrator's suggestion that Joe's competency in music should be encouraged, suggested to Joe that he play the piano for a dance at the hospital recreation center that evening. Joe refused, saying, "A jazz musician is well aware of the value of money. For 15 or 20 dollars I might consider it." At the time he seemed genuinely contemptuous of such an affair as a hospital dance. Viewed in retrospect, his response to this offer of a supplementary role seems to have contained, besides obvious scorn, an implicit question as to whether the proffered job—or supplementary role—was real, with pay as a stamp of social reality, or whether it was make-believe. The possible effect upon Joe had his offer to perform, with pay, been immediately accepted will unfortunately never be known.

Throughout his hospital career Joe showed his greatest capacity for positive interaction when approached in the role of expert musician. Several trips to jazz concerts with aides who shared a high interest in jazz music were quite successful. Considerably later, after Joe had been disorganized for many months, the administrator hit upon the idea of asking Joe to help him with some harmonica music he was attempting to master. After initial suspiciousness and hesitancy Joe gradually warmed to the role of music teacher, and when the administrator had learned the music, Joe played the accompaniment for him. During this time he showed a manifest attachment to his administrator, occasionally dropping by his office with nothing particular to say but apparently content to sit quietly while the administrator went about desk work.

Another opportunity to fill the role of musician arose at a hospital dance. The pianist asked Joe if he wished to play. Joe shook his head in seeming disinterest, but shortly afterwards, when the pianist got up for a breather, Joe jumped to the piano and began to play. The band joined in and the audience applauded in genuine appreciation. For several days subsequently Joe was much more responsive to routine requests by the ward staff.

Just before his disorganization Joe made several efforts to establish another type of supplementary role. He would approach the administrative physician and suggest that they go for a walk, play a game, or otherwise share some personal, nonprofessional activity. These overtures were often self-defeating, since he made them when the administrator was busy with other patients. The administrator felt reluctant to commit himself to a somewhat special relationship with one patient, and usually parried the suggestions by indicating that an aide could join Joe in the suggested activity. In retrospect it appears certain that Joe must have experienced this as a "brush-off" and rejection of his effort to establish a more personal, companion role with the administrator. Joe's subsequent manner toward the administrator became increasingly haughty and condescending as he grasped at various grandiose identities for himself.

Joe occasionally approached the administrator with the demand that arrangements be made for him to start work. However, at this point his thinking was so grandiose that he dismissed with scorn the type of jobs available in the patient work program.

Another type of supplementary role effort cropped up a few times—a literal wish to be the son of the administrator or other staff members. He had quite often called the administrator "Dad" or "Daddy-o" in "beatnik" vernacular, but during a period of grossly manifest passive withdrawal, as he lay in bed in pajamas, he used this form of address literally, asking if the administrator would have him as a son. On another occasion he requested a third person to ask the senior aide to take him to the aide's apartment. He added, "I wish he would take me in and feed me." This type of supplementary role had a strong regressive tinge which the others did not.

Joe had come to the hospital with a background of strong and conflicting career ambitions held for him by his family, along with his own acute sense of failure to establish a satisfactory identity and career. He strongly protested the identity and role of patient, not only verbally but in repeated attempts to run away. The reaction of the staff to these protests consisted mainly of efforts to convince him that he was ill and in need of hospitalization, considerable anger, and a temporary policy of restricting Joe to the ward as if to force him into the role of patient. In addition, Joe's parents refused his pleas that he be allowed to leave the Lodge. Efforts by both Joe and the staff to establish some type of supplementary role met with little sustained success. As the identity-role conflict continued, Joe reacted by phases of withdrawal and physical struggles, and then by identity diffusion. He was convinced at first that he was other persons in the immediate situation. Subsequently his identity became a mélange of fleeting, grandiose fragments, including some role reversals in which he viewed himself as the doctor, and others as patients. Gradually he disorganized further and clung to identity remnants and various substitute objects.

In general, throughout his hospital career Joe functioned best when offered a role opportunity supplementary to that of patient, especially when afforded the role of music teacher of his administrative physician. Much of this patterning of events emerges only in retrospect, but it is tempting to speculate how his hospital career might have differed had a better and more sustained identity-role fit been achieved. After two and a half years at Chestnut Lodge, at a time when he had begun showing distinct signs of improvement and reconstruction of his identity, Joe unfortunately was transferred to another hospital.

Case 2

Pete was in his early twenties when admitted to Chestnut Lodge. He had spent almost all of the preceding three years in a series of hospitals. His personal background contained much identity uncertainty in terms of religion, social status, and occupation, which contributed to deep inner uncertainties and a sense of being different. Although his family was part of a small Jewish minority in a small city, its Jewish identity was blurred by his father's participation in a civic organization that tried to lessen the distinction between Jews and Christians, and by his mother's affiliation with other religious groups, including Christian Science and Unitarianism. Socially ambitious and conscious of class distinctions, the mother regarded her husband's family heritage as lower than her own, and disparaged his relative lack of education and his occupation of businessman. She was eager that her only son excel his father in education and in the social prestige of his career; in a sense, Pete was expected to be the standard-bearer for an enhanced family identity. Pete's predominant intrafamilial alliance was with his mother and an older sister. His loyalty shifted only when his father developed a fatal illness one and a half years prior to the overt onset of Pete's psychosis; Pete became very attentive to his father, while bitterly castigating and blaming his mother for the impending death. Undoubtedly the conflicting loyalties were associated with competing identifications which rendered more difficult Pete's task of constructing an integrated identity for himself. In the course of his stay at the Lodge he expressed grave uncertainty as to his sexual and filial identities, asking perplexed questions such as "Am I a son? Whose son am I?"

Although noticeably troubled after his father's death, Pete managed to complete college. However, he never worked at his chosen career, and a period of service in the Navy was terminated when he became psychotic. The onset of his overt psychosis occurred when his mother became fatally ill. In a highly dramatic incident while he was on emergency leave, a rose fell apart as he presented it to his mother in the hospital.[6] To him this signified something terribly wrong in his attitude toward her; that evening he attempted suicide and went into a catatonic stupor. His long series of hospitalizations followed. He made another suicidal effort when he read a medical report that his mother's illness would be fatal. Pete evidently felt deeply and guiltily that the deaths of his parents were his responsibility, and that they stamped his identity with the hateful self-appraisal, "There is something terrible about me."

Previous hospital experiences and advance reputation: Reports from previous hospitals described Pete as alternating between cheerful optimism and violent assaultiveness and self-destructiveness, including at least one attempt to castrate himself—an indication of the depth of his conflict about his sexual identity. Seclusion and physical restraint were frequent. At the same time, he also developed at least two intense and involved relationships with older, married women, from whom he evoked sympathy and attachment. One of them described Pete as especially solicitous of the welfare of sicker patients, toward whom, in an apparent denial of his own patient role, he adopted a helping role while viewing himself as only temporarily incapacitated.

Thus Pete's advance reputation was that of an extremely difficult patient, likely to arouse both special sympathy and antagonism which might prompt serious staff dissension. Even before Pete's arrival at the Lodge, therefore, his administrative physician advised a staff attitude of firm, matter-of-fact consistency.

A most important further circumstance of his admission to Chestnut Lodge was its trial basis. After six months a court-appointed guardian was to decide whether continuance was advisable. This provisory agreement, of course, placed everyone in the situation under pressure and, in particular, intensified the importance of the question of how well Pete could adapt to the role of patient at the Lodge.

Initial efforts at identity definition: Upon admission Pete presented an extremely mixed picture indicative of his identity variegation and instability. With some staff members he spoke clearly, making little or no mention of his long series of prior hospitalizations, and voicing optimism about a future outside a hospital within a few months. He told others that

---

[6] This incident, as the patient reconstructed and told it, probably represents a blend of fact and fantasy, but is nonetheless a valid symbolization of his feelings.

he was hopeless, and castigated himself as a murderer, adulterer, and bastard. He also voiced fears of world destruction. Occasionally he called himself a bear or other animal. He also spoke of dying or of already being dead.

With his therapist Pete initially was less chaotically disorganized and was partially able to discuss some of the problems which beset him. He described poignantly his lack of a clear sense of identity, his lack of capacity for self-control, and his vulnerability to influences from his surroundings. He said, "I am what I am in a situation. If I am writing, I am a writer. If I am drawing, I am an artist. This is terrible, Doctor. I can't seem to be me; I've never been me; I died a long time ago. It doesn't make sense to feel this way. I feel as if I had been railroaded but I know this isn't just something done to me by somebody else."

He also spoke of inability to make decisions, or to control his feelings, or even to know which were genuine feelings. He feared losing control of his impulses and he feared what others might do to him. He described feeling like a puppet sometimes, totally dominated by others. He vaguely alluded to muscle twitchings as evidence that his body was being controlled from the outside and said he thought he could communicate with animals, thus indicating not only his vulnerability to the influence of the environment but also his part-identity as an animal. Once he said to his therapist, "You think I'm a gorilla." As with the ward staff, he also described himself to his therapist as a terrible criminal, guilty of adultery and murder.

From the outset Pete also showed intermittent lack of clarity in his definition of others as well as himself. For instance, he misperceived one aide as his father, and later attacked him. For a time he perceived his therapist and his administrator as one and the same person. In talking with the ward staff he sometimes spoke clearly and rationally one moment, only to be seized by a violent, delusionally based impulse the next moment.

Attitudes toward the role of patient: Regarding the role of patient, Pete was highly contradictory. Often he protested that he was well and needed only to get a job and to leave the Lodge. He demanded to see a doctor who would arrange for his return home. At other times he partially accepted the role, acknowledging that he was mentally ill and in need of help, and saying that he expected to receive help at the Lodge and was optimistic about a stay of only a few months and a return to good health. Clearly these statements still contained considerable denial of illness and refusal of patienthood.

Still another attitude toward the patient role was his conviction that he was a beast, hopelessly ill, and depraved beyond any hope of rescue. He indicated that he deserved no treatment other than punitive electric shock and permanent incarceration in a state institution. This hateful, derogatory view of himself was further demonstrated by various self-destructive acts. He tried to burn himself with cigarettes, banged his head on the wall, punched himself in the nose, picked his gums until they bled, and stuffed paper in his nose until it bled.

Attitudes toward the staff members and their roles: Pete's attitudes toward the staff fluctuated sharply and unpredictably between passive dependency and furious bursts of protest against the influence and control of others. His passivity was manifested by his remaining in bed in pajamas for his initial interview with his therapist. He expressed a wish that his therapist be strong, powerful, and able to take care of things for him, and showed disappointment and annoyance when the therapist did not take the lead or arrange various features of the ward living situation. He seemed to want a magical, omnipotent protector who could make him comfortable by rearranging the situation at will. This wish for a strong, active, decisive mentor was associated with an abysmal sense of weakness, and inability to guide or control himself.

He told the ward staff he didn't know what to do and seemed to invite and depend upon their suggestions. A few times he in effect handed himself over to them in a wave of passive resignation, saying, "Crucify me."

His deep fear of and attempts to struggle against his passivity and control by others manifested itself, for example, in a phobic abhorrence of a catatonic patient who, lying helplessly at the mercy of his environment, seemed to epitomize passivity. Within days after admission, Pete made several abrupt assaults on others, including various aides and the administrator, while protesting that they were dominating him. Several of these assaults apparently were wild efforts to fight off an engulfing sense of enslavement. At other times he disavowed the assaultive impulse, saying that voices had commanded it.

Along with impulsive assaults, he made equally impulsive efforts to kiss and attach himself in clinging fashion to women, either nurses or patients. One assault was provoked when in the course of a walk a male aide intervened between Pete and a student nurse, suggesting that the nurse walk with another patient. After they returned to the ward, Pete violently attacked the aide, and later in the day stood before the nurse in mute appeal with tears streaming down his face.

Staff responses: Initially the ward staff made a concerted effort to show Pete that despite his reputation from previous hospitals he would be met with respect and a reasonable balance between permissiveness and control. Staff attitudes toward him soon crystallized around his unpredictable changeability. At times he was described as "energetic, courteous, and possessing a keen sense of humor," or as "a great guy—real good personality, intelligent, gets along in most situations, nice to be around." However, he seemed to the staff almost to try to undo and spoil relationships begun so pleasantly and productively. Seemingly without reason he would become disdainfully disinterested or violently assaultive. This was interspersed with fits of despair and self-mutilative efforts. His sudden and violent reversal of behavior confused and disappointed the staff members and engendered distrust. They said, "You don't know what he's going to do next. You just can't trust him." Their distrust was compounded by the assumption that much of the time Pete was able to exercise conscious control. Pete's asking an aide to remove his glasses before attempting to hit him was cited as clear evidence of his willful purposiveness.

Lack of fit between staff and patient: The difference in their appraisals of his capacity for conscious control formed a major discrepancy between Pete and the staff, which must have rendered his identity definition all the more uncertain. Pete told his therapist that he often felt more controlled by his surroundings than by himself and that he was frightened by his inability to regulate his feelings and impulses. Of course, he also attempted to conceal and deny his incapacity for self-regulation. One reason the staff members were so puzzled, disappointed, and angered by his unpredictable shifts was that they overestimated his capacity for conscious self-control.

Certainly Pete was far from fitting the role of ideal patient. He seemed to oscillate between two extremes, neither of which fit the staff's expectations of the patient role. At one extreme he viewed himself as completely well and was intolerant of the slightest delay in his leaving the hospital. At the other extreme he regarded himself as so hopeless and bestial as to be beyond treatment and suitable only for permanent incarceration in a state institution. He explicitly requested inhumane treatment, asking, for example, to be locked in a seclusion room without clothing and treated as an animal.

Both extremes refused the role of patient, one because he had no illness and no need for treatment, the other because he was so hopeless and nonhuman that treatment was senseless. Both denials correspondingly denied the staff members their reciprocal identities and roles as therapeutic agents—doctors, nurses, and aides. The staff complained that Pete didn't seem to try and that he didn't seem to want to help himself. They might have added, "Nor does he want us to act in the therapeutic role and help him." His passive resignation was a major source of staff complaint. One staff member said, "Perhaps he would do better in a hospital where less was done for him. There he might have to do more for himself and make more of an effort to change himself." The question of the degree to which Pete "really tried"—that is, exerted conscious effort to help himself and to change—probably was another crucial point at issue between him and the staff. Undoubtedly Pete felt himself to have exerted enormous effort, at least prior to sinking into a state of despair in the latter stages of his stay.

The closest approach to an identity-role fit was an unconstructive one between Pete's self-hateful image of himself as terribly destructive and the staff's growing conception of him as a problem patient, which developed despite the original determination not to prejudge him. Certainly the intensity and pervasiveness of Pete's manifestations of a negative identity (Erikson,

1959)—complete failure and loathsome beast—made it difficult for the staff to perceive his positive aspects.

At times Pete made quite explicit the threat to staff identities and roles posed by his refusal of the role of patient. He called his therapist and administrative physician liars, double-talkers, and fakers. In words and actions he indicated that they served no useful purpose for him. His therapist reported that with Pete he felt far more doubt and uncertainty regarding his own particular actions and general competency than he did in working with other patients. With Pete he was prey to serious erosion of his professional identity as a psychotherapist. Ward staff members also often felt impotent and useless in their dealings with Pete. Pete's later attempts to reverse roles constituted another kind of refusal to acknowledge staff roles.

Phase of running away: After about three months, Pete's protest of the patient role took the concrete form of several episodes of running away. At least twice he made his way to towns over fifty miles distant, there to be recognized as mentally ill by passersby and police when he paced the streets talking to himself. Once he handed an accosting policeman a note which stated that he had died several days previously and that the end of the world was impending—a striking example of the link between threatened loss of identity and fantasies of world destruction.

In the course of this escape effort, Pete showed a pattern of ambivalence and shifting loyalty very similar to that which he had demonstrated within his family. While talking with police, he expressed strong dislike of the hospital and said he had no wish to return to Chestnut Lodge. However, when hospital aides arrived, he greeted them warmly, saying, "Well, back to civilization again," and complained about the hardships of jail life. On the return trip, his attitude again switched; as they approached the hospital he began to manifest fear and protest about reentering it.

His ambivalence regarding dependency and the role of patient was further evidenced on another escape venture when he phoned the Medical Director asking him to wire money so that he could return. When the money was sent, Pete did return.

After still another runaway effort, Pete offered the delusional explanation that his leaving was dictated by a need to go home to care for his (nonexistent) wife and children. This assertion of the identities of husband and father served to deny and project his own deep dependent needs and urges.

Following Pete's unsuccessful and ambivalent efforts to protest the patient role by running away, his suicidal efforts, mostly hanging attempts, increased in frequency and seriousness. Once he set fire to his bedding; it was unclear to what extent this destructive action was aimed at himself or others.

Phase of withdrawal: In this phase a pattern of mutual withdrawal predominated. Pete spent more and more time alone in his room, often lying in bed with the covers over his head. In many of his therapy sessions he was mute. Although they regarded him as the major ward problem, the ward staff members withdrew from him. This was strikingly indicated when a questionnaire administered to the staff showed that although Pete ranked highest of all the patients on behavior requiring nursing attention, he was almost the lowest in time spent with him by the staff.

Pete's behavior gradually became predominantly catatonic. He ate little, lost weight, and frequently was mute and unresponsive for hours at a time. Often he refused to wear clothing and presented a most unkempt, pathetic appearance. Several persons described him as the picture of a weak, helpless, chronic invalid. Intermittently he lashed out in bursts of fury at persons who came into his room.

Phase of identity diffusion: Approximately nine months after admission, Pete began to emerge somewhat from his withdrawn state and to show distinct identity diffusion. He seemed to be attempting rebirth with a new identity, appropriated from others. He claimed that he was other patients, and attempted to affirm these assertions by taking their clothing, climbing into their beds, and mimicking their actions.

His assumption of the identities of other patients had been foreshadowed earlier by his special sympathy and identification with the same patients. For example, several months earlier he had angrily criticized the administrator as inhuman for neglecting the needs of these patients. At the time he implied that he spoke for them because they were helpless and unable to stand up for themselves. Toward one patient, Tom, he had shown a special concern which was a blend of solicitude, fear, and phobic avoidance. Tom was the oldest and had been at the Lodge the longest of all the patients on the ward. He suffered periods of wild violence and chaotic lack of control, which Pete must have seen as mirroring that which he feared most in himself. Furthermore, Tom seemed almost a symbol of a patient doomed never to recover—a fate which Pete desperately feared might be his in the role of patient. The fire which Pete set in his room had followed by only a few days a fire set by the other patient. For a time Tom apparently served as the repository for unacceptable aspects of himself which Pete had to deny and project. As Pete slipped more into a hopeless mood, the projected fragments of self returned in the form of close identification with the older man, culminating finally in the conviction that he was Tom. During the period of identity diffusion, Pete made his most serious suicidal attempt.

During this period he also manifested sporadic attempts at role reversal. He called himself by his therapist's name and tried to treat the doctor as his patient. He made similar efforts at role reversal vis-à-vis the ward staff, including attempts to carry out staff role functions such as cleaning up the ward.

With his therapist he made a few efforts to establish a role alternative to that of patient. For instance, he suggested that they become buddies and go out night-clubbing, and the like. At another time he directly asked if he might become the therapist's son and pleaded to be taken to the therapist's home.

With the administrator he occasionally assumed the identity of a soldier reporting to his commanding officer. He would snap to attention, saying, "What are your orders, sir?" This apparent eagerness for orders was in sharp contrast to earlier protestations that the administrator was nothing but a villainous jailer, interested only in bossing others. That he was still ambivalent about orders was indicated by his requesting them and then demanding his immediate release. He once expressed his wish for strong leadership by saying most pleadingly to his therapist, "Lead me." Similar expressions were contained in such statements as, "Take me to my father," "Take me to my home," "Take me home with you." His conflict over whether to submit passively to the orders of others or to frantically assert independence and a protest against domination by others was central and recurrent throughout his stay. It was a major factor in his conflict of acceptance versus rejection of the role of patient.

During his period of identity diffusion, Pete expressed grave uncertainty regarding his sexual identity. He feared that he was being changed into a woman. In rapid sequence during the same day he made a clumsy effort to rape a woman activities worker, to whom he had become quite attached and whom he occasionally had addressed as "Mother," and a frightened venture into homosexual play with Tom. He also occasionally brushed against his therapist in a vaguely sexually suggestive manner. His uncertainty about sexual identity undoubtedly was associated with conflicts of activity versus passivity, and dominance versus submission. Many of his attacks on others seemed prompted by a desperate urge to break out from the mire of passivity and to assert manliness.

The pervasiveness of the activity-versus-passivity conflict was further evidenced during this phase by much overt indecision and vacillation. He might get up from a chair, start to leave the room, walk only a few steps, then return to the chair. If he started to speak, he often interrupted himself and muttered half-sentences of apology.

Pete's identity diffusion seemed not just an indication of ego disorganization, but also a positive struggle and search for a new identity. Although several of the identities which he appropriated from other patients were those of "hopeless patient," he was less totally despairing than he had been during the preceding phase of withdrawal and helpless self-neglect.

Final phases: Unfortunately, Pete's identity struggle in Chestnut Lodge was terminated by extrinsic circumstances which dictated his transfer to another hospital after he had been at the Lodge a year. During his last month at the Lodge Pete was aware of the impending transfer and also of the nearly simultaneous departure of his therapist to a position elsewhere. When the therapist told him of the latter, Pete responded with an angry "good-by." It was especially unfortunate that one more separation was added to the series of identity-shattering losses and separations. Upon re-

ceipt of definite notice of his transfer to another hospital he gave little response, except for a few fragmentary comments indicative of helpless
resignation. The staff responses were mixtures of disappointment, detachment, and relief.

This man's background contained much identity uncertainty, with an
especially pronounced conflict over which parent to align and identify himself with. In a series of prior hospitalizations, he had failed to establish a
satisfactory identity-role fit, and at Chestnut Lodge the trial nature of his
stay diminished the likelihood that he would establish a more successful fit.
He alternated between an illness-denying protest of the patient role and an
image of himself as a hopeless beast or criminal not worthy of patienthood.
Both attitudes interfered not only with his fitting the role of patient but
also with the staff's ability to function in professional roles. The staff members were also uncomfortable when he abandoned all self-determination
and asked to be led and directed; their expectations of the patient role
did not allow for such an absolute degree of helplessness.

A stable identity-role fit was hindered by central conflicts of activity
versus passivity, masculinity versus femininity, and self-control versus control by others. Differing appraisals of his capacity for ego autonomy and
conscious purposiveness probably accentuated his lack of identity definition.
The form of identity diffusion which ensued was shaped by identification
with patients who were the sickest and presumably least likely to recover,
although it did seem to contain some elements of constructive rebirth
efforts. His unpredictability and tendency to undo constructive interactions
by self-defeating hostility and withdrawal made it difficult for the staff to
offer him alternative roles when he refused the traditional role of patient.
Probably the closest approach to an identity-role fit was an unconstructive
one between his hateful negative identity of terribly destructive person and
the staff's picture of him as a problem patient.

Case 3

When this report was written, Bill, 30 years old, had been a Chestnut
Lodge patient for approximately six months, having been transferred after
18 months spent intermittently in other hospitals.

His background history contains many data pertinent to problems of
identity and role. An only son, with one older sister, he was predominantly
dependent on and dominated by his mother. She was highly conscious of
minority-group status and social prestige and proud of being native-born
in contrast to her immigrant husband. She always wanted the best of everything for her children, including schools, clubs, hospitals, and doctors. She
spoiled and indulged Bill, sometimes verging on romantic adulation as she
spoke of his handsomeness, his dancing skill, and his many girl friends.
She also excused his difficulties and failures by blaming them on others,
saying that he was unjustly accused; at times she almost assumed the "para-

noid twosome" position of feeling that everyone else was against her and her son. Bill voiced the same sentiment during his stay by saying, "My mother, I can really count on her, can't I?" as if he felt she was his only reliable source of support in the world. His father, whom Bill was said to resemble in physical appearance, suffered a chronic, hereditary, neurological illness, which had forced his premature retirement when Bill was 12. The mother and the rest of the family tended to deny the fact or at least the extent of the father's illness, terming him lazy and attributing his difficulties to his stopping work rather than vice versa. Their general disparagement of the father contributed heavily to rendering him an unsatisfactory identification model for Bill. One measure of his situation was the fact that in his teens Bill turned to his mother rather than his father for sexual information. In an unguarded moment Bill himself said, "How would you like to have someone around you like that for a father? What can you expect of me?"

Two maternal uncles, both aggressive, wealthy businessmen, filled the role of strong masculine figures in the extended family, and the mother looked to them as such. At the same time she hated them for their power and success. Bill's attitudes toward them were a mixture of envy, dependency, fear, and anger. As potential identification models, they were not only unattainable, in the sense that Bill felt he could not emulate their drive and aggressiveness, but also undesirable because they were hated by the mother.[7]

Bill had had numerous difficulties in school, attending several, including one for problem children, and being expelled from at least one. At 13 his disobedience in school had led to a psychiatric consultation, followed by sporadic treatment interviews for the next five years. He managed to graduate from college, taking longer than the usual four years. He also achieved modest success in college athletics. His interest in athletics had been stimulated originally by a teacher who had befriended him. However, an attempt at graduate school failed. There was an unconfirmed report that he had attempted suicide after this blow to his identity aspirations.

A period of barely acceptable military service followed, including failure to achieve the status for which he had initially aimed. Upon return to civilian life, while living at home with his parents, he lost a series of jobs, most of which had been obtained through family connections. He had often failed to show up for work, instead remaining in bed much of the day and spending his night drinking alone in bars. During this period his mother frequently nagged him to be more active and diligent in work efforts. His attitude at home alternated between aloofness and sullen surliness.

Approximately three years prior to his Chestnut Lodge admission Bill

[7] It seems likely that underlying his failures to identify successfully with males was an earlier inability to solve serious problems in his infantile relationship with his mother, including the achievement of a separate sense of self.

undertook psychiatric treatment. After nearly a year of treatment he experienced a rather sudden subjective personality change, in the form of a surge of self-confidence and outspokenness. At this point he terminated his psychiatric treatment against advice. He then attempted to assert independence by moving out of the parental home, and to affirm a masculine identity as well as separation from his mother by intensively courting a girl. The courtship was both hectic and unrealistic. He lost weight and sleep, while faking business records and repeatedly borrowing money from his mother in order to impress the girl with his fictitious wealth and business success. His rather frantic pose was shattered by the girl's refusing his proposal of marriage, whereupon he assaulted her. He attempted to rationalize being jilted on the grounds that his wealth and social position were insufficient to win the girl. Then in a desperate effort to gain these prestige symbols by force he went to one of his uncles threatening violence if not given an important job and a large sum of money, and blaming the uncle for his failures in jobs and the love affair.

Police were called and immediate hospitalization arranged. He received electric and insulin shock treatments and after four months was released to his mother's custody. For the next few months he remained at home, mostly depressed, drinking heavily and reversing his day-night cycle. Rehospitalization, again with police assistance, was precipitated when he threatened his parents and tore up the home in a night of wild violence.[8]

During the next year at two different hospitals he made a poor adjustment. He made little or no constructive effort to fit into the hospital programs, instead attempting to rely upon verbal magic by repeated assertions that he was not ill and should be granted full privileges and prompt release. He used another type of verbal magic by reiterating, like a little boy, that he had had enough punishment to learn his lesson, and, accordingly, should be released. His transfer to Chestnut Lodge was largely due to his mother's urgent wish that he receive more active treatment; she pressured her wealthy brothers so insistently that she generated in them an irrational sense of guilty responsibility for Bill's illness, and, ultimately, they agreed to support his treatment.

Initial efforts at identity definition: Upon arrival at Chestnut Lodge Bill denied illness, saying that he was all right now, that he had been railroaded, and that all he needed was to move to another city and make a new start with a new job and social contacts. In the last statement he revealed not only his projection of blame onto the environment but also the dependence

---

[8] The role of the police in Bill's hospitalizations undoubtedly aggravated his own lack of clarity as to whether he was a criminal or a patient and whether he was in a jail or a hospital. In addition, the threatened uncle labeled Bill much more a potential murderer than a sick person.

Wood and coauthors (1960) have discussed some of the differences between patient-initiated and family-initiated hospitalization—clearly a significant factor in the patient's identity definition in the hospital setting.

of his sense of identity upon the environment. To change his surroundings would be to change his identity.[9]

Bill's denial of illness was neither complete nor constant. To one aide with whom he initially was quite friendly he once confided that he regarded himself as a paranoid. Shortly thereafter Bill's attitude toward the aide changed quite abruptly. He accused the aide of pushing him around and picking on him, and subsequently assaulted him. To his therapist, although for the most part denying illness and protesting hospitalization, he occasionally voiced fears of losing control, killing someone, and further wrecking his life.

He showed pervasive concern over identity. He was quick to announce that he was a "college man" and to let it be known that he had distinct identity assets such as good looks, intelligence, and athletic ability. He said that he had belonged to one of the best country clubs, where he was not only the best athlete but also the handsomest and smartest. His assertions tended to balloon into grandiose fantasies of becoming a fashion model, Hollywood star, or athletic or dance instructor. The narcissistic quality of the fantasies was clearly demonstrated by his standing before a mirror, saying, "Yes, you're a very good-looking fellow, Bill—you really ought to be an actor."

He revealed the reason for these narcissistic fantasies by acknowledging concern over his failure to achieve a solid identity. He spoke of flunking out of graduate school, his series of job losses, and being jilted. Clearly each of these meant loss of an important identity support if not of an essential constituent.

In his struggle to define himself and his life situation, he often constructed a picture of himself as a criminal incarcerated in a jail. This not only served to deny illness but also afforded him a positive identity of a sort which was even a source of some pride. He said that the only reasons for his being here were his threatening and violent actions. He termed himself a murderer and said, "To tell the truth, I felt I was nobody, and being against people is better than being nobody." With the ward staff it was clear that Bill rather wished to be perceived as a tough, menacing person. From the beginning he made occasional threatening gestures toward staff members, such as cocking his fist or raising a pop bottle as if to strike. Then he would grin and say, "Thought I was going to hit you, didn't you? But I was only kidding." His partial disavowal of these threatening motions as kidding or as testing to see what the staff would do did not erase their meaning as indicators of shaky impulse control.

Precarious ego organization: Bill manifested a variety of other indications of precarious ego control. In initial interviews with his therapist he con-

[9] Interestingly, in the social worker's initial interviews with the family, the father, with little or no recognition of Bill's illness, said that he hoped that the family could assist in getting Bill a job at the Lodge, as if this were the only task to be accomplished.

veyed an impression of on-and-off blocking and sudden waves of loss of reality contact, with possible hallucinations. At times he blinked, shook his head, and said, "What did you just say?" Or he might begin a sentence, "Well, I'll tell you . . . ," only to lapse into silence.

On the ward he was quite sloppy in his dress and reluctant to bathe regularly. He often was extremely restless, pacing the hallway; chain-smoking, and drinking water, coffee, and juice, sometimes until he regurgitated. It soon was necessary for the staff to limit his smoking and fluid consumption. At the hospital canteen he ate with compulsive voracity. At times his oral insatiability was so strong that he ate bits of paper. He was extremely intolerant of any delay or frustration. If refused a cigarette, he might grab one from another patient's mouth. This hunger-driven lack of respect for the personal boundaries and property of others soon provoked several scuffles.

He was unable to sustain an activity requiring concentration for any length of time. Ball games were interrupted when he began pacing. Similarly, he could stay with card games only briefly, and if he picked up a newspaper he soon laid it down and began pacing. In any type of even mildly competitive activity he showed extreme intolerance of possible defeat and would stop immediately if the score was against him.

Also highly relevant to the problem of identity-role fit was the most conspicuous indication of his precarious ego organization—an incessant, repetitive questioning of any and all staff members and other patients as to the circumstances of his being in the Lodge and his prognosis. He asked, "Why am I here? Is this a jail? How does one get out of here? Tell me how long it will be." He asked other patients, "How long have you been here? What are our chances of getting out? What does one have to do to get out? Have patients ever gotten out of here? Has a patient here ever committed suicide? Do you think you will ever get out?" Of the staff he queried, "Do you think I'm sick? Do you see any need for me to be here? Am I getting better? What are my chances? Will I be here the rest of my life?" His constant questioning seemed to be a desperate plea to be given an unqualified definition of his situation. It had the same driven, insatiable quality as much of his other behavior. The staff noted that he sometimes hardly waited for an answer, or when given one would return in a few moments with the same question. It was as if he sought magical reassurance which would bring certainty to his own overwhelming uncertainty as to his identity and life situation.

Bill's questioning of the staff members included efforts to define their identities. For example, he went to some pains to inquire whether his therapist was a psychoanalyst or a psychiatrist and what type of treatment he was providing. He asked one of the aides questions seemingly designed to clarify the identity of the aide: Had he ever graduated from high school? Was he married? Had he ever been in fights or in jail? These questions clearly reflected Bill's own preoccupations and uncertainties about himself.

In the meantime Bill protested the role of patient, saying that he was not ill and that anyway, this wasn't a hospital but a jail. He said that his main goal was to leave and announced that he would run away at his earliest opportunity. He said, "All I want to do is live outside as every normal person should. I'll be all right if I can move somewhere else and get a job."

Therapist's responses and expectations: Bill's therapist immediately was struck by how much Bill resembled Joe, Case 1. The therapist perceived Bill as attempting much of the time to strike a tough, threatening pose— a pose, however, which was mitigated by a certain boyishness and an appearance younger than his actual years. The therapist said further that Bill was engaged in a desperate, struggling quest for a solid identity, a sense of belonging, and a social niche into which he could fit. In this process Bill seemed to be attempting to erect a façade which he could not sustain. The therapist said, "He wants to think of himself as much more than he actually is." At another point the therapist remarked, "Basically he realizes that he is a brat who doesn't know how to get along in the world."

Bill made repeated requests of the therapist for definition of his personal situation. In denying illness he asked, "Why am I here? How can I get out of here? Can you tell me how to get out? How long will I be here?" In response the therapist sometimes said, "I don't know"; at other times he attempted to formulate reasons why Bill needed treatment—for example, he said that Bill seemed simultaneously to want to be friendly to people and to be unable to be so, and that a major goal in treatment would be to understand the reasons for this problem. Such formulations sometimes were followed by Bill's temporarily relaxing but soon he resumed his stereotyped protestations and queries. This pattern somewhat annoyed the therapist, who was relieved by brief intervals in which Bill dropped his denial and acknowledged personal difficulties, such as his series of failures to hold a social role and his sense of being nobody. The therapist attempted to use these fleeting acknowledgments as starting points for a therapeutic alliance and Bill's acceptance of the role of patient. However, Bill persisted in his denials of illness and patienthood.

Ward staff responses: One depersonalizing staff response from the outset was the preconception that Bill might be "another Jim Doe," a former chronically assaultive patient who had been a serious ward problem. There were several predictions in the admission conference that Bill was likely to become more disturbed. The major response to Bill's pretensions to the identities of great athlete and potential movie star was that he was trying to put up a "big front" and to be a "real big man." Several of the ward staff members derived distinct pleasure when Bill's claims to athletic prowess were deflated during a hospital athletic event. In general, he was regarded as an aggravating bore who was untidy and unclean in his personal habits. The charge nurse characterized him as a spoiled problem child. She described his response to ward rules and restrictions as being that of a little boy who promised he wouldn't be bad again and expected this to have magical undoing effects. One of her major goals was to have Bill become more cooperative and even obedient. Further evidence of the image of Bill as a spoiled child was afforded by a persistent memory slip of the social worker—she repeatedly referred to him as an only child, although, of course, she knew of his older sister.

Bill's incessant questions and pleas for definition of his status were met initially by efforts to give him straightforward answers. He was told that he was in a hospital, not a jail, and that the goal was to help him. He was urged to "work with your doctor" and to "try to learn to cooperate with people." When he attempted to airily dismiss any possibility of illness, one aide told him that it was a serious matter and that he did have serious problems. In short, the ward staff encouraged Bill to accept the role of patient.

Soon the staff became wearied by the repetitiousness of his questions and the apparent ineffectiveness of their answers. Nursing notes began to refer in stereotyped fashion to his asking "his usual, standard questions" and "the same old stuff." Such stereotyped reactions must have further eroded the patient's already tenuous identity.

The various manifestations of Bill's precarious ego controls also bothered the staff. They perceived him as unpredictable, untrustworthy, and destructive. Significantly, several of his destructive actions seemed designed to provide him with a way out of the situation. For instance, he picked a hole in a security screen and dug a hiding place in his mattress for sharp instruments such as scissors and nail clippers. His insatiable requests for food, liquids, and cigarettes, coupled with his restless pacing and encroachment on the property of others, prompted rationing and restrictive measures. Such efforts at external control by the staff often seemed to provoke Bill to further protests that this was a jail and that he should leave. He spoke with increasing frequency of running away.

His ambivalence regarding dependency prompted behavior further puzzling to the staff. As several of the aides put it, he seemed insatiably hungry for attention yet simultaneously intolerant of the sustained presence of others. Repeated requests for answers to unanswerable questions and for food and services were countermanded by snarling demands that others get away from him and leave him alone. He rejected the staff's concern over his regurgitation of excessive fluids by saying, "Go away. I'll be all right. I'll take care of myself." This paradoxical mixture of incessant, basically insatiable demands, and protests that he had no need or wish for help rendered him an extremely poor fit with the patient role. In turn, the staff members were unable to feel confirmed in their roles of helping persons; instead they felt there was little they could do to either satisfy or assist this patient who refused to be a patient. The charge nurse commented simply but tellingly, "It's hard to be nice to him."

Being a problem was not without some identity value for Bill. Being negativistic, annoying, and aggravating undoubtedly afforded him some relief from the sense of being nobody—to wit, his own earlier statement that being a criminal was better than being nobody.

Subsequent developments: escapes, withdrawal, and assaults: After this initial period, Bill resorted to further modes of protesting the situation and the patient role. He made several escape attempts, two or three times managing to stay away from the hospital for periods of several days. During one of these he worked as a caddy at a golf course. When he was returned to the hospital, he said with obvious pride, "See, I proved I could make it outside. All that I need is a job." It was noteworthy that this flush of success in an occupational role endured for several days during which he was calmer and less frantically driven in his general behavior.

However, his protests quickly resumed. In addition to further escape efforts he was in several fights which he himself provoked or initiated. Once he attacked the aide with whom he had earlier been quite friendly and confiding. Now this aide seemed to him more like a toxic intruder to be avoided, driven away, or destroyed. This drastic switch of attitude was partly related to the aide's enforcing a gratification delay regarding some of Bill's requests, but also seemed related to Bill's basic ambivalence. His attitude toward the aide changed again toward greater acceptance when he developed a bête-noire feeling about another aide, who he said was always "bugging" him and wouldn't leave him alone.

At times Bill became quite withdrawn, spending much of the day on his bed, tending to reverse his day-night cycle, as he had at home, and saying little to the staff. Periodically, instead of eating compulsively, he ate very little; occasionally while disdaining his own food he took food from the plates of other patients. Possibly this represented a blurring of the distinction between himself and others and an excessive fluidity of introjective-projective processes.

The predominant staff response to Bill's running away, assaultiveness, and violation of the property rights of other patients was an increasing reluctance to escort him to activities off the ward. As a result he was further restricted and confined, to which he reacted with a mixture of protest and withdrawal.

Bill made one major effort to obtain release from the hospital by contacting a lawyer. The lawyer requested an outside psychiatric consultant, who rather skillfully told Bill that although at present he thought Bill was ill enough to require hospital treatment, once Bill was well the consultant would be glad to assist him should anyone interfere with his leaving the hospital. Bill was considerably reassured and mollified by this statement. However, he soon resumed his repetitive pleas for a definite discharge date and his protests that he shouldn't be at the Lodge.

Often his questions had a desperate note, as if he had to have a definite answer that very instant. Their incessant, moment-to-moment repetition seemed related to an urgent need for almost constant replenishment of supplies of reassurance, which kept slipping from his grasp almost immediately.

It was as if he said, over and over again, "Say the magic words once again. Tell me I'll be all right." The desperate urgency of his questions was clearly indicated by an incident with his therapist. In answer to Bill's questions as to whether he should be in the Lodge, the therapist one day shifted from saying that he didn't yet know Bill well enough to say definitely, to a direct opinion that Bill did need to be at the Lodge. Bill then asked, "How long?" and pressed for a definite date while insisting that six months ought to be long enough. The therapist refused to commit himself, saying that he could not give a definite date, especially in view of the fact that if the date proved incorrect Bill might feel that the therapist had lied. Bill then became extremely tense and said that he felt barely able to restrain the impulse to put his fist in the therapist's mouth.

Uncertainty regarding the capacity for conscious control: As with the other patients described in this chapter, the question of Bill's capacity for conscious control and purposive action was a focus of uncertainty. Several of the staff members tended to attribute deliberate willfulness to much of his aggravating behavior, such as his repeated questions and demands, his threats to run away or to assault others, and his misappropriation of the property of other patients. Opinions were uncertain and divided as to whether Bill really wanted to run away. Undoubtedly this reflected his own uncertainty and ambivalence, and probably the staff's uncertain appraisal was reflected back to him and increased his own uncertainty.

Bill himself expressed considerable fear of loss of control. In fact, this was a major element contributing to his fear and refusal of the patient role. He said that previous treatment had ruined him by making him release his impulses, lessen his inhibitions, and generally lose control, so that he was exceedingly reluctant to accept treatment and the status of patient for fear of history's repeating itself.

Still another indication of his precarious ego control was the manner in which he sometimes imitated statements made by others about him. He parroted the staff's answers to his queries as to when he could leave and what he must do in order to be ready to leave. He might say, "Oh, yes, I'm supposed to learn how to get along with others and then I can leave." Such mechanical parrotings had the hollow ring of ritualistic formulas rather than sounding like a realistic appraisal of his situation.

Occasionally there were glimpses of possible gross underlying confusion. For instance, at the swimming pond he forgot where he had placed his outer clothing, and sometimes he seemed bewildered about finding his way to the dining room. The extent of his possible confusion was obscured by his own efforts to present himself as a person in complete possession of his faculties and the situation. The staff, in turn, was puzzled in attempting to appraise his capacity for self-control, a situation which had many potentialities for a vicious cycle.

Bill's repetitive requests for services, such as delivery of coffee or cigarettes, seemed to derive part of their meaning from an urge to achieve at least a momentary sense of mastery and control over the situation. But here again, whatever reassurance he gained from fulfillment of his demands evaporated almost immediately. In addition, their endlessly repetitious quality came to have high nuisance value for the staff. A further possible meaning of his demands was role reversal or at least derogation of staff roles, especially when he cast his therapist in the role of servant, asking him to fetch this or that immediate want, as if this were his only useful role.

Supplementary role efforts: The supplementary role most meaningful to Bill was the job as a golf caddy which he had held for a few days during one of his escapes. Within the hospital context most efforts to establish supplementary roles were unsuccessful. His efforts to assert the identity of a superior athlete were hampered by his difficulty in concentration, his exquisite sensitivity to possible defeat, and the downright pleasure of several of the ward staff members, irked by his air of superiority, at seeing his boasts deflated.

Attempts to organize a supplementary role in the patient work program largely met defeat. Bill's propensity for running away required that an aide escort him to work assignments such as care of the grounds, and instead of fitting into the role of worker, Bill would become absorbed in testing the aide-patient role structure, with his repeated questions about the fairness, legality, and probable duration of his patient status. Bill himself requested work in the woodworking shop, but the ward staff, fearful of his unpredictable assaults, preferred that he not be allowed access to potentially dangerous tools. For a brief time Bill was interested in piano lessons from another patient but this soon lapsed.

Of distinct supplementary-role significance were his reactions prior to and during an all-hospital dinner party. Earlier in the day Bill had been so tense, pacing restlessly and asking his incessant questions, that the staff members had doubted the advisability of his attending the party. However, they decided to chance it. Shortly after arriving at the party Bill changed remarkably. He relaxed, mingled rather easily, and made small talk. He told his administrative physician, "You know, this is more like it. I used to be a pretty civil fellow. I used to go to cocktail parties." When introduced to a staff secretary, he smilingly said, "I'm just an ex-gangster on the lam for a while." This semiflip, semiserious definition of himself contained many elements of his identity-role problems. His transformation in the party setting was not fully sustained; after an hour or so he reverted to his restless tension and made an effort to escape. Although temporary, the effect of the blurred staff-patient role distinctions at the party on lessening Bill's identity-role conflict was striking.

In general, Bill's capacity to create and adapt to supplementary roles was limited by specific features of his personality organization. His low threshold for frustration and his intolerance of defeat or any status-lowering experience were related to his reliance upon a passive, narcissistic mode in which he expected things to come magically to him. These factors, combined with limitations in the hospital role organization, made probable at least a stalemate between the patient's efforts at identity definition and the staff's expectations of the patient role, if not further disintegration of his flimsy identity structure.

This man's background contained heavy emphasis on social status and a series of unsuccessful attempts to establish a confirmed identity. He lacked a satisfactory male identification model and his overprotective mother encouraged him in magical, narcissistic modes of enhancement of his self-esteem as opposed to active, industrious pursuit of realistic goals. His general intolerance of frustration and defeat accentuated his unwillingness to accept the downgrading implicit in accepting the role of patient. His hospital course featured denial of illness, statements assuming the identity of criminal, protests against the patient role, and incessant requests for reassuring definitions of himself and his life situation. Neither the staff's efforts to encourage him to accept the patient role nor its attempts to afford supplementary roles met with success. Increased restriction and control, prompted by his instability and his attempts to run away, accentuated his protests of the situation. Staff uncertainty in appraising his capacity for conscious control and purpose probably increased his own doubts regarding himself.

Case 4

John, a young man in his early thirties, was twice admitted to Chestnut Lodge, for stays of six and 20 months respectively. Prominent in his history was an identity-definition struggle marked by deep conflict over which parent to align himself with. Although named for his successful father, a self-made businessman with professional training, John identified with him less successfully than did his younger brother, his only sibling. Identification with his father was hampered by a sticky mutual attachment with his mother, who herself was extremely dependent. During John's late adolescence she had suffered a depressive-paranoid illness and had remained in bed most of the time for nearly three years. Highly conscious of family background and social status, she was ambitious for John, but at the same time so possessive and blindly admiring that she hindered his development of independence and a constructive self-critical capacity. When he became overtly ill, she ignored the seriousness of his difficulties, which she excused and blamed on others.

John's mother-versus-father identification conflict was further accentuated by turmoil over professional schooling. He had attended college near home, which pleased his mother, and then, upon her urging, he chose to study for his father's profession. However, after vacillation and much turmoil he decided, with his father's backing, to attend a graduate school away from home. His mother opposed this, expressing her fear that if John went to a distant school, he eventually would marry and settle far from home. Earlier she had been distressed by her son's showing pubertal changes and an interest in dating.

His attempt to break away from his mother and align himself with his father by going to a distant school was fraught with much difficulty. During his second year at graduate school he became upset and troubled about his relationships with his classmates. The next year he transferred to his father's alma mater, where his brother was an undergraduate. He was urged to make this transfer by a professor friend of his father who was himself making the same transfer. Thus for John the move had multiple connotations of greater affiliation with his father.

In this context he failed dismally. Upon receipt of his nonpassing grades, he phoned to tell his father with great anguish that he had disgraced him.

The following year he returned to the first school, where he managed to pull up his grades and graduate. However, he failed professional examinations and again was distressed that he had disgraced both himself and his father. It now seems clear that much of his anguish stemmed from his awareness of inability to identify successfully with his father.

After six months in a routine, nonprofessional job he was called to active duty as an Army Reserve officer. His assignment involved rather close confinement within a group isolated from outside contacts for extended periods. After six months he was hospitalized with infectious hepatitis for several months. Subsequently he said that the hepatitis had weakened both his general physical strength and specifically his sexual powers. Another event, approximately concurrent, that probably also helped to precipitate his overt manifestations of mental illness was a nonfatal heart attack suffered by his father.

A few weeks after his return to duty, John began to act peculiarly. He stared fixedly at the post nurses and was convinced of their sexual interest in him. At the same time he startled his commanding officer by the question, "Are you a woman? Are you what you think you are?" Hospitalization followed shortly with a diagnosis of paranoid schizophrenia. Hallucinated voices accused him of weakness, homosexuality, and failure. He attempted to hang himself. His uncertainty regarding the masculine-feminine component of his identity was strikingly indicated by his hearing voices which classified his gender after each of his actions. Because his every movement was followed by the hallucinated comment, "That's a man" or "That's a woman," he felt that his slightest gesture might alter the judgment of his sexual identity.

After nearly a year of hospitalization in military and veterans hospitals he was retired from the Army and released to his home. He made several abortive job efforts, leaving one because he could not countenance working under the supervision of a woman. Another attempt to identify with his father by taking professional examinations failed miserably. His preparatory studying was rendered hopelessly ineffectual by hallucinated voices, which he attributed to women in the house next door who reiterated their opposition to his passing the exams because it would make him too independent. That this represented his mother's attitude is abundantly clear. His ambivalence then was demonstrated by his arriving a day late for the exams. He blamed this on a plot, and left home in a rage telling no one where he was going. Subsequently he reported that the voices had said he could escape them if he went to Mexico. To his dismay he found in Mexico that this promise was not fulfilled: he felt that advance notice had been passed along the route to arrange that microphones and other persecutory devices be planted in his hotel rooms. John fled back to the United States, where he made disorganized, grandiose efforts to establish an export-import business. Rehospitalization ensued shortly, and soon afterwards he was transferred to Chestnut Lodge.

First Chestnut Lodge admission: Upon arrival, John was well dressed and overly polite. Although he attempted to maintain a genial manner, he appeared quite anxious and guarded. For the most part he tended to deny illness and to shy away from discussion of personal problems; occasionally, however, he acknowledged previous sickness and craziness and said that he still was troubled by voices derogating his sexual nature and his capacity to work.

John tried to structure the role relationship with his therapist as if they were colleagues and buddies who were on a par with each other. He called the therapist by his first name and, in an effort to impress him, referred in offhand pseudosophistication to matters of big business and high finance. Sometimes he affected cryptic mannerisms such as chuckling or nodding to himself with an air of being "in the know about some big deals." With the ward staff he was overbearing and opinionated although he participated fairly well in group activities, played the piano, and sang. For a time he worked on a model of an Army tank, a task perhaps related in some way to his brief Army career.

He evidenced great underlying concern over questions of strength and potency and whether masculinity could be defined in terms of muscular power. He was also enormously concerned with defining proper role behavior between men and women. For instance, he was startlingly outraged by his therapist's lightly frivolous tone in a phone conversation with the charge nurse. On another occasion he protested that the doctor did not deal strongly enough with the nurses who were running his life. Similarly he stated that his father was weaker and not as forceful as he once had been. John occasionally affected a blasé manner about the "good-looking babes" around the Lodge, as if he were a sophisticated man of the world.

John's first stay ended when he refused to return after a trip home from his brother's wedding.

Interim between Chestnut Lodge admissions: John and his father quarreled when his father urged him to return to the hospital and refused to lend him money for a vaguely defined business venture. The climax was a violent outburst in which John accused his father of trying to kill him. It seems likely that John felt that his father was murdering him by refusing to allow him to assume the identity of businessman.

During the next 15 months John lived first at home and then in various hotel rooms. He made an autistic attempt to establish the identity of businessman by renting an office, buying expensive furniture, and putting in time at the office every day. He spoke vaguely of an export business to deal in nonexplosive chemicals through Greek and Italian companies.

Gradually John became more and more disturbed and spent money recklessly. When his unpaid bills mounted precipitously, his father realized that John could no longer manage outside a hospital, and arranged that John be sent Army orders to report for an examination at a military hospital. There he was found to be flagrantly delusional. His readmission to Chestnut Lodge was arranged in a fashion which lent itself to John's thinking that it had been ordered by the Army, a circumstance which undoubtedly contributed to his uncertainty regarding his identity and role.

Initial efforts at identity definition: Upon his readmission the major change was that he seemed distinctly less puzzled and troubled by the nature of his experiences than previously. He now spoke with an air of satisfied certainty that he had everything figured out.

Although at the time much of his behavior seemed obscure and fragmentary, it is possible, with retrospection and detachment from the emotional intensity of the situation, to pick out distinct patterns. John attempted to assert an identity featured by manliness, success, importance, and strength. He dressed meticulously in the conservative attire of a successful businessman, which identity he claimed. With a stiff, pompous, condescending air he attempted to impress others and himself that he was perfectly well and in full command of the situation. However, he managed only an extremely brittle façade, or perhaps merely the rudiments of a façade, which was seriously marred by the repetitive intrusion of inappropriate gestures and grimaces. Occasionally he acknowledged that he was hearing voices. His effort to assert an identity of importance was so desperately tenuous that he had recourse to magical delusions such as the repetitive, blandly confident assertion that he was soon to marry Princess Margaret Rose. He took great pains to state that he had British blood and connections with various important persons and big businesses. His discussions of other persons were often in terms of their belonging to such and such a category. In fact, identifying persons by categorization was an overriding concern—for example, he recited lists of names and genealogies. One solution to the problem of identity definition seemed to be his membership in an ancestral line, so that his identity had little to do with personal capacities and achievements. It also was in keeping with his mother's great emphasis on family background as the major source of one's identity.

In a brief undefensive and relatively undelusional interval, he clearly stated his concern regarding loss of identity and role, although not using those exact terms. He said he had lost his honor when he became a mental patient and that he felt forsaken by the Army and the government in general. He mentioned that perhaps he could join the Navy since the Army was such a miserable outfit anyway. The only other alternatives were to kill himself or to emigrate to Australia. The latter became a recurrent theme which he elaborated in various ways. He said that he wished to go there because no one here wanted to help him, and that Australia was similar to America 200 years ago in needing new immigrants, especially men. The idea of living in Australia was further associated with an urge for autonomy and self-sufficiency. He said he planned to build a solid house there, with its own electric generator. At times he made out lists of what he would need in Australia, adding that it was a long distance from the United States, from this hellhole called a hospital, and especially from his parents. He spoke unrealistically of contacting the Australian ambassador to make immediate arrangements, and a few times asked his therapist to help him with these arrangements.

Another preoccupation which belied his efforts to assert a strong masculine identity was a deeply pervasive anxiety regarding bodily weakness. He feared that he didn't have enough blood, and that his heart was breaking down and failing to push enough blood to his brain cells. He was certain that his heart was slowing down and beating only once or twice a minute. He repeatedly made a ticlike clicking sound with his tongue, saying that this washed or squashed his brain and strengthened the brain cells.[10]

John associated his fear of loss of strength with his father, complaining, "He is derogatory of me. He has a bigger head than I and is always doing things to knock me out. He's going to take away my heart. He will cut it out and give me his bad heart, his broken-down heart." This apparently was a reference to the father's heart attack, which coincided approximately with the onset of John's overt psychosis. John's statement concretely expressed his changed appraisal of his father; instead of being a source of strength and support, he was perceived as threatening to steal John's all-too-limited supplies of strength. Several times John complained that his father had changed and was now weak.

A further gross contradiction of John's assertion of a strong masculine identity was evidenced in his periodic open statements that he wished to be transformed into a woman. He said that women have a better life than men and occupy a position of dominance over everything. Somewhat incoherently he described having attempted between hospitalizations at the

---

[10] This likely was a compulsive effort to clear his mind of confusion and intrusive disturbing thoughts. A similar tic is described by Phyllis Greenacre (1952).

Lodge to transform himself by consuming huge quantities of cream and other soft, fattening, and, to John, feminizing foods. He also had purchased a large supply of soft pencils with which to "scratch the muscle fibers to make them female." The wish to change to a woman was mixed in varying proportions with a fear of such a change. It might be noted parenthetically that in the subsequent course of John's illness the wish gradually predominated over the fear. He seemed progressively to abandon his struggle to achieve a masculine identity patterned after his father and instead to helplessly accept identification with his sick mother. Increasingly his behavior resembled that of his mother in her illness 17 years before, especially in the features of helpless passivity and retreat to bed.

Staff responses: Staff responses were distinctly unenthusiastic toward John's attempts to assert the identity of an important businessman and to deny illness and serious personal problems. His therapist found him a dull, unstimulating patient, boring in his repetitive attempts to maintain a formal role. He felt that most of John's attempts at identity definition were so flagrantly delusional, empty, and stereotyped that little about them could be realistically supported. John seemed to wish from him only responses confirmatory of a delusional identity, and arrogantly brushed aside any other responses.

The administrator and ward staff also found themselves quite disinterested in John. His grandiose notions of marrying Princess Margaret Rose and of various other important business and social connections were so monotonously repeated that the staff members soon heard them as relatively meaningless prattle. This reaction was reinforced as they found that their efforts to make meaningful responses had no noticeable effect.

Phase of autistic work activity: Approximately three weeks after admission a brief episode occurred which marked a change in John's efforts at identity definition. He dropped his pompous denial of illness, voiced fear that he was going "batty," and requested tranquilizing drugs. Then he became greatly preoccupied with the notion that his heart was slowing down and becoming too weak to push sufficient blood to his head. He complained of general body weakness and took to bed for several days.

He was reassured that his heart was normal and encouraged to get out of bed and to be more active. He complied, but with a gradual change from his behavior of the first few weeks. In place of much of the stereotyped recitation of his grandiose marriage and business plans there appeared a more solitary effort to assert the identity of businessman. At the rear of the ward hallway, he set up a working area with a table as a desk, where he spent many hours a day mechanically and laboriously copying word for word such printed material as statistical manuals, sorting and resorting his mail, and reading lists of names from the telephone book. This evidently was similar to his behavior between Chestnut Lodge admissions when he had put in time conducting a totally autistic export-import business.[11] John himself commented that to work was to be healthy and that working was a means of preventing sudden death.

Approximately coinciding with the appearance of this pattern of identity definition via autistic work was a distinct shift in the relationships to which John turned for emotional support. Specifically he turned away from his father and his therapist and toward an uncle by marriage, a retired Navy officer of high rank who apparently had not been especially significant in John's life prior to his illness. However, within the first few months of John's second stay he began writing his uncle almost daily and continued to do so throughout the remainder of his hospital stay. The development of this attachment to his uncle was concurrent with growing distrust of and distance from his father. After four or five months at the Lodge, John requested that his uncle be made his legal guardian in place of his father. Although writing his uncle almost daily, he seldom if ever replied to his father's letters. He refused to sign checks which his father had sent for endorsement. He also complained that his parents were trying to wreck his life and were connected with large trusts plotting to ruin him. It seems plausible to suggest that John may have turned to his uncle as a source of masculine strength and support when, subsequent to his father's heart attack, he began to think his father weak. John's wish to change guardians may have been an effort to change his identity, an attempt to find a stronger male ally, or a wish to escape his father's influence and supposed domination.

Another by no means insignificant factor in this development was increasing conflict about his therapist. During this period John had become less communicative with his doctor and had, for the first time, flared up in open anger at him. After seeing a young woman patient emerge from the doctor's office, he angrily accused the doctor of raping her, and threatened to kill him. He then managed to control his rage, saying, as if to dissuade himself, that since women apparently were fond of the doctor perhaps he should not be killed.

Phase of withdrawal: John's autistic work routine began to disintegrate and he became generally more withdrawn and uncommunicative. He sat on the toilet and stood before the bathroom mirror for hours. Perhaps

[11] Quite revealing were the attitudes of his parents regarding disposition of the expensive office equipment after John was rehospitalized. His father favored and his mother opposed selling it. All along she apparently had been pleased with John's preoccupation with his autistic work. She showed no appreciation of its unrealistic and totally unproductive nature, but said she was glad as long as it gave John the *feeling* that he was working. One suspects a schizophrenogenic significance in her emphasis on the private meaning of John's activity in his internal world, to the almost total neglect of its socially shared meaning in the external world. A mother might seriously weaken her child's capacity for reality-testing by encouraging him to ignore harsh reality in favor of comfortable fantasy. As a purchase price for symbiotic intimacy, the mother and child may eventually pay in terms of isolation from the rest of the world in a *folie à deux*.

staring in the mirror was a desperate attempt to solidify or fix his body image and identity; this is not uncommon in schizophrenic disorganization and identity diffusion. He ate so little that several tube feedings were required.

During this generally uncommunicative period John did afford a few glimpses of the precariousness of his sense of control over internal forces. He said, "I think I will never be able to really describe what's going on in me." At another point he asked, "Would a jury acquit me of being crazy?" His increasing immobility and inability to eat were associated with crippling indecision. At times he sat rigidly and breathed deeply as if in a last-ditch effort to control himself. His stilted pose of a proper gentleman and his obsessive, empty work routines can be regarded as partly in the service of self-control. Although often seemingly indifferent to the therapist's presence, occasionally he said, "Please don't leave now," and in office interviews remained fixed to his chair after the therapist had indicated the end of the appointment. Such clinging behavior was indicative of enormous dependency and devastating separation anxiety that also seemed linked to fear of a lack of capacity for self-regulation and control. The fact that during John's general withdrawal the therapist was his only tenuous link to real and immediate persons rendered the therapist an object of intense ambivalence. The therapist in turn found this a position of oppressive intensity.

John also voiced fears of a cosmic explosion brought about by the collision of two planets. He said that the moon was rushing toward the earth and that disaster was imminent. Once he asked the administrator for books on astronomy which he might study. John's fears of cosmic collisions and explosions seem to represent his dread of loss of control of destructive forces within himself.

Incongruity between patient and therapist: Differing appraisals of John's capacity for self-control and conscious purpose constituted a major but largely unspoken disagreement between his therapist and himself. In addition to feeling enormously threatened by impending loss of control, John indicated by his behavior that his sense of conscious purpose was extremely tenuous; much of the time he apparently experienced himself as an automaton helplessly responding to forces beyond his control and even beyond his knowledge. Of course, he attempted to maintain a façade of one who was in control of himself and the situation. This defensive effort—producing stiff, manneristic control—contributed heavily to the therapist's perceiving him as resistive, stubborn, and controlling. He described John as the master of the situation, who so controlled their interviews that the therapist felt futile, castrated, and worn out. The therapist partly viewed John's behavior as consciously, purposively designed to control the therapist, rather than John himself. The therapist ascribed a purposive quality to various features of John's behavior: his uncommunicativeness was labeled evasive and indirect; his refusal to eat was an effort to blackmail others into greater capitulation to his wishes; his social withdrawal was an effort to drive others away from him; and his smiling to himself was an indication of a supercilious, this-is-something-I-won't-let-you-in-on, private thought.[12] It should be emphasized that this was not the therapist's only view of this complex situation, but much of John's behavior was so willful, stubborn, and even arrogant that it obscured the extreme lack of autonomous control underlying it.

There was further incongruity between John and his therapist concerning definition of the role of patient. The therapist believed that ideally a patient should acknowledge illness and accept his need for hospitalization and treatment. He should place some measure of trust in the therapist as someone in whom to confide personal thoughts. For the most part John eschewed this role definition and instead attempted to structure the situation as if both he and the doctor were either businessmen who might talk of matters of high political and financial import, or college buddies who might share smutty jokes and casual boasts of their prowess with women. Thus the therapist would urge John to speak about what was troubling him, only to have John arrogantly walk to the phone insisting that he must call the Pentagon on important business and could not be bothered with anything else. To some extent the therapist perceived John's refusal to conform to the role of patient as willful contrariness rather than as a defensive necessity.

The therapist experienced a distinct threat to his own identity and professional role status. At times after sessions with John he felt the weakening of his identity with special acuteness, particularly when John's overt behavior had denied any need whatsoever for the doctor as a helpful person.

Phase of loss of control: The next major development was the breakdown of John's controls as he erupted into violent physical attacks on others. It was noteworthy that this occurred at a time when two major sources of support were unavailable. John's therapist was on vacation when the first major assault occurred. Then while the therapist was still away, John received word that his valued uncle had suffered a serious heart attack. Although the uncle's illness undoubtedly was a critical blow to John, his reaction to it was quite realistic. He sent appropriate "get-well" letters and flowers to his uncle. In addition, John was almost always responsive to inquiries from the ward staff regarding his uncle's health, while minimally communicative regarding most other topics. It is difficult to know whether this was simply because the topic was of greatest interest to John or because all along his relationship with his uncle had been a

---

[12] The significance of attributing a purposive quality to a patient's behavior has been pertinently discussed by Cumming and Cumming (1956). They suggest that hospital staff members are likely to feel more anger toward a patient whose behavior differs quantitatively from normative group behavior than toward one whose behavior differs qualitatively and is perceived as less intentional. They further suggest that this may be a factor which makes some patients become chronic and others not.

relatively lucid, intact island in John's thinking and action. At any rate, John did not take recourse to the familiar mechanisms of denial and delusion regarding his uncle's illness.

In other painful sectors of reality John used misperceptions and delusions in a frantic effort to retain control and meaningful organization of his experience. For instance, the target of his first major assault was a Negro aide, whom John misperceived as Nasser of Egypt. Occurring at the time of the Suez crisis between Great Britain and Egypt, this delusion incorporated John's ideas that things British symbolized good and desirable objects. Thus when an assaultive impulse escaped control into abrupt discharge, John retained a measure of logical meaning in his representation of reality by misperceiving the target as an enemy of the good object. It seems plausible to assume that without this device to salvage meaning, John might have been plunged into even greater disorganization when the assaultive impulse erupted.

Similar examples were evident as John's assaultiveness became more frequent and was aimed toward several different persons. He insisted that the persons he attacked were notorious criminals, wanted by the FBI. Once he gave a student nurse a dime and pleaded that she phone the FBI to notify them of the presence of these criminals. He attacked another patient, who he was certain had bullied him in childhood. It is unclear whether these rationalizations occurred before, after, or concurrent with the assaults. Misperception also was employed in last-ditch efforts to restrain, as well as to explain, the impulses. A striking instance of this occurred once when John's therapist was urging him to talk more—in effect, to conform more closely to the ideal patient role. John, already holding himself rigidly and breathing deeply, retorted angrily to his German-born therapist, "How do you expect me to talk when I think of a dirty, corrupt bunch of swine who have caused two world wars?" The startled therapist acknowledged this as an insult, whereupon John hastily said, "I know you are actually British." When the therapist in a reality confrontation insisted that he was German rather than British, John burst into a violent physical assault. Previously, John had intermittently categorized the therapist as British, with such comments as "You have a British nose. You look like Prince Philip. How is Queen Elizabeth?" Presumably these distortions of reality were an effort to construct and preserve a good-object image of the therapist.

A few days prior to his attack on his therapist, he had assaulted his father, who was visiting. Immediately following these attacks on two of the most significant persons in his life, John was extremely disturbed for several weeks. He refused to eat, was incontinent on the floor of his room, and violently attacked persons who attempted to enter it. Gradually the acute disturbance subsided, but John continued a pattern of general withdrawal interspersed with unpredictable attacks on others.

The eruption of aggression as a major feature of John's behavior, especially when directed at his father, was most disconcerting to his family. He had always filled a family role of model of good behavior, and this drastic change threatened the entire family equilibrium. Their anxiety fed back still further pressure into the therapist-patient relationship.

John's assaultiveness also raised again the question of his capacity for conscious control of his behavior. His therapist thought that some of John's attacks showed planning and deliberate intent rather than uncontrollable impulse discharge. He thought, too, that John discriminated in his choice of targets, picking only those certain not to fight back, although in several instances this was not the case. John did show a remarkably persistent specificity in his choice of targets, which contributed to an impression of purposiveness. However, John saw himself more the passive victim than the active director of forces impelling his actions.

Phase of helpless passivity: Gradually John slipped into a state of helpless passivity, except for sporadic assaultive outbursts. He ceased his efforts to dress the part of a businessman and no longer affected the manner of an important man-of-the-world. He lay in bed much of the day. For a time, although eating very poorly, he was preoccupied with food, clipping numerous recipes from magazines, and showing a distinct preference for cream and similar soft or liquid foods.

During this period, while manifesting increasing passivity, he also definitely preferred the company of women. While pleasantly responsive to student nurses, he was almost continuously hostile and negativistic toward male aides. John's therapist was rather critical of this situation, saying that the attention of the student nurses seemed to afford John a secondary gain from his passive, dependent behavior. He added that John was like a pasha awaiting the ministrations of his servants. The therapist's resentment was very similar to annoyance expressed by John's father at his son's open indulgence in passivity.

Thus during the final phase of his hospital stay, John's efforts at identity definition clearly swung from a masculine to a feminine image. Although continuing to write his uncle, he seemed to abandon his attempts to emulate male models of assertiveness and active mastery. Instead he increasingly accepted a passive, recipient, and even feminine role, aside from intermittent, brief flurries of assaultiveness. The staff in turn perceived John in increasingly stereotyped and depersonalized fashion. John, the nursing care problem, eclipsed John, the person.

John's transfer to another hospital was arranged when his father became discouraged by this turn of events.

This man's construction of an integrated identity was severely hampered by a deep conflict over whether to identify with his mother or his father. The dilemma was prominent in the onset and throughout the course of his illness. His efforts to assert an active masculine identity took on increasingly unrealistic and magical qualities, which fit poorly with the patient role expectations held by the hospital staff. He, in turn, looked to autistic measures—a fantasied business, a new beginning by emigration to Australia—and to persons geographically distant, such as his uncle, for support of his identity, rather than to persons in the immediate real environment. Thus he denied the staff members their roles as helping persons. The hospital role offered him probably accentuated his drift toward a helpless, passive identification with the sick aspects of his mother, a trend already likely because of the precarious state of his ego organization. Nonetheless, one wonders whether roles alternative to that of passive invalid might have been found which would have strengthened his efforts to achieve active mastery and positive identity. At the same time a strong question can be raised as to whether the course of events should also be viewed as a therapeutic regression with potential for reorganization.

DISCUSSION

We have presented these cases in such detail because we believe they illustrate well the pervasive significance of identity-role conflicts in the hospital careers of schizophrenic patients. Upon entering a hospital, the patient all too often views himself in the words of Frost (1945) in "The Death of the Hired Man":

> . . . nothing to look backward to with pride.
> And nothing to look forward to with hope,
> So now and never any different.

For a person in that predicament identity and role are of vital concern, all the more so because his personality organization is so vulnerable to influence by the environment.

We do not believe that identity-role conflicts and the danger of identity disintegration in the hospital setting are limited to a few special patients. Quite the contrary; we are convinced that it is exceedingly prevalent (Erikson, 1957). We deliberately focused upon patients in whose hospital careers identity and role failed to mesh and unfortunate consequences ensued. There were other patients who managed to establish at least partially satisfactory identity-role fits. In several instances supplementary role opportunities were important. For example, Glen, whose claim to the dual identity of concert pianist and horse trainer we described at the outset of this chapter, was able to give a semiformal piano recital in the hospital recreation center. Another patient, formerly a professor, gave a series of technical lectures. Still another managed the hospital canteen. It may not be too great an exaggeration to say that for patients whose identities are perilously shattered such supplementary role opportunities may be lifesaving.

In this regard, several patients come quickly to mind who refused to collaborate in treatment, even to the point of long periods of muteness, until they became outpatients or established themselves in schools or jobs outside the hospital. As soon as they had one foot outside the hospital in supplementary roles, their acceptance of the patient role increased dramatically.

Other studies of the effect of hospital organization on patient functioning may be cited, including the work of Jones (1952), Sivadon (1957), and Stanton and Schwartz (1954). Sivadon (1960) also reported a remarkable side effect of the German invasion of France during World War II. In the face of the oncoming German Army, the staff of a government mental hospital fled, leaving the patients to fend for themselves. Follow-up after the war indicated that many of the patients had fended astonishingly well, not only in terms of survival but in terms of subsequent success in jobs and other social roles.

A somewhat similar account is that of a hospital in Israel for chronic mental patients which for economic reasons was changed into a work camp. Here, too, with fresh role opportunities, many of the ex-patients did surprisingly well (Bruch, 1960). Revealingly, when the workers were provided with a truck which still had a red cross painted on it, they objected vigorously that they no longer were patients and that the red cross should be erased.

These various sources of data argue, we believe, for a careful review of the various determinants of traditional hospital role organization, with a view toward increasing the availability of a range of roles supplementary to that of patient. It is important that supplementary roles be as real as possible and not simply "make-work" or a type of occupational "therapy." In this regard it is worth recalling the question of Joe, Case 1, as to whether he would be paid for performing in the role of musician. The importance of positively valued and socially necessary roles for the patient was also emphasized in the preceding chapter on time as an organizing factor in the lives of patients.

For certain types of patients perhaps a hospital is not the proper treatment setting, and alternatives such as halfway houses, foster homes, work camps, clubs, and day-hospital-schools might be more suitable.

This is not to say that the whole problem of lack of identity-role fit is the result of hospital organization. As the illustrative cases amply demonstrate, patients bring to the situation serious ego instabilities and records of failure to achieve stable identities in any previous situation. Certainly patients who are desperately close to losing autonomous ego control will be most disturbed by features of hospital procedures and organization which anticipate a patient's helplessness and lack of control. Another common phenomenon consists of persons with only "negative identities," who, in a sense, have a need *not* to fit any role (Erikson, 1959). Their major identity is that of misfit. Another consideration is that by increasing and broadening role expectations of the patient, the hospital staff might run the risk of pushing him into still another failure. One also can argue that to provide roles supplementary to that of patient might aid and abet denial of illness, projection of blame, and resistance to therapy.

Perhaps the most cogent argument mitigating the disadvantages of identity-role conflict is that the apparently disintegrative course of the illustrative cases should not be regarded as entirely negative. Conceivably the described clinical courses constituted regressions with distinct therapeutic and reintegrative potential. For certain patients a phase of regression is perhaps not only unavoidable but also necessary and desirable if thoroughgoing personality change is to occur. Particularly for patients organized along rigid paranoid lines a phase of disintegration or, in a sense, a melting of their rigid personality structure may be required as a preliminary to reorganization. Some authors have suggested that by means of schizophrenic illness a person effects a drastic personality shift which he cannot accomplish by any other means (Boisen, Jenkins and Lorr, 1954). Although we believe one should guard against the self-deluding quality of the dictum, "Patients have to get worse before they get better," the possibility of a necessary therapeutic regressive phase cannot be dismissed lightly. In the case histories described, the periods of identity weakening and diffusion contained elements of a positive quest toward a new identity. It is possible that had treatment progressed further without termination by external circumstances, a phase of reintegration might have developed.

These various considerations further emphasize the complexities of attempting to achieve a constructive identity-role fit for patients. At best the hospital career of a schizophrenic patient is a dreadful and tortuous experience. One patient, having seen on a hospital bulletin board the title of an earlier version of this chapter which had been prepared for presentation at a staff meeting, wrote a note to the authors saying, "My God! Do you call this a career?"

BIBLIOGRAPHY

Boisen, A. T., Jenkins, R. L., & Lorr, M. (1954), Schizophrenic Ideation as Striving Toward the Solution of Conflict. *J. Clinic. Psychol.*, *10*:389-391.

Bruch, H. (1960), personal communication.

Burnham, D. L. (1959), unpublished research.

Cumming, J. & Cumming, E. (1956), Affective Symbolism, Social Norms, and Mental Illness. *Psychiat.*, *19*:77-85.

Erikson, E. H. (1959), Identity and the Life Cycle. *Psycholog. Issues*, Vol. 1, No. 1. New York: International Universities Press.

Erikson, K. T. (1957), Patient Role and Social Uncertainty—A Dilemma of the Mentally Ill. *Psychiat.*, *20*:263-274.

Frost, R. (1945), *Collected Poems of Robert Frost*. New York: Holt.

Gibson, R. W. & George, G. (1959), Patient-Staff Relationships Change with Environment. *Ment. Hosp.*, *10*:18-19.

Goffman, E. (1957), The Characteristics of Total Institutions. In: *Symposium on Preventive and Social Psychiatry*, Washington, D.C., Walter Reed Army Institute of Research.

Greenacre, P. (1952), *Trauma, Growth, and Personality*. New York: Norton.

Jones, M. (1952), *Social Psychiatry*. London: Tavistock.

Loeb, M. B. (1957), Role Definition in the Social World of a Psychiatric Hospital. In: *The Patient and the Mental Hospital*, ed. M. Greenblatt, D. J. Levinson, and R. H. Williams. Glencoe, Ill.: Free Press.

Parsons, T. (1951), Illness and the Role of the Physician: A Sociological Perspective. *Amer. J. Orthopsychiat.*, *21*:452-460.

Polansky, N. A., White, R. B., & Miller, S. C. (1957), Determinants of the Role-Image of the Patient in a Psychiatric Hospital. In: *The Patient and the Mental Hospital*, ed. M. Greenblatt, D. J. Levinson, and R. H. Williams. Glencoe, Ill.: Free Press.

Searles, H. F. (1959), Integration and Differentiation in Schizophrenia: An Over-All View. *Brit. J. Med. Psychol.*, *32*:261-281.

Sivadon, P. (1957), Techniques of Sociotherapy. In: *Symposium on Preventive and Social Psychiatry*, Washington, D.C., Walter Reed Army Institute of Research.

—————— (1960), personal communication.

Stanton, A. H. & Schwartz, M. S. (1954), *The Mental Hospital*. New York: Basic Books.

Talbot, E., Miller, S. C., & White, R. B. (1960), Roles for Hospitalized Psychiatric Patients. Unpublished paper, Stockbridge, Mass., Austen Riggs Center.

White, R. B., Miller, S. C., & Polansky, N. A. (1955), Sanctuary Versus Social Demand: The Dilemma of the Therapeutic Community. Presented at meeting of the American Psychiatric Association, Atlantic City.

Wood, E. C., Rakusin, J. M., & Morse, E. (1960), Interpersonal Aspects of Psychiatric Hospitalization. *Arch. Gen. Psychiat.*, 3:632-641.

XV
STRATEGIES OF CLINICAL ADMINISTRATION AND THE NEED-FEAR DILEMMA

ROBERT W. GIBSON

OUR PURPOSE IN THIS CHAPTER is to discuss the applicability to clinical administration of our theoretical formulations, particularly the need-fear dilemma.

First, we wish to comment generally concerning the clinical administrator's part in hospital treatment of the schizophrenic patient. The patient's lack of stable internal organization requires that the hospital pursue, among others, two major treatment goals. These goals may at times seem contradictory, but actually are not, if they are blended in proper proportions. We refer to the goals of providing necessary external control and regulations for the patient while simultaneously facilitating his development of adequate internal controls and regulatory capacities.

Another formulation of this twofold goal is in terms of providing supports for the patient's weak ego while at the same time confronting him with challenges and opportunities for ego growth. Support may involve direct control and management of major symptoms, while facilitation of ego growth involves encouraging fundamental personality changes and assumption of personal responsibility by the patient.

The sharing of the treatment responsibility for the patient by both a psychotherapist and a clinical administrator is one means of attempting to effect a balance between these treatment goals. It has been a major feature of treatment strategy at Chestnut Lodge for over 25 years. It would not be accurate to say that the administrator concentrates exclusively on providing external regulation while the therapist works at facilitating growth of the patient's internal regulatory capacities, although the division of labor is somewhat along these lines. For example, the administrator is responsible for such matters as the patient's daily schedule, his physical health, how much freedom he should be permitted, and so forth. In brief, a primary concern of the administrator is the management, or at least the supervision of the "other 23 hours" of the patient's daily life outside his one psychotherapy hour. In this capacity the administrator functions partly as an agent of social control, charged with protecting society from possibly destructive behavior by the patient.

However, the administrator's task consists of much more than managing or controlling the patient. He shares with the psychotherapist the goal of facilitating the patient's development of self-regulatory abilities. The administrator is well aware that too much external structure, control, and direct symptom management will stifle the patient's growth.

To illustrate the task of effecting a balance between direct behavior management and facilitation of self-regulation we cite the following clinical example.

In the course of treatment a schizophrenic man with predominantly paranoid symptoms became withdrawn, less communicative, and eventually stopped eating. It was noted that he maintained an adequate fluid intake and his nutrition was good. Efforts at encouraging the patient to eat were at first successful but gradually he resisted these. Discussions with the ward staff were not too illuminating until one of the nurses mentioned that she thought the patient sometimes tried to smell the food. She speculated that he might think that it had been contaminated or poisoned even though the patient had said nothing about this. From discussions with the therapist it was learned that just prior to the change the patient had been more open in discussions about himself but had then become somewhat hostile and suspicious. The history of the patient's early development and childhood seemed consistent with the hypothesis that whenever he became closer and more open to a person he began to fear that an effort might be made to influence and control him—in effect, to poison him. On this basis he was asked if he might wish to observe or even assist in the preparation of his food. In response, he visited the kitchen prior to several meals, and then resumed eating. Presumably his fear of control had been relieved.

In this example refraining from direct and immediate measures of external control, such as electric shock, drugs, or forced feeding, permitted the discovery of an approach which gave the patient a greater measure of autonomous control over a frightening situation. Had direct measures of external control been employed, the patient might have begun eating, but it is highly likely that his fears of being influenced or poisoned would have been reinforced. Careful attention to his physical state had helped us to conclude that drastic intervention was not immediately required. Observation of the patient's behavior gave a clue, which when tied into the therapist's observations, resulted in a plausible hypothesis for the cause of the patient's behavior. The approach that finally succeeded increased the patient's trust and helped him to feel less vulnerable to external influence and more under his own control.

As we indicated earlier, the task of providing external controls while simultaneously facilitating growth of the patient's internal controls also involves finding a balance between support and challenge for the patient. The administrator will seek specific ego-supportive techniques for each patient. This does not mean that the administrator will always function in a supportive fashion—much of the time he will not. For instance, he does not ordinarily use his supportive techniques to foster repression. Rather, he uses them to lessen the disruptive impact of overwhelming anxiety. He must institute supportive measures when anxiety reaches dangerous proportions or disrupts communication for a prolonged period. Some of the specific techniques that can be used will be discussed in a later section of this chapter. At this juncture we simply wish to emphasize that a major task of the administrator is to discover and apply measures which will provide sufficient support not only to avert the patient's greater disorganization but also hopefully to facilitate constructive reorganization.

Along with support, however, the administrator seeks to provide the opportunities and challenges which are necessary if genuine ego growth is to occur. A purely supportive environment might relieve the patient of terrifying psychotic disorganization but might also lack sufficient challenge to impel him to growth and forward movement. Under those circumstances he might drift into chronic stagnation in a relatively comfortable equilibrium with a supportive social structure. To avoid this the administrator must keep in mind the ultimate goal of greater independence and self-regulation for the patient. Toward this end he will seek to provide the patient with appropriate opportunities for initiative, choice, decision, responsibility, and independent action.

Perhaps foremost among the growth-fostering conditions which the administrator seeks to provide are opportunities for constructive object relations. It is our firm belief that object relations are the essential context for ego growth. The relationship with his psychotherapist is, of course, very important in this regard, but this relationship alone may not suffice for the severely disabled schizophrenic patient. Additional opportunities for significant object relationships must be provided. For one thing, the patient may be unable to contain his violently conflicting feelings within a single relationship. He may need for a time to spread his feelings among many relationships. A tenuous therapist-patient relationship may require supplementation if the patient's intact abilities are to be preserved and if he is to be encouraged to develop new areas of competence. At the same time the patient should not be overwhelmed with demands that he form and maintain multiple relationships all at once. Here, too, in planning treatment strategy the administrator must strike a balance.

The administrator, in seeking a proper balance of external and internal controls, of support and challenge, and of an appropriate number and type of relationships for the patient, needs a theoretical framework within which to interpret the patient's behavior and to plan his overall treatment. The administrator not only must deal effectively with day-to-day problems but also should have a consistent long-range plan. In the course of our study we found that the theoretical considerations presented in earlier chapters, particularly in Chapter II, could provide the administrator with a very useful framework for planning administrative strategy.

In particular, we have found it helpful for the clinical administrator to organize his thinking and planning around the concept that the schizophrenic patient struggles with a basic dilemma—the need for an object from which to borrow ego strength, and the fear of the same object because of its threat to ego organization. To some extent this need-fear dilemma is a part of the experience of all human beings capable of relating to an object. However, it has an all-pervasive effect on the life experience of those persons whom we call schizophrenic. It is especially apparent in psychotherapy because the very nature of the interaction intensifies the dilemma. The need-fear dilemma arises out of a deficit in ego functioning.

The ego functioning of a schizophrenic person has at least three cardinal features: (1) a vulnerability to disorganization of executive functions of the ego; (2) a relative lack of autonomy from internal drives and external stimuli; (3) an inability to maintain a reliable and enduring concept of reality. These disturbances are overlapping and interrelated. For example, the vulnerability to disorganization makes control of drives exceedingly difficult; poor reality testing presents an obstacle to organized ego functioning, and so forth.

Taken together, these disturbances in ego functioning all work to make the schizophrenic person peculiarly dependent upon objects, but simultaneously seriously threatened by them. His vulnerability to disorganization of ego functions makes him desperately need objects to provide the support and structure which he lacks. His lack of ego autonomy leaves him unable to resist the influence of objects and thus makes them frightening to him. The poor reality testing of the schizophrenic person makes all object relations extremely tenuous.

The consequences of the dilemma lend themselves more readily to study because they unfold before the clinician as he treats his patient. In brief, the schizophrenic patient's reaction to the need-fear dilemma falls into three major patterns. (1) *Object Avoidance*—If the fear is dominant he avoids objects. This can range from mild aloofness to profound catatonic withdrawal. (2) *Object Clinging*—If the need is dominant he clings to objects. This can involve seeking a dependency relationship that provides an auxiliary ego. In the extreme it can include such phenomena as the automatonlike behavior of echolalia and echopraxia. (3) *Object Redefinition*—He may seek a compromise solution through a redefinition of the object. He overlooks or actually distorts various features of his relationship to the object. This solution represents an attempt to maintain the belief that the object will always be reliable and available.

These three reactions—(1) object avoidance, (2) object clinging, (3) object redefinition—are rarely seen in pure form in a particular patient. One pattern may predominate for a long period and then give way to another. Frequently we see sudden shifts between the poles of object clinging and object avoidance. This is the characteristic ambivalence of the schizophrenic person's object relations.

The psychotherapist inevitably activates the need-fear dilemma. Through regular contacts with the patient he attempts to establish a relationship of trust. The therapist becomes an object to which the patient can cling to strengthen his weakened ego. He may also perceive the therapist as a threat to his autonomy and may suffer intense feelings of rage and helplessness.

At times the clinical administrator may wish to mobilize the environmental forces in what amounts to an assault on the patient's defensive responses to the need-fear dilemma. At other times he may try to provide the support and controls that are needed as the schizophrenic patient experiences the anxiety, even panic, encountered in his struggle to solve the need-fear dilemma.

In the day-to-day handling of the patient's behavior, the clinical administrator is usually most concerned with the responses to the need-fear dilemma—object clinging, object avoidance, and object redefinition. Much time will be spent in interpreting such behavior to the ward staff and guiding them toward constructive interventions. To some extent each patient poses a unique problem, but some generalizations can be made about typical situations encountered. These will be presented in a later section of this chapter.

The long-range goal of the total therapeutic endeavor is to modify the ego deficit. Much of the definitive work in this area must be done by the psychotherapist through the transference relationship, genetic interpretations, and working through. In this process the patient must repeatedly face both poles—the need and the fear—of his dilemma. The severely ill patient can seldom do this with the psychotherapist alone; he must have additional experiences with other significant persons in the environment. The clinical administrator must try to provide a setting that will promote such interactions and, at the same time, provide the security needed for a successful resolution.

Object Clinging

Object clinging is the simplest and most direct response to the need-fear dilemma. Hospitalization tends to encourage this response. Even the process of psychotherapy itself fosters such a relationship.

The history of such patients usually reveals evidence of previous object clinging. They usually have been highly dependent on one or two relationships. Frequently the rupture of one of these relationships has precipitated a psychotic disorganization and hospitalization. The initial response to hospitalization is often one of marked symptomatic improvement. The institutional organization of the environment substitutes for the weakened internal ego organization of the patient. This may lead to a prompt disappearance of the psychotic symptomatology of regressed behavior, thinking disorganization, and hallucinatory experiences. Such patients may pose little problem initially for the clinical administrator because support is readily supplied by the environment. Nevertheless, several problems in connection with object clinging do regularly occur.

Certain object-clinging patients do not find spontaneous support from the hospital environment. These are the patients who display their needs in such primitive, intense, and bizarre forms that the staff withdraws. They desperately seek an object relation, but in a fashion that guarantees failure. The administrator can utilize two approaches to this situation. In the first he organizes a fairly detailed program that meets the patient's basic needs. This involves bathing, shaving, oral hygiene, feeding, and the like. Such a program gives tacit acceptance to the patient's regression and it also spells out for the hospital staff the mode of interaction through which object relationships are established. The second, and more or less complementary approach, is an effort to educate the staff to the meaning of the patient's behavior. For example, they may be encouraged to place a positive value on any effort by the patient to make contact even in the form of an assault. Although some patients remain in such regressed states for prolonged periods, most do not, and within the hospital achieve levels of more conventionally acceptable behavior.

Another set of problems centers around the disruption of significant relationships, which may occur for a variety of reasons. The treatment of the severely ill schizophrenic patient usually extends over a period of years, in the course of which the patient is bound to experience separation from and loss of staff members important to him. Even the most stable of staffs will change in composition over an extended period. The schizophrenic patient is extremely sensitive to these changes. As we indicated in Chapter XII, separation anxiety and lack of object constancy are major problems for him. Relationships may assume a life or death significance to him. Staff members may withdraw from what they feel to be an unbearable burden. Such withdrawals are usually clouded by complex rationalizations but patients usually detect the rejection. The patient himself may become frightened by the intensity of his feelings. The more dependent he becomes on the object, the more terrifying is the prospect of loss. Unless skillfully handled, the patient may resolve this dilemma by object avoidance.

Once object loss has occurred, there is little to do but again begin the slow process of establishing a relationship. Preventative measures are far more effective but must be started early. Certain obvious steps can be taken to maintain a constant ward staff. Supervision, group discussion, and even group therapy may help the staff to deal with the anxieties created by the intense needs of the schizophrenic patient. Reduction of staff anxiety does much to prevent the traumatic rejection that comes from staff withdrawal.

Still, inevitable losses do occur. To reach the regressed patient special relationships must be recognized and encouraged. But once such a relationship becomes established every effort must be made to bring other persons in as additional objects. For example, an administrator or a psychotherapist may, by giving instructions to the staff in the presence of the patient, invest in them some portion of his relationship to the patient. If additional relationships can be established they protect against the devastating impact that occurs when a patient is thrust into an essentially objectless state.

A striking illustration was provided by Henry Harrashaw, the young man described in Chapter X who suffered from a chronic catatonic reaction. For several years this patient had undergone the gamut of hospitalizations and physical therapies. He gradually regressed to a state of mute inactivity and was about 50 pounds below his proper weight. Through the utmost gentleness and patience a psychotherapist managed to establish a relationship with him. Although the patient did begin to speak a little, most of what went on was at a nonverbal level. The patient gradually began to eat and finally regained his lost weight. After some two years of painstaking effort he was considerably improved though still seriously psychotic.

At this point psychotherapy had to be interrupted because the therapist moved to another city. Although some reaction from the patient was expected, we were not prepared for the cataclysmic response that occurred. Shortly after being told of the therapist's imminent departure, he hurled himself on the floor and writhed about with such fury that we feared he might seriously injure himself. His speech was fragmented but he seemed to be saying that he was some kind of a vicious beast and that his body, perhaps even the whole universe, had been dismembered. Even when placed in a cold wet sheet pack he continued to struggle to such an extent that his temperature rose to 105° F., and we feared that he might die from exhaustion. Massive doses of sedatives and ataractic drugs had only a temporary quieting effect.

This reaction began in the late afternoon and continued until the following morning when a particular attendant from the day shift went into the room with the patient. In the presence of this young man the patient stopped his struggling, became much calmer, and spoke more clearly. The attendant had for several months been assigned to work especially with this patient. He was often present, at least on the periphery, during psychotherapeutic appointments. He had helped the patient to dress, look after his room, and encouraged him to attend activities. Outwardly the patient had given little indication that this attendant was of special significance. Over several days the reaction gradually subsided, but throughout that time the attendant was the only person who could make contact with the patient. In his efforts to assure himself of the presence of the aide, the patient not only repeatedly reached out to touch him, but even licked him with his tongue. Within a month the patient had regained his level of functioning prior to the change of psychotherapists.

We interpret this sequence of events along the following lines. The patient had experienced disturbances in early object relations that interfered with the processes of ego differentiation and integration. This ego defect drastically limited the attainment of autonomy. By a reassuring, nonthreatening approach, the therapist had helped the patient overcome his fear of closeness so that an object relationship could be established. This relationship had supported the patient's fragile ego, but relatively little enduring change in ego structure had as yet been achieved. When the patient learned that the therapist was leaving he was confronted by total ego disorganization and went into a panic state. Because he had already started to develop a second relationship, it was possible for him to shift much of the libidinal attachment from the psychotherapist to the attendant. Had this not been so he probably would have regressed to his earlier state. Not only would it have meant starting all over again, but the task would have been immeasurably more difficult because the traumatic experience would have reinforced the patient's conviction that object relations are dangerous.

Another strategy for lightening the impact of inevitable object losses is to help the patient achieve relationships to nonhuman objects. For example, a patient may establish a relationship to a daily program and a set of specific responsibilities. When confronted by a loss he may get considerable ego support from knowing that he has his art lessons, his job at the snack bar, and his position of hall representative. Patients often achieve a relationship to the gestalt of the entire institution and even after a short hospitalization lapse into referring to it as "home."

In some ways the hospital in its total organization offers a patient more support than can a relationship with one other person. The hospital is always there; it has a visible structure; it provides a vast array of routines, policies, regulations, and traditions. Schizophrenic patients functioning with reasonable adequacy within a hospital setting number in the scores of thousands. By clinging to the institution as an object, they have relieved their need-fear dilemma and compensated for their deficient ego capacities.

Thus far we have discussed some strategies that may help in establishing a relationship with the schizophrenic patient, some precautions that may help to avoid its premature disruption, and some methods for protecting the patient against the blow of unavoidable losses. An even more difficult problem is to help a patient relinquish relationships —to go beyond object clinging to relationships which require greater autonomy and initiative on his part. The schizophrenic person seldom finds people outside the therapeutic setting who make a concerted and largely unilateral effort to achieve and maintain a relationship. Hence it is not surprising that the patient is reluctant to give up a relationship he has achieved within the hospital. Staff members, too, may find it difficult to end the relationship. Rather strong countertransference determinants are needed for a person to persist in the ordeal of relating to a severely regressed patient. As treatment progresses we often discover a symbiotic patient-staff relationship that rivals that of a schizophrenic person and his mother.

It follows from what has been said thus far that the patient will not have to cling to objects once he has been able to overcome the need-fear dilemma. Before this happens sufficient ego growth must occur to give the patient a degree of autonomy; he must neither be totally dependent on objects nor a slave to internal impulses. This brings us face to face with a lack in our theoretical knowledge. Much is known about how to modify those synthetic functions of the ego concerned with the resolution of conflict. We know something about how the executive functions of the ego develop during the course of normal maturation. However, we know very little about how to promote growth of the executive functions of the schizophrenic patient's ego. Nevertheless, such growth does occur.

To promote ego growth, the environment should provide not only the opportunity but an expectation that the patient use his intact areas of ego functioning. At the same time he requires sufficient constancy of object relations to relieve the anxiety involved in the need side of his dilemma. Experiences must be provided that permit him to gain mastery over exceedingly complex sets of interrelationships. In this way be acquires what John Cumming (Cumming, 1962) has called "ego sets" that apparently are used as the building blocks of the ego. Anxiety must be anticipated; it often is experienced as the patient moves into a new and less structured situation. Everyone concerned with the patient must be prepared for this progress through resolution of crises. If not, they are apt to abandon the effort just when the most valuable work is being done.

A crucial step is the discharge from the hospital. The patient must adapt to a more complex set of demands and at the same time give up many opportunities to fulfill his needs. Much has already been written about the value of continuity of psychotherapy as the patient leaves the hospital. Additional support can be provided through various types of partial hospitalization such as day care and night care programs.

While it is important to maintain the relationship to the hospital it is equally important to establish new contacts away from the hospital. For example, the patient can undertake school or start to work well in advance of the time of discharge. Sometimes if circumstances or hospital policy make it necessary for him to change therapists, he might make such a change prior to discharge. The threat of loss that inevitably is aroused by discharge is less terrifying if some new object relations have already begun.

OBJECT AVOIDANCE

The schizophrenic patient has an inordinate need for objects to compensate for a deficit in ego functioning. This need leaves him dependent on his objects and vulnerable to their influence. A whole set of painful feelings may arise from this vulnerability and dependence. The patient will have constant reminders that he cannot control the object and may lose it. His weak ego structure makes any relationship a threat to his ego autonomy. His fear and helplessness may evoke such rage that he comes to perceive himself as destructive and insatiable.

The schizophrenic patient may avoid objects in an effort to escape the painful experiences they bring. Such a solution of the need-fear dilemma may range from mild aloofness to profound withdrawal. Avoidance of the object creates serious problems. It eliminates the meaningful object relations that may promote ego growth. Developing a therapeutic environment that will facilitate object relations is one of the greatest challenges to the clinical administrator.

Much has been written about the intrusive controlling quality of the parents of some schizophrenic patients. Object avoidance is sometimes considered a natural, even adaptive, response to such parents. This formulation may lead to an approach calculated to be just the opposite of the so-called schizophrenogenic parent. The patient is given a minimum of direction and a maximum of permissiveness. Personnel through word and action try to convey the message: "We know you have been pushed around. We are not going to do this. We respect your right to be unconventional, deviant, even crazy."

One patient on the research ward had for a two-year period, prior to coming to Chestnut Lodge, remained in his room and seldom permitted anyone to enter. He refused to bathe and had been unwilling to shave or cut his hair. Since the staff at the other hospital had been unwilling to force these issues, he had acquired a luxuriant beard and growth of hair to his shoulders. For this patient the two-year experience had made no noticeable change in his pattern of object avoidance.

Gentleness and patience may certainly be helpful in the approach to the withdrawn patient. Regardless of his manifest behavior, the schizophrenic patient who avoids objects feels frightened and helpless. A nonthreatening approach may do much to allay his fears. To advocate such an approach because it conveys respect for the patient's integrity is probably beside the point. The patient's deficient ego structure lacks integrity. He must relate to an object having structure and giving him direction sufficient to compensate for his own lack of ego organization.

Ward staff can attempt to establish a relationship with a withdrawn patient in many ways. These may range from a gentle approach like that conveyed by Fromm-Reichmann (1950) in her writings, to the sometimes violent attack described by Rosen (1946). The personality and experience of the particular staff member will have a decisive influence on the technique chosen. But whatever the particular approach, the staff should be encouraged to go to the patient. They must be encouraged to open themselves to the severely ill schizophrenic patient. Most of all they must be helped to persist in the sometimes prolonged effort to make contact with the patient. We consider it axiomatic that ego growth can only take place within the context of an object relationship.

The assaultive patient who holds people off by physical threat is a difficult problem to the clinical administrator. It is sometimes suggested that the patient should not repress his hostility—he should get it out of his system. All too often the patient does not get it out of his system but just continues interminably. Hostility must be worked with, but failure to establish some reasonable controls may have damaging, even disastrous consequences.

The assaultive patient can easily get into a vicious circle. He feels vulnerable and threatened. He avoids contact because of his fear and tries to hold people off by menacing behavior. The hospital staff rapidly comes to look upon him as dangerous and conveys this through a multitude of verbal and nonverbal cues. In the mirror of his object relations the patient sees himself as dangerous. Lacking a well-defined ego structure he fulfills the expectations of the staff and continues his assaults. Once his reputation has become firmly established the effect is devastating. The psychosocial forces can be so powerful that nothing short of transfer to another institution can interrupt them.

We are not suggesting that the treatment of the schizophrenic patient can or should be conducted without the patient's behavior ever becoming grossly disturbed, even if only in transient episodes. We do not consider that tractable patients in a quiet ward mean things are going well. We are suggesting that intervention is indicated when the vicious circle of fear and assault begins to congeal.

The ward as a whole shows several symptoms as the vicious circle develops. Discussions about the patient begin to focus on his assaultiveness. Staff members are dominated by fear (often unrecognized) in their handling of the patient. There is less interest in understanding the behavior and more emphasis on judgmental appraisals of it. The various neurotic symptoms of vacillation, projection, displacement, and the like are easily observed in the relationship of the staff to the patient.

On Third Floor considerable reliance was placed upon staff discussions of such problems. Often in these discussions no solution was readily forthcoming, but simply identifying the problem brought about a remarkable change. In some instances it proved helpful to bring the patient into the discussion so that he received a direct and unambiguous statement of staff's discomfort.

Electroshock therapy is never used at Chestnut Lodge so we had no direct experience with this on the research ward. Ataractic drugs were used sparingly but with sufficient frequency to permit us to form some impressions concerning their usefulness in psychotherapeutic work with severely ill schizophrenic patients. The experience with one patient, Robert Feldman, is described in Chapter XI in some detail. The ataractic drugs make most patients more tractable. They may, in some cases, promote a sealing over of the psychotic reaction through denial and refusal to face the fundamental problems. On the other hand, such drugs may be effective in breaking up the vicious circle that has been described. The patient's communications become more intelligible, he is less threatening, and the staff is less fearful. They interact in a more positive way that promotes the development of an increasing circle of object relations. When used in this way, we found the ataractic drugs useful and consistent with the general proposition that ego growth can occur only through relationship to significant persons in the environment.

OBJECT REDEFINITION

In addition to object clinging and object avoidance there is still a third response that patients may have to the need-fear dilemma. We have chosen to call this object redefinition. In a general way object clinging involves a movement toward the object and object avoidance a movement away from it. Object redefinition involves a change in the perception of the object so that its need-fulfilling characteristics are recognized and its fear-evoking characteristics are excluded from awareness.

We have observed several ways in which object redefinition can be accomplished. A common method employs the use of two objects. The need-fulfilling qualities (supportive, dependable, nondemanding —good) are seen as residing in one object while the fear-producing qualities (demanding, intrusive, controlling—bad) qualities are seen as residing in another object. This can be done without a gross break from reality if the objects are selected carefully and the patient limits the amount of information he obtains about the object. Selective inattention and autistic thinking are often used to facilitate this kind of object redefinition. In more extreme cases a frankly delusional paranoid system may be present.

For some patients object redefinition may be so successful that it becomes apparent only when the patient is forced to deal with a situation that repudiates his ideas. Object redefinition may even have some positive aspects. It is a solution that circumvents extremes of avoidance and clinging. It is probably present to a degree in all persons and becomes pathological only when it does serious violence to reality testing.

Redefinition subjects an object relationship to a variety of vicissitudes. Human beings seldom fit into neat compartments that are all good or all bad. When information is made available that contradicts his view of the object, the schizophrenic person is pushed toward more extreme distortions in his perception of reality. If these fail he is forced into object avoidance and all its damaging consequences. Confrontation occasionally leads the schizophrenic person to correct his redefinition and in the process achieve greater ego integration and differentiation. Such an outcome seldom occurs fortuitously; it must be made to occur through psychotherapy and special handling of the environment.

Redefinition can be particularly stressful to the object. Being cast in the bad role is unpleasant, but with some experience staff members can usually handle this. The staff group shares the problem and provides sympathy and support. Such a situation may become more complicated if the redefinition happens to activate some neurotic trait of the staff member. For example, an emotionally constricted nurse who has difficulty in giving of herself may be quite troubled by a patient who continually suggests by his words and actions that the nurse is failing to meet his needs and even actively depriving him.

In our experience more difficult problems occur when the staff member is cast as the good object. Most people working with psychiatric patients want to be helpful and, latently at least, have some Messianic aspirations. If a patient casts such a person in the role of the all-loving, all-giving object neither participant may recognize the redefinition. Inevitably the staff member fails to fulfill the patient's expectations and the relationship comes to a shattering and painful end. Another variation of this problem is the autistic love affair that reaches an advanced stage before its recognition by the person who is the object. Typically, the denouement is startling and leads the staff member to withdraw abruptly.

Frequently a staff member may overextend himself in attempting to fulfill the patient's needs, feel increasingly burdened, and, when he reaches the limits of endurance, withdraw from the relationship. In such situations the staff member is apt to get very little sympathy from his colleagues unless they are unusually understanding and enlightened. Insofar as they may well have envied and resented his special relationship to the patient, they may be quite pleased by his distress.

It is very difficult to avoid exploitation of the patient's object redefinition. The staff member in the good role may find it a convenience to allow the patient to attribute bad qualities to someone else. Either by design or just plain human nature, the staff members in the good role may spend more time with the patient while those in the bad role tend to avoid him. This can easily serve to reinforce and perpetuate the object redefinition.

The presence of object redefinition in an object relationship is not necessarily damaging. Staff members must become involved with patients. This becomes antitherapeutic only when the termination of a relationship occurs in such a way that it strengthens the patient's conviction that object relations are dangerous.

Object redefinition takes many forms as illustrated in the case presentations, particularly that of Glen of Chapter VI. The diversity of problems makes it impractical to discuss specific tactics to meet the many situations. Nevertheless, certain general principles for the approach to object redefinition can be identified.

Object redefinition has certain positive values; it may be the only type of relatedness possible for a patient at a given time. If these positive values are to be retained, ward personnel require a great deal of assistance. Intensive work with schizophrenic patients characteristically evokes serious countertransference problems in even the most experienced psychotherapist. The difficulties are greatly increased for psychiatric nurses and aides. They have seldom had the experience or training of the psychotherapist. They work in a far less structured situation than the therapeutic hour. The single most effective tool for helping ward personnel with their problems is the ward conference. A more complete picture of the patient's relationships is obtained by pooling experiences. By seeing that an individual relationship may be only a fragment the staff can identify object redefinition. The sharing of experiences has a corrective influence on the intense personal reactions felt by the various individual staff members.

In planning his strategy the administrator may be forced to choose between two unattractive alternatives. If he rigorously confronts the patient with the distortions involved in his relationships, he risks forcing him into object avoidance. If he tries to preserve the relationship by avoiding confrontation, he runs the risk of reinforcing the underlying conflict involved in the patient's need-fear dilemma. A compromise solution is to provide the patient with the maximal information that will permit him to recognize the inaccuracies in his object redefinition. It is possible to do this without a frontal assault. Major efforts must be made to provide experiences and to permit the patient to see that objects are neither all good nor all bad. This can be done in a variety of ways. For example, decisions about the patient can be made through open and candid discussions in his presence. This is particularly effective when it involves a good object and a bad object since it gives the patient an opportunity to see that objects can fuse and need not be rigidly separated. In this case the patient learns by observing the interaction of the objects.

Another method is to provide an opportunity for the patient to have a variety of experiences with the same object, usually over a period of time. This allows him to see that the person who at one time may seem threatening and intrusive, at another time may be supportive and kind. Serious obstacles often interfere with the accomplishment of this kind of approach. Shifts in patients and personnel may occur before a relationship can be fully worked through. Traditional hospital organization fosters the withholding of information from patients rather than a full exposure. Our experience on Third Floor impressed on us the importance of sustained relationships and open communication among patients and personnel.

Much of the therapeutic work on object redefinition must occur in the psychotherapy. We believe, however, that it is seldom possible for the chronically ill schizophrenic patient to work this problem through unless the therapist has consistent assistance from other significant persons in the environment. The psychotherapist primarily attempts to clarify and interpret so that the patient becomes aware of the genetic links involved in his object redefinition. The therapist himself also becomes an object of the redefinition, and if this becomes too intense, a therapeutic impasse may develop. Auxiliary relationships can help to dilute such relationships so that they stay at a workable level of intensity. In addition, these relationships provide the life experiences that are needed to confirm the therapist's interpretations.

Object redefinition is a resistance. It is used in the service of denying hostility. But it is something more. It is a way of maintaining an object relation and as such should be treated with care. Eventually it must be dealt with but only after a great deal of work has been done on the core issue—the need-fear dilemma.

Conclusion

In daily practice it often seems as though it is administration versus therapy. The demands on the administrator are different from those on the therapist; the interventions of the two take a different form; but the differences do not make therapy and administration antithetical.

In the treatment of the schizophrenic patient, psychotherapy and administrative management are inextricable. Together they form a potent therapeutic force.

Psychotherapy is sometimes considered as the center of the treatment process about which all else revolves. In this view of things, management of the environment is just an unpleasant chore that must be done while the real therapeutic work goes on in the individual sessions. This conceptualization, taking its model from psychoanalytic treatment of the neurotic patient, is totally inadequate for the treatment of the severely regressed schizophrenic patient.

At the other extreme, the milieu including physical therapies may be seen as the real mode of treatment. It is pointed out that patients have always gotten well "spontaneously" and that a humanitarian approach with an ordered life is all that is needed. Psychotherapy is at best seen as just another relationship. This milieu-based orientation is equally one-sided and inadequate in the treatment of the severely regressed schizophrenic patient.

In psychotherapy, the schizophrenic patient does develop a transference relationship. In addition, the therapist becomes extremely important to the patient as an object in his own right. This inevitably activates the need-fear dilemma and as such may open the way for a different resolution of this dilemma. By opening himself to the patient the therapist provides a model and encourages the patient to expose himself to what he has found to be the hazards of object relations. The therapist helps the patient to identify and live through the conflicts at either pole of the need-fear dilema. By sharing in the need-fear dilemma the psychiatrist establishes a new kind of relationship for the patient—a relationship that nurtures ego growth.

The administrator works to create a milieu in which the schizophrenic patient can develop object relations. He must use his leadership to encourage the staff of the ward to go to the patient. He must provide the kind of support needed to face the anxiety that inevitably occurs in relating to the severely ill person. Through his experience the administrator guides the staff in the technical handling of the specific problems and complications that develop as therapy progresses. From his own knowledge of individual psychotherapy he strives to collaborate so that the total experience of the patient will facilitate the psychotherapeutic work.

BIBLIOGRAPHY

Cumming, J. & Cumming, E. (1962), *Ego and Milieu: Theory and Practice of Environmental Therapy*. New York: Atherton Press.

Fromm-Reichmann, F. (1950), *Principles of Intensive Psychotherapy*. Chicago: University of Chicago Press.

Rosen, J. N. (1946), A Method of Resolving Acute Catatonic Excitement. *Psychiat. Quart., 20*:183-198.

APPENDIX: THE RELATIONSHIP QUESTIONNAIRE

Arthur I. Gladstone

1. The Development of the Questionnaire

In planning our research project we agreed that the major focus would be on the personal relationships of patients on Third Floor. We wanted to find out, for each patient, which people were significant to him (and just what meaning each had for him), what went on between the patient and these significant people when they were together, what changes might take place in each relationship in the course of time, and what might be happening in each relationship that would have a more general effect on the patient and on his other relationships. We wanted to study several relationships for each Third Floor patient and to describe each relationship in a standard way that would make possible systematic comparisons. We decided, therefore, to use a detailed questionnaire, to be administered at regular intervals.

When we examined existing questionnaires, the Lorr Scale (Lorr, 1953) and the Interpersonal Check List (LaForge & Suczek, 1955) appeared the most promising. Both were tried, with the ICL receiving an especially careful trial, but we decided that neither was suitable for our study. The Lorr Scale emphasized symptomatic rather than interpersonal behavior. The ICL, although more useful, still omitted many things we wanted to know which were not related to its two principal dimensions (love-hate, and dominance-submission), and included many items that were not appropriate for our psychotic patients. We therefore undertook the construction of our own questionnaire.

In the fall of 1957 we had talked about studying relationships from three points of view: the staff member's conceptions and feelings, the patient's conceptions and feelings, and the actual behavior of the two people when together (as it might be observed by an objective observer). We wanted to compare the patient's and the staff member's conception of their relationship since difficulties in appraising reality and in reaching interpersonal consensus are of great importance in schizophrenia. We planned to use a questionnaire to obtain data on the conceptions and feelings held by patients and staff members and to use direct observation to obtain data on actual behavior. We found there was staff opposition to the idea of administering any questionnaire to patients, based not only on fears that this might have undesirable effects on patient-staff relationships or on patients' anxieties and misconceptions, but also on skepticism about the ability of most patients to provide any useful information. (The result of this opposition was that no attempt was made to collect data from patients until two years later.) As we developed our own questionnaire and as we began to make various kinds of direct observations, our ideas about how to use these two sources of data shifted. The questionnaire was to be used as the principal source of data about the relationship, and direct observation was mainly a way of checking on the validity of the questionnaire as a data-gathering instrument. An important reason for our coming to emphasize the questionnaire as a source of data was the large number of relationships to be studied, which made regular direct observation completely impracticable. We tried to make the questionnaire items as objective, factual, and unambiguous as possible, by referring to kinds of behavior which could readily be noted by an observer if there were one. We hoped to develop a separate procedure for reaching the subjective, internal aspects of a relationship.

In planning our questionnaire we talked about various "aspects" or relationships. By an "aspect" we meant any characteristic of a relationship which could be observed and described (just as "personality trait" refers to any characteristic of personality). A set of such aspects and a consistent procedure for assessing them would provide us with a systematic framework for the description of relationships. On this basis it would be possible to compare one relationship with another and to discover changes in a single relationship over the course of time.

The first version of our questionnaire was developed in February, 1958. It contained 20 scales of six items each. This questionnaire was administered to nursing personnel on Fourth Floor and the data were examined to see whether items which were expected to form scales were actually related. As a result of this procedure, the questionnaire was considerably revised, with some scales eliminated, new scales added, some individual items rewritten, and answer categories changed. This revised version of the questionnaire was administered to Third Floor nursing personnel in May 1958 and again in August 1958.

In the fall of 1958 we undertook a major revision of the questionnaire. This involved considerable discussion of which aspects of relationships were of most importance for description and understanding. We hoped to develop a framework that would have some general applicability, although we were mainly interested in its usefulness for hospitalized schizophrenic patients. We finally settled on five aspects: approach-avoidance behavior, communication, feelings expressed, influence and control, and activities. (These aspects are described and discussed in Chapter V.) On the basis of this set of aspects and the results from previous versions, a new form of the questionnaire was developed. This form, consisting of 74 questions, was administered to Third Floor nursing personnel in January 1959. Succeeding forms were administered at approximately three-month intervals until March 1960, and again in December 1960. There was considerable revision between January and April 1959, but after that the questionnaire remained substantially the same for the remaining six administrations. (A copy of the latest form of the Relationship Questionnaire will be found at the end of this Appendix.) The revisions that were made had to do mainly with the elimination of unsatisfactory and unnecessary items, attempts to improve scales, the addition of a few items that had not been thought of earlier, and standardization of answer categories. Starting in June 1959, each question was answered for all patients on a single sheet (whereas previously the staff member had answered all the questions with respect to one patient, then all the questions with respect to a second patient, and so on). The main purpose of this change was to simplify the task and reduce the time required, but it should also have reduced halo effect.

As mentioned earlier, we had hoped to use the questionnaire as a source of information about particular relationships. We wanted to be able to characterize the relationship between a particular patient and a particular staff member and to note change in this relationship in the course of time. However, our methodological studies of the questionnaire, to be reported in section 3 of this Appendix, showed that it could not be validly used in this way. We found variations in response style from one staff member to another (section 3A) which suggested that the questionnaire data from different staff members could not be directly compared. The use of direct observation to study validity (section 3C) confirmed this. However, when the questionnaire reports about a given patient by different staff members were pooled, the validity coefficients of many of the scales became fairly good. Thus the questionnaire is fairly satisfactory as a way of characterizing the relationship behavior of a patient but not for describing or comparing particular relationships. However, we did develop a method for comparing the particular relationships of a staff member in certain respects (see section 4E). This tells less than we had originally hoped for, but can still be useful. Nevertheless, the major use which we made of the questionnaire in this study was to characterize the overall relationship behavior of a particular patient (pooling the data from his various relationships with staff members).

2. CORRELATION ANALYSES

Two types of correlation analyses were made with data from the Relationship Questionnaire. Individual items were correlated with one another in order to determine whether they could appropriately be combined to form scales. Later, scales were correlated with one another to discover groupings into clusters. For simplicity of computation the Spearman rank correlation coefficient was used. All the analyses to be reported in this section made use of grouped data; averages were computed from the answers given by different members of nursing personnel to a particular question about a particular patient.

A. The Development of Scales

In the fall of 1959 correlations were computed with data from the April and September 1959 administration of the questionnaire. All sets of items which we expected to be related were intercorrelated. For a set of items to qualify as forming a scale we required that each item have a correlation of at least .50 (or −.50) with all or most of the other items in the set, and that any correlations which did not exceed .50 at least be fairly close to that value.[1] Only scales for which the correlations from both the April and September data met this criterion were included. Furthermore, items were not combined into a scale unless we had a clear conception of the characteristic or kind of behavior with which they all dealt. Using these criteria, 15 scales were formed.

Before the January 1960 administration of the questionnaire, several new items were added in the hope of forming additional scales. Subsequent item correlations justified the addition of one scale and the revision of three others. Because of other item changes, the item intercorrelations of four other scales were also checked with these January 1960 data and found to be satisfactory.

The grouping of items into scales was further checked by analyses of the data from the December 1960 all-hospital administration of the questionnaire (see section 2D). A list of scales showing the items belonging to each scale, in the latest version of the questionnaire, will be found in section 6B.

In the initial planning of the questionnaire we had thought of it as composed of parallel scales, that is, each scale dealing with patient behavior was to have an exact counterpart dealing with staff behavior. In the latest version of the questionnaire there are 16 scales, eight of which form such parallel pairs (Approach, Personal Communication, Expression of Positive Feelings, and Expression of Negative Feelings). Even among these four pairs of scales only one pair (the Personal Communication scales) contains exactly corresponding items in both patient and staff versions; the others vary somewhat in wording and inclusion of items. The discrepancies were forced upon us either by the correlation analyses or by other findings from ques-

[1] The value of .50 was used as a rough-and-ready cutoff point in all our work with correlation coefficients. This gives a *rough* approximation to the .05 level of significance with a one-tailed test. Since the Ns on which the correlation coefficients were based varied from 8 to 16, the *exact* value of the Spearman coefficient for the .05 level varied from .643 to .425. It would have been more precise to vary the cutoff point with the N, but a rough screening to eliminate low and chance correlations seemed adequate for our purposes. As a further screening, we considered only correlations which reached the criterion on at least two separate occasions.

tionnaire data. For example, one of the items dealing with the Expression of Positive Feelings by the patient read, "When he was with you, how often did he show you or let you know that he felt *friendly?*" whereas the corresponding item for the staff scale was "When you were with him, how often did you show or let him know that you felt *especially friendly?*" Before we added the word "especially," staff members reported being friendly to nearly all patients virtually all of the time, so it was necessary to change the question to make it somewhat more discriminating.

For the seven scales which did not form parallel pairs, the lack of parallelism was due in most cases to actual differences between patients and staff members, or to staff member conceptions of such differences. Thus there was no counterpart to the Clarity of Communication by patient scale because staff members engaged in less obscure communication than patients. Furthermore, they probably would not have been willing or able to report their own obscure communication. The same was true for Problem Behavior and for Avoidance. There was an attempt to construct a patient scale that would have corresponded somewhat to the staff scale dealing with Use of Control Techniques, but the items did not correlate very well with one another. (Even if the correlations had been better this scale would not have been an exact counterpart, simply because the methods available to patients for influencing staff members are somewhat different from the methods available to staff.)

B. Cluster Analysis

The second kind of correlation analysis that we performed was analysis of the relationships among scales. A correlation matrix was prepared, showing the correlation of each scale with every other scale. This was first done with data from the September 1959 administration. This matrix was used as the basis for determining clusters—groups of scales, each of which correlated at least .50 (or −.50) with all or most of the others. Correlation matrices were later prepared and cluster analyses performed with data from the January 1960 and December 1960 administrations of the questionnaire. The two clusters which were found with all three sets of data from Third Floor, and also on all other units in December 1960, have been described and discussed in Chapter V. (In that chapter only two of the three cluster analyses with Third Floor data are mentioned. The analysis with September 1959 data is not mentioned because two of the scales which appear in the clusters had not yet been added to the questionnaire at that time. For this reason, Active Activities did not appear in the first cluster and Lack of Compliance did not appear in the second cluster. In all other respects these clusters were the same in September 1959 as in later data analyses.)

The two clusters reported in Chapter V include all interscale correlations above .50 which appeared consistently. There were additional interscale correlations above .50 which appeared at one time and not at another; examination of the data showed that the appearance and disappearance of such correlations was related to the presence and absence of particular patients. For example, in January 1960 the correlation between Approach by the patient and Approach by the staff member was −.22, whereas in December 1960 it was .83. Five patients who contributed to the high positive correlation in December had not been on Third Floor in January.

C. Clusters among Change Scores

In addition to the three cluster analyses mentioned above, two cluster analyses were performed with "scale change scores." A scale change score is the difference between the average score which a patient received on a particular scale at one time and his average score on the same scale at a later time, with the direction of the change indicated by the sign. Such scores were computed for the nine patients who were on Third Floor both in April 1959 and in March 1960, and for the eight patients who were there both in March 1960 and in December 1960. (Four patients were included in both groups. To make the scores as comparable as possible from one time to the next, the data were drawn only from the questionnaires of staff members who were present on both occasions. There were five such staff members for the first interval and six for the second interval.) A positive correlation between such change scores would indicate that the scales involved tend to vary together, so that as one goes up or down the other would go up or down correspondingly. If two scales are correlated, it does not necessarily follow that their changes will

also be correlated. For example, among adults there is a positive correlation between height and weight but no correlation between weight
changes and height changes. All of the correlations between scale
changes which were above .50 for both intervals can be grouped
into two clusters.

The first cluster consists of changes in the following four scales:
Approach by the patient, Personal Communication by the patient,
the Expression of Positive Feelings by the patient, and Personal Communication by the staff member. This corresponds to the first cluster
which was consistently found in the static correlation analyses, except for the absence of Active Activities, which is missing presumably
because it did not appear on the April 1959 questionnaire. (Changes
in Active Activities are included in the first cluster obtained from
the March to December 1960 interval.)

The second cluster consists of changes in the following five scales:

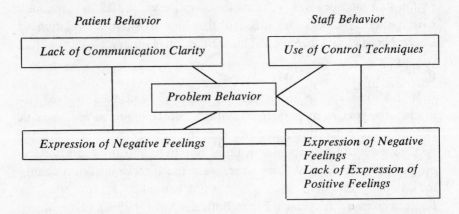

Patient Behavior   *Staff Behavior*

Lack of Communication Clarity   Use of Control Techniques

Problem Behavior

Expression of Negative Feelings   Expression of Negative
                                      Feelings
                                      Lack of Expression of
                                      Positive Feelings

(In the above diagram lines connect those scales whose change scores
show correlations with one another that are generally over .50.
Change scores for Expression of Negative Feelings by the staff member and Expression of Positive Feelings by the staff member are negatively correlated with each other, and both correlate with change
scores for the other same three scales, except for difference in sign.
As in Chapter V, the phrase "lack of" signifies that changes in that
scale correlate negatively with changes in the other scales.) This
cluster strongly resembles the second cluster found in the static correlations. The scale of Compliance by the patient is missing; it did

not appear on the April 1959 questionnaire. Two scales appear here which did not appear previously, the Expression of Negative Feelings by the patient and the Expression of Positive Feelings by the staff.

D. All-Hospital Questionnaire Administration

In December, 1960, the questionnaire was filled out by all the nursing personnel at Chestnut Lodge, each person answering in terms of the patients with whom he worked. The purpose of the all-hospital administration of the questionnaire was to replicate the correlational findings on Third Floor, to see whether the same relationships would be found with other groups of patients and staff members.

In the correlation analysis of the data from the all-hospital administration, the first step was to check the composition of the scales. This was done by computing a correlation matrix for each scale of six nursing units. (One nursing unit was omitted because it contained a number of geriatric patients whose behavior and treatment were rather different from that of other patients in the hospital. Only data from aides and nurses were used in this analysis because responses by administrators and student nurses tended to be somewhat different. The data used were from a total of 54 staff members reporting on a total of 74 patients. The number of staff members on each unit varied from six to 10 and the number of patients from 10 to 16.) Examination of these correlation matrices showed that five of the 16 scales (Personal Communication by the patient, Active Activities, Personal Communication by the staff member, Expression of Positive Feelings by the staff member, and Use of Control Techniques by the staff member) met our criteria for scales (see section 2A) on all six units. One scale (Problem Behavior) was unsatisfactory on all units. The other nine scales were satisfactory on some units but not on others. However, even the scales which did not meet our criterion for interitem correlations in all instances still showed mainly positive correlations, and the few negative correlations were mostly close to zero, suggesting that the items do have some relation to one another. This was true even for the Problem Behavior scale. Therefore, it appeared to be worth examining the interscale correlations for all scales despite the unsatisfactory interitem correlations.

Using the data from aides and nurses which we have just been discussing, interscale correlations were computed. There were nine pairs of scales whose intercorrelations were above .50 on all six units. (All nine pairs also correlated above .50 on the seventh nursing unit, despite its inclusion of geriatric patients.) Five of these correlations are involved in the first cluster (friendly approach by patient) reported in Chapter V. All the other pairings of scales in that cluster have correlations of .50 or greater on at least 3 units, and most of the remaining correlations are close to .50. In other words, of the 90 correlations represented by that cluster, 74 are .50 or greater, 10 are between .40 and .49, and six are below .40.

The other four pairs of scales which universally correlated above .50 all appear in the second cluster (patient problem behavior). As shown in the diagram in Chapter V, Lack of Clarity of Communication by the patient and the Expression of Negative Feelings by the staff generally have little or no correlation with each other but these five scales are otherwise well correlated. Of the 54 correlations involved, 42 are .50 or greater, nine are between .40 and .49, and three are below .40 (none are below .30).

The administrative physician of each unit also filled out the questionnaire for the patients on his unit. This involved some problems, partly because the questionnaire had been developed for use by nursing personnel and was not as suitable for the administrators, and partly because the administrators spent much less time with patients than did nursing personnel and therefore had much less interaction on which to base their replies to the questions. Therefore the administrator's replies included a high proportion of omissions and much use of the "never" category. The three most completely and satisfactorily filled-out questionnaires from administrators were used as the basis for interitem correlation analyses with the items that comprised the scales. For many scales these correlations were generally satisfactory. The principal exceptions were the scales concerned with the Use of Control Techniques by the staff member, Problem Behavior, Active Activities (very little reported), Passive Activities (little reported), Approach by the staff member, Personal Communication by the staff member, and the Expression of Negative Feelings by the staff member (little reported by two administrators, good correlations for the third).

3. METHODOLOGICAL AND EVALUATIVE STUDIES

A. *The Use of Answer Categories*

In the latest version of the questionnaire nine answer categories are provided for each question. Five of these categories are labeled and the other four (each of which was between two labeled categories) do not bear labels. (In the earliest versions of the questionnaire five answer categories, all labeled, were provided for each question. In the major revision of the questionnaire in the fall of 1958 we decided to provide nine categories for each question. This was done for nearly all questions on the January 1959 version and for all questions on the April 1959 version and thereafter.) Two main sets of labels are used: (1) Most of the time, ½ of the time, ¼ of the time, Hardly ever, Never; (2) Many times a day, 5 or 6 times a day, A few times in the past week, Once or twice in the past week, Never in the past week. A few questions had other answer categories, dealing with the number of hours spent during the past week in the kind of activity the question referred to.

The use of answer categories was examined a number of times, most intensively with the data from the January and April 1959 administrations of the questionnaire. This was done in several ways. One was to compare the answers to a particular question given for different patients. If these did not show much variation from one patient to another, the question was generally revised or eliminated in subsequent versions of the questionnaire since there seemed little point in including questions that did not discriminate.

Data from the January 1959 questionnaire administration were used to examine the distributions of answers given to questions with different sets of answer categories. On the basis of this examination the answer categories were revised slightly in order to secure more even distributions (since the more evenly the answer categories are used, the more information is secured.) Similarly, the distributions of answers to particular questions were often considered in making revisions, attempts being made at times to reword questions in order to secure better distributions.

The use of answer categories by different staff members was also tabulated and examined. Considerable variations in the distributions were found in central tendency, in flatness of the distribution, and in the extent to which the in-between (unlabeled) categories were used. These considerable differences in use of answer categories raise serious doubts about the comparability of questionnaire responses by different staff members. A study of the tendency to give generally high or generally low answers to questions was made with data from the January 1960 questionnaire administration. From these data we got for each scale the average score which each aide gave to patients on that scale. If these scores were accurate reports, we would not expect aides to give consistently high or low scores on all or most scales, but that is what they tended to do. A particularly striking example is provided by the Approach by patient and Avoidance by patient scales. If an aide gives high scores on the Approach scale (meaning that patients approach him more than they do the average aide), we would not expect him also to give high scores on the Avoidance scale (meaning that patients avoid him more than average). Yet, there is a positive correlation of .49 between average scores given by aides on these scales. For each of the 16 scales the aides were ranked in order of the average scores based on their reports. The rank orders tend to be quite similar for the different scales. (There are two exceptions to this: the Compliance scale and the Clarity of Communication scale. The reason they are exceptions is that ⅔ of the items on each of these scales had been reversed. When the rankings on these two scales are reversed, they become similar to those on the other scales.) Five of the aides appear in one of *two* adjacent ranks on at least half the scales. Four more aides appear in one of *three* adjacent ranks on at least half the scales.

We considered two ways of dealing with these response tendencies. One would be to construct scales so that half of the items in each scale are positive and half are negative (scored in the reverse direction). Thus the tendency of an individual to use mostly the high answer categories (or mostly the low ones) would be automatically compensated for. In the final version of the questionnaire there are two scales which provide a rough approximation of such balancing. These are the Compliance and Clarity of Communication scales (which, as mentioned above, have proportions of ⅔ to ⅓ instead of half and half). However, it did not seem feasible to make additional balanced scales without radically changing the basis of the questionnaire. As long as answers are in terms of frequency of occurrence of a particular kind of behavior, it is only when there are two kinds of behavior that have really opposite significance that one can be used as the basis for an item to be reversed. Some kinds of behavior may seem at first to have such opposite significance, but further thinking shows that they are not so completely opposite that a score for one can be subtracted from a score for the other. For example, the expression of positive feelings and the expression of negative feelings appear to be opposite, but if we subtract a score for one from a score for the other, the person who expresses much feeling of both kinds and the person who expresses little feeling of either kind will be indistinguishable.

Another conceivable way of dealing with response tendencies would be to use a correction factor for each person filling out the questionnaire which would raise or lower his scale scores so that their mean would correspond to that for other people filling out the questionnaire. Aside from the cumbersomeness of this procedure, there is the serious problem that this would probably obscure some real differences among nursing staff members in the way they behave and in the way patients behave toward them. Some aides interact more with patients than other aides do. With questionnaire data alone there does not seem to be any way of distinguishing precisely between higher scale scores which accurately show greater interaction and higher scores resulting from inaccurate use of higher answer categories.

Because of these objections, we did not attempt either of these proposed methods of dealing with response tendencies. This suggests that we cannot directly compare questionnaire data from different staff members.

B. Reliability

In order to study the reliability of the questionnaire data we administered the questionnaire an extra time in Steptember 1959, one week after the regular administration, explaining to the staff members that we wanted to see what kinds of changes took place in the course of a week. We expected that changes over a one-week period would be generally less than changes over a three-month period. If this were not so, it would seriously question our intended use of the questionnaire to study long-range changes.

Correlations were computed for each scale over the one-week

period in September 1959 and the four-month period from September 1959 to January 1960, using data from five staff members about eleven patients, all of whom were involved in all three questionnaire administrations. These correlations are presented in Table 1.

TABLE 1

Reliability Coefficients over One-week and Four-month Periods

Scales:	Sept. A '59 with Sept. B '59	Sept. A '59 with Jan. '60
Approach (Pt.)	+.68	—.05
Communication, Impersonal (Pt.)	+.93	+.58
Communication, Personal (Pt.)	+.94	+.16
Communication Clarity	+.96	+.53
Problem Behavior	+.99	+.65
Positive Feelings (Pt.)	+.94	+.56
Negative Feelings (Pt.)	+.97	+.89
Approach (Stf.)	+.79	+.71
Communication, Personal (Stf.)	+.87	+.33
Positive Feelings (Stf.)	+.92	+.82
Negative Feelings (Stf.)	+.93	+.22
Use of Control Techniques	+.91	+.59

It will be seen that for the one-week period nine of the twelve correlations are over +.90 whereas none of those for the four-month period are that high. The scales with the lowest correlation for the one-week period are Approach by the patient and Approach by the staff.

Except for these two scales, the test-retest reliabilities of the scales over a one-week period are highly satisfactory.

C. Direct Observation

Another method which we used to evaluate the questionnaire was the comparison of questionnaire results with data collected by direct observation. Two series of observations were undertaken for this purpose. The first series of questionnaire-checking observations was made between March 31 and April 5, 1959. (A number of different kinds of observing had been tried out at various times prior to this.) Questionnaires were administered to Third Floor staff members on April 6; therefore the observation period was roughly the same as the period of "the past week" which was asked about on the questionnaire. A sampling plan was made by picking at random 20 starting times, each between 9:00 a.m. and 9:00 p.m. on one of the six days. The research assistant and the research psychologist divided the starting times equally between them and made five observations for each starting time, at 25 minute intervals. (For example, one starting time was 11:10; so observations were made at 11:10, 11:35, 12:25, and 12:50.) 100 sets of observations were made during the six days. For each set of observations the observer went through the ward systematically in a predetermined order and noted, for each patient, where he was, whom he was with, what he was doing, whether anything was being said by him or to him and what it was, and whether any feeling was being expressed by him or to him and what it was. If there were any patients who could not be found, a staff member was asked where these patients were and what they were doing. The observers experienced most difficulty in judging expressions of feeling. A few other specific points gave some trouble, such as trying to judge whether a patient was "with" somebody when nothing was going on between them.

After making the observations each observer coded his own notes in terms of questionnaire items. Of the 81 items in the questionnaire at that time there were 68 that referred to kinds or aspects of behavior that might have been observed by this procedure. Of these 68 items there were 28 for which 10 or more instances each were observed. For these items we computed rank correlations between the observation data and the mean scores which the patients received on the corresponding items on the questionnaire. (Note that a mean score combines the data from different staff members. Thus we are dealing here not with particular relationships but with composites, each one being an overall picture of the relationships of a particular patient with the various staff members who reported on him.) Only eight of these correlations were below +.50. The five most valid items, with validity coefficients of .80 or above were: 24, 42, 44, 48, and 74. (The wording of each item will be found in section 6A.)

We also used our observation data to check the validity of the questionnaire as a report on the *aide's* behavior (and on the behavior of patients when with a particular aide). We tabulated the frequencies of various kinds of behavior shown by each of the eight aides observed (or by a patient in the presence of a given aide). There were 42 items on which we had some data, and for all these items we made comparisons with the medians on the corresponding questionnaire items as reported by the aides about themselves. (Here we are dealing with composites of each aide's relationships.) The correlations were generally poorer than for the patient data, the majority being well below +.50.

At the time these observations were made the questionnaire items had not yet been grouped into scales. After scales had been constructed we used the observation data to check the validity of the scales. For this purpose the observation data were also formed into scales by combining the observation items which correspond to the questionnaire items belonging to a single scale. As we have already pointed out for individual items, the data for scales can be pooled either by patients (all interactions with a given patient combined, to give a composite picture of that patient's relationships) or by aides (all interactions with a given aide combined). Both kinds of pooling have been done and the correlations computed from the pooled results will be found in Table 2 (pooled by patients) and Table 3 (pooled by aides.)

TABLE 2

Correlations between questionnaire reports and direct observations for 10 scales. (April 1959 data, pooled for each of 11 patients.)

Scales:	Correlation	Number of Instances Observed
Positive Feelings (Pt.)	.90	41
Clarity of Communication	.83	224
Problem Behavior	.74	40
Control Techniques	.67	55
Approach (Pt.)	.59	123
Personal Communication (Stf.)	.53	15
Personal Communication (Pt.)	.48	16
Impersonal Communication (Pt.)	.43	6
Positive Feelings (Stf.)	.24	4
Negative Feelings (Pt.)	.21	65

Examining Table 2 we see that five out of the 10 correlations are significant at the 5% level.[2] We can also see in that table that there is a relation between the size of the correlations (and hence their significance level) and the number of instances on which the direct observation scale scores are based. All of the significant correlations

---

[2] With 11 cases a correlation coefficient of at least .54 is necessary for significance at the 5% level and .73 is necessary for significance at the 1% level.

involve 40 or more instances. With one exception, all of the non-significant correlations involve 16 or fewer instances, certainly too few for an adequate test. The one exception to this is the correlation for the Expression of Negative Feelings by the patient, which is the lowest despite being based on more cases than most of the others. The validity of this scale must therefore be considered unsatisfactory. (However, see the evaluation of this scale in section 3G.)

After the correlations in Table 2 had been computed we noticed that for some of the scales there were no observation data for one of the items. In other words, the behavior described by that item had not been seen at any time by the observers. (This was never true of more than one item in a scale). Looking at five scales for which this was true, the unobserved item had the lowest average score in the questionnaire data for four of the scales and was tied for lowest in the fifth scale. Nevertheless, thinking that the omission of an item (in scales containing four to six items each) might make a difference, we recomputed the correlation coefficients for these scales using questionnaire scale scores from which the unobserved item had also been omitted. The resulting correlations differed from those shown in the table by an average of only .03 and were not consistently either higher or lower.

TABLE 3

Correlations between questionnaire reports and direct observation for 9 scales. (April 1959 data, pooled for each of 8 aides.)

Scales:	Correlation	Number of Instances Observed
Problem Behavior	.53	28
Positive Feelings (Pt.)	.32	15
Impersonal Communication (Pt.)	.28	4
Control Techniques	.23	62
Personal Communication (Pt.)	—.04	6
Negative Feelings (Pt.)	—.16	14
Approach (Pt.)	—.29	69
Clarity of Communication	—.29	65
Personal Communication (Stf.)	—.29	7

Let us turn now to Table 3, which shows the correlations found when the results are pooled for each aide.[3] Even the highest of these

[3] These correlations are based on observations on eight aides, which means that a correlation of .64 is necessary for significance at the 5% level.

correlations is not significant, and the fact that approximately half of them are negative strongly suggests that the true relation between questionnaire and observation results is close to zero when the results are pooled by aides. It is true that we do not have as good a basis for judging validity here as in Table 2. There are eight cases instead of eleven and the numbers of observations per scale tend to be considerably smaller. However, the correlations for the three scales on which we have the most observations (Approach [Pt.], Clarity of Communication, and Control Techniques) are certainly no better than for the other six scales, so that there does not seem to be much hope that more data would improve the correlations.

Our comparisons of questionnaire and observation data all involved the use of pooled data; we did not directly test the validity of the questionnaire for describing individual relationships. In the observations reported in this section we did not secure sufficient data to make possible comparisons of observation and questionnaire data for particular relationships. However, the unsatisfactory results obtained with data pooled by staff members indicate that the validity of the questionnaire for individual relationships would also have been unsatisfactory. The responses of different staff members to the questionnaire are not sufficiently comparable to one another. The differences in response style described in section 3A are obviously one reason for this. Other reasons may be differences in interpretation of items and differences in attitude toward the questionnaire (willingness to be candid, conscientiousness in filling it out, etc.)

D. Comparison of Intercorrelations from Direct Observation and from Questionnaire Data

Using the data from the two sets of observations, we also computed intercorrelations which would be comparable with those computed from the questionnaire data. Our objective was to check the possibility that the correlations among questionnaire scales might be affected by the expectations and preconceptions of the staff members filling out the questionnaires. The possibility of such an effect has been much discussed and has been demonstrated by at least one investigation. Newcomb found that when counselors at a summer camp rated boys on 26 behavioral traits, the mean intercorrelation was .49, while direct observation on the same traits yielded correlations with a mean of only .14 (Newcomb, 1931). Apparently the counselors' expectations that certain kinds of behavior should go together influenced their impressions of the boys they reported on, resulting in spuriously high correlations among the traits. It seemed worthwhile to use our observation data to check on the possibility that something similar occurred with correlations among the scales of our questionnaire. Therefore, we computed correlations among eight of the scales based on the April observations (shown in Table 4). The scales for Impersonal Communication by the patient and for the Expression of Positive Feelings by the staff member were omitted because of the extremely low number of observations for each. These interscale correlations and those from the questionnaire data on the same patients are shown in Tables 4 and 5.

It will be seen that the correlations based on the observation data are generally lower than those based on the questionnaire data. If we take the 56 correlations in the two tables together, exactly half of them have values of .36 or lower, while the other half have values of .39 or higher (ignoring signs). However, in the table of correlations from

TABLE 4

Interscale Correlations: Observation Data for 11 patients, April 1959

		1	4	5	6	7	8	12	15
1	Approach (Pt.)								
4	Communication Personal (Pt.)	+.04							
5	Communication Clarity	—.44	+.13						
6	Problem Behavior	—.27	—.51	—.39					
7	Positive Feelings (Pt.)	+.40	+.45	—.17	—.29				
8	Negative Feelings (Pt.)	—.36	+.23	—.15	+.05	+.10			
12	Communication Personal (Stf.)	—.12	+.16	—.04	+.05	+.04	—.53		
15	Use of Control Techniques (Stf.)	—.19	—.55	.00	+.66	—.16	—.33	—.02	
		1	4	5	6	7	8	12	15
	Total for each scale (absolute value)	1.82	2.07	1.32	2.22	1.61	1.75	.96	1.91

TABLE 5

Interscale Correlations: April 1959 Questionnaire Data, for 11
patients (Scales comparable to those used with observation data)

1	Approach (Pt.)							
4	Communication Personal (Pt.)	+.67						
5	Communication Clarity	+.19	+.28					
6	Problem Behavior	—.30	—.52	—.57				
7	Positive Feelings (Pt.)	+.95	+.60	+.32	—.30			
8	Negative Feelings (Pt.)	—.63	—.49	—.33	+.41	—.66		
12	Communication Personal (Stf.)	+.54	+.88	+.23	—.60	+.45	—.68	
15	Control Techniques (Stf.)	—.35	—.47	—.84	+.71	—.45	+.40	—.40
		1	4	5	6	7	8	12 15
	Total for each scale (absolute value)	3.63	3.91	2.76	3.41	3.73	3.60	3.78 3.62

observation data, 20 of the 28 have values of .36 or lower, whereas in the correlations from the questionnaire data only 8 have values of .36 or lower. In fact, there are only two correlations in the observation data which are higher than the corresponding correlations in the questionnaire data (those between Approach by the patient and Clarity of Communication by the patient and between Personal Communication by the patient and the Use of Control Techniques by the staff member, both negative in the observation data).

The correlations from the observation data may be lower because many of them are based on very few observations or because the observers were using somewhat different criteria from the staff members. Let us examine the correlations among those scales for which we have the best observation data (as shown both by number of observations and correlation between observation and questionnaire reports). These are the first five scales in Table 2. The intercorrelations among them from the observation and questionnaire data are shown side by side for convenient comparison in Table 6.

TABLE 6

Interscale Correlations: Comparison of Questionnaire and Observation

	From observation data				From questionnaire data			
5	—.44				.19			
6	—.27	—.39			—.30	—.57		
7	.40	—.17	—.29		.95	.32	—.30	
15	—.19	.00	.66	—.16	—.35	—.84	.71	—.45
	1	5	6	7	1	5	6	7

(The scales are: 1. Approach by the patient, 5. Clarity of Communication by the patient, 6. Problem Behavior by the patient, 7. Expression of Positive Feelings by the patient, and 15. Use of Control Techniques by the staff member).

In Table 6 we find four correlations above .50 from the questionnaire data. For one of these, the correlation between (6) Problem Behavior by the patient and (15) the Use of Control Techniques by the staff member, we find a correlation of very nearly the same size from the observation data. (Indeed, it would be very surprising if this correlation were not confirmed by the observation data!) The negative correlation between (5) Clarity of Communication by the patient and (6) Problem Behavior by the patient has a somewhat lower counterpart in the observation data, which probably does not differ enough to mean anything. The extremely high correlation between (1) Approach by the patient and (7) Expression of Positive Feelings by the patient has a much lower, but still positive, counterpart in the observation data. If the observation data are correct, this suggests a staff member stereotype which influences their questionnaire responses. Staff members may tend to see patients who are harder to understand as requiring more control or vice versa. There is also a suggestion of a difference in the opposite direction in the one observation correlation which is larger (absolute value) than the corresponding questionnaire correlation. This is the correlation between Approach by the patient and Clarity of Communication by the patient. The questionnaire data show little or no relationship, but the observation data yield a negative correlation which does not quite reach significance. If the observation data are valid, the patients whose communication was less clear did more approaching. This would make sense if the patients with clearer communication were more independent, as they might well be. However, if the staff members are maintaining a stereotype that more approach behavior is healthier or more normal, that would interfere with accurate reporting.

The material in this section shows that some of the correlations among our questionnaire scales were inflated and suggests that there may be a general tendency for questionnaire correlations to be inflated, as Newcomb found with his boys' camp data. However, there is also an indication that questionnaire correlations may occasionally be deflated. This clearly deserves further investigation.

E. Comments and Questions of Respondents

We also received indications of the difficulties and shortcomings of the questionnaire from the comments and questions of staff members as they answered the questionnaire. During the December 1960 administration a record was made of spoken comments and questions. Many staff members also wrote comments on the questionnaire itself. All written and spoken comments which indicated ambiguity of an item, or possible misunderstanding of it, or uncertainty about how to answer it were tabulated. The item which received by far the largest number of such comments was 42A ("How often do you think your ideas about how to handle this patient agree with those of his therapist?"); a great many staff members said they did not know what the therapist's ideas were. In addition to 42A, the items about which three or more problem-indicating comments were made were 1, 17, 18, 34, 42B, 46, 52, 53, 72, 77, and 78. We also tabulated the items for which answers were omitted by staff members of three or more nursing units, further evidence of difficult-to-answer items. The items for which such omissions occurred were 13, 14, 15, 17, 18, 19, 21, 38, 38A, 38C, 42A, 42B, and 78. Taking the comments and omissions together as indicators of problem items, the following scales are involved: Clarity of Communication by the patient (17, 18, 19, 21), the Expression of Negative Feelings by the staff member (34), Compliance by the patient (38, 38A, 38C), Impersonal Communication by the patient (53), Problem Behavior by the patient (72), Approach by the patient (13, 14), and Avoidance by the patient (15, 77, 78). The remaining items (1, 42A, 42B, 46, and 52) did not belong to any scales.

Among the difficulties we found in examining the items and the comments about them were the following: Some ideas were not clearly and precisely expressed; for example, it was not always clear just what was to be included in being "with" a patient (1). Some items caused difficulty by asking about a kind of behavior that depends on something else happening first; an example of this is item 78 ("When I ask him to go somewhere or do something with me he refuses"). If the staff member rarely or never makes such a request, how is he to respond to this item? In some items the use of several different terms proved confusing for some staff members who were not clear about what these terms had in common, as in item 18 ("The things he said to me were unrealistic (imaginary, delusional, outlandish"). With many items, including many not tabulated above, it seems clear that the research staff was using words and phrases somewhat differently from the people who filled out the questionnaire; often there are a number of different ways an item can be interpreted. Among the words capable of a variety of interpretations are: approach, attack, threat, gesture, distorted, unhappy, ignore, speak.

F. Comparison of Patient and Staff Questionnaire Responses

Another study carried out primarily for methodological purposes involved the comparison of responses to the questionnaire by patients and by staff members. We had attempted to get patients on Third Floor to answer some of the questions on our questionnaire, but with little success. The all-hospital administration of the questionnaire in December 1960 provided us with a more satisfactory opportunity to secure such data. A special version of the questionnaire was prepared for this purpose. Many of the items were identical with those already in the questionnaire, especially those which appeared in pairs, asking about patient and staff behavior in the same terms. Where necessary, additional items were prepared to correspond to items already in the staff version. To avoid offending the patients, questions about problem behavior were omitted, and questions about clarity of communication were replaced by a single pair of items ("He understands clearly what I say to him" and "I understand clearly what he says to me").

A number of patients on Hilltop I and II filled out questionnaires for us during the week that staff members were also filling out questionnaires. Five patients on each unit filled out the questionnaires with reasonable completeness and with indications that they had worked with care and understanding. The questionnaires filled out by these 10 patients were used for intensive analysis and comparison with the questionnaires filled out by the staff members on Hilltop.

In comparing data from patients and staff members we can make the assumption that items about which there is agreement are more likely to represent a valid report of what actually happened than items about which there is disagreement. This can only be taken as a general tendency; it certainly does not hold in every instance, for it is clearly possible for two people to make the same report and for both to be wrong. However, as a general assumption this seems fairly safe. Examples of specific applications of this assumption would be: Comparison of different questionnaire items for amounts of patient-staff agreement; the items with more agreement probably yield more valid reports. Comparison of different individuals for amounts of agreement with their interaction partners; those individuals showing higher average agreement with their partners are probably reporting their interactions more accurately.

In studying these data we also had the following questions: What are the common differences between the reports given by patients and the reports given by staff members? (The answer to this may indicate common difficulties and sources of friction in patient-staff relations and may also indicate specific items of questionnaire data which should be interpreted with caution because of possible inaccuracy.) What are the characteristics of relationships in which there is much agreement between the participants, and of those in which there is little agreement? (The answer to this may cast some light on the factors which contribute to agreement or disagreement. Furthermore, since consensus is likely to be closely related to the quality of communication and to be easily affected by feelings, this may indicate the quality of a relationship. It is obviously important to examine not only the amount of agreement but just what the agreement or disagreement is about.)

Patients vs. staff. We will consider first the overall differences in the pictures presented by patients and by staff. There is a general tendency for staff member reports to involve somewhat higher frequencies than patient reports. Thus, whenever the patients report something as happening more often than the staff members do, this is worthy of attention. Of the 63 items which were asked in comparable form of both staff and patients there are seven which patients on both Hilltop units answered with higher average frequencies than staff members. Four of these items are in the scale of Avoidance by the patient (and they comprise the entire scale). One item has to do with the use of force by staff members (Control Techniques scale), and one has to do with the use of commands, warnings, and ultimata by staff members (not included in any scale). The seventh item has to do with the expression of unhappiness by patients (Expression of Negative Feelings scale). These items clearly suggest that patients are more likely than staff to regard the interaction with ward staff members as something unpleasant which they actively try to avoid.

Looking at the other extreme, the items for which the frequencies reported by staff members exceed those reported by patients by the greatest amounts, we selected the six items for which there are the greatest discrepancies on both units. Three of these items have to do with time spent together (total time, time spent in conversation, and being together without talk). The other three items have to do with approach (two are in the Approach by staff scale and one in the Approach by patient scale). In other words, the patients report less time spent in interaction and less effort on both sides to initiate or maintain interaction than do the staff members.

Another way of looking at the patient and staff reports in relation to each other is to determine the absolute amounts of disagreement between members of interacting pairs. This measure does not show which member of a pair reports higher frequencies, but simply how close together or far apart their reports are. Using such measures, we can determine which items patients and staff members agree upon most and which they agree upon least.

There are four items for which the average amount of disagreement is less than 1.5 categories on both Hilltop I and II. One of these has to do with time spent in nursing care, and the agreement is mostly in reporting that little or no time is spent this way. (In other words, most of the agreement comes from both partners marking the "never" category). Another item has to do with the patients responding when approached. Here the agreement is at the other end of the scale; in other words, this is what usually happens. The third high agreement item has to do with the use of force and the agreement is predominantly to the effect that this never happens. The fourth one is item 46 ("He stayed around me but didn't speak to me unless I spoke first"). Here most of the agreement is to the effect that this never happens, but there is also a fair amount of agreement about once or twice a week and a few times a week.

At the other extreme, there are four items for which the average disagreement is 3.0 or more categories on both units. Two of these items have to do with admiration and approval, although they are not worded the same way. The item concerning patient behavior asks about "admiring or praising (complimented you on appearance, behavior, accomplishments, belongings)" whereas the staff behavior item asks about being "pleased with him (approving, grateful, or admiring)". A third item with high disagreement on both units has to do with securing compliance just by asking. There tend to be wide disagreements between members of pairs except for one patient on Hilltop I (who was reported as being very compliant by both himself and staff members). The fourth high disagreement item has to do with the use of reasoning, coaxing, and explaining.

Why should these particular items elicit so much disagreement? One possible explanation might be that the meaning of those items is less clear, so that there are considerable differences in interpretation of them. Another possible explanation might be that these items for some reason were answered in a more perfunctory or careless fashion so that agreement occurs mainly by chance. Still another possible explanation is that these particular items refer to matters which are most likely to be seen quite differently by the two participants in a relationship. Let us see what evidence we can find for or against each of these possibilities.

If the disagreements are the result of differences in the interpretation of these items we would expect that the reports of different people would vary from one another more than usual. In other words, the reports made by different staff members with respect to the same patient (or by different patients with respect to the same staff member) should be more varied than usual. To check this we used the range as a rough measure of variation and found the total of the between patient ranges for all staff members and the total of the between staff member ranges for each patient for each question. (For this purpose we used data from the five patients and six staff members on Hilltop II who seemed to have had most to do with one another). It turned out that all eight of these total ranges (eight because there are two for each question) are above the median of the total ranges; five of them are in the highest one-sixth of total ranges. It is clear that for these four items the reports made by different people with respect to the same person are indeed more varied than usual.

If the high disagreement on these items were due to their being answered in a perfunctory or careless fashion, this might be hard to detect. However, one form which a perfunctory answer might take would be the marking of the same category for everyone listed, straight down the page. On the two approval items this was done only once (by a patient who marked "never" for each staff member on the question about staff member expressions of approval). Taking the two units together there was an average of more than two such nondiscriminating answers per question by the five patients and of more than one per question by the six staff members, so these two items are *below* the average for this type of perfunctory answer. The item on securing compliance simply by asking for it received nondiscriminating answers from four patients (three of whom marked "Most of the time" and one of whom marked "Hardly ever" for everybody) but no such answers from any staff members. The item of reasoning, coaxing, and explaining received nondiscriminating answers from three patients (two marked "Never" and one marked "Hardly ever" for everybody) and three staff members ("Most of the time" for everybody). For these two items, then, there is somewhat more indication that they were marked in a perfunctory fashion but there were a number of items which had higher totals of nondiscriminating answers. Even for the nondiscriminating answers the categories marked by patients and staff members suggest that the answers are tendentious rather than simply perfunctory, which brings us to the third possible explanation.

The third explanation is that the disagreement is real, that it is not due to carelessness in answering or differences in interpretation but shows a difference in the way the partners see their interaction. This might take several forms. There may be disagreement associated with role difference; patients may tend to see things one way and staff members another. We have already given some examples of such disagreements, revealed by differences in the total amounts of certain kinds of behavior reported by patients and staff. However, none of these high disagreement items is among those for which there are high differences in total amounts on both units. (Of the six items mentioned earlier for which staff members tend to report much higher frequencies than patients on both units, only one has an especially high average of disagreement. This item, which deals with staff attempts to prolong time together, had an average disagreement of three categories on one unit and nearly three on the other). Another possibility is that the distortions which produce the disagreement take different forms for different individuals (one person may see himself as expressing more approval than other people are aware of, another may see himself as expressing less than others notice, another may tend not to notice the approval expressed by others, still another may have little distortion in his awareness of his own and others' expressions of approval, etc.). A third possibility is that distortions may be associated with particular relationships, as a result of things going on in those relationships rather than as a general characteristic of either partner. Both these possibilities (of individual-specific and pair-specific distortions) can be checked only by examination of the data in terms of particular individuals and relationships.

Differences between individuals. To examine differences between individuals we computed averages for the various patients and staff members and compared these averages with one another. (An average gives a rough composite of the way a person deals with his interaction partners.)

As mentioned earlier, a result which is of great interest is the average amount of disagreement each person has with his interaction partners. Such averages have been computed for each patient and each staff member. In analyzing differences between individuals in amounts of agreement with their interaction partners we did not at first make any distinction between different kinds of agreement. However, after some analysis of the data it became clear that there were at least two kinds of disagreement that should be distinguished: disagreement about the "never" category, and disagreement about other categories.

The "never" category is the most clearcut, and therefore people should find it easier to achieve agreement about it. Furthermore, the less two people have to do with each other, the easier it is for them to answer "never" to a great many questions and therefore agreement about the "never" category does not indicate good communication and understanding, which we might expect agreement about other categories to indicate. We therefore computed two scores for each patient, a never-category agreement score and a non-zero agreement score (each score showing the proportion of answers of a given kind on which he was in agreement with his partners). The rank correlation between the two kinds of scores is .04; this suggests that different factors must be influencing the two kinds of agreement. For example, patients' intelligence quotients correlate .46 with non-zero agreement but only .16 with never agreement. This fits in with the expectation that non-zero agreement has more to do with communication and mutual understanding than never agreement. Another patient characteristic that might be related to agreement is diagnosis. There were three patients who were relatively low on both kinds of agreement; two were psychotic and one was manic-depressive. There were two patients who were relatively high on both kinds of agreement; they were both diagnosed inadequate personality, impulsive. Both I.Q. and diagnosis are related to the same underlying characteristic, adequacy of cognitive functioning.

Another patient characteristic that might be related to agreement has to do with a style of filling out the questionnaires. On some questions a patient would give exactly the same response for all staff members. Every patient did this on at least two questions, one did this on 45 out of the 63 questions. Occasionally such a uniform response may be accurate, as when a given kind of behavior never occurs. For example, a patient may not have received any nursing care from any staff member, so that for him to mark all staff members "never" on this item would be completely accurate. However, it seems likely that most of the time a uniform response indicates carelessness or impatience with the question and hence a large number of such uniform responses indicates carelessness or impatience in filling out the questionnaire as a whole. Therefore, we determined for each patient the number of questions to which he gave uniform responses and correlated these with agreement. Most of the uniform responses were in the never category. Category 9 ("Most of the time" or "Many times a day") was second in frequency of uniform responses. The number of uniform responses had a high negative correlation (−.90) with agreement about the never category on Hilltop I, but a positive correlation (.70) on Hilltop II. Number of uniform responses had hardly any correlation (.20) with non-zero agreement on Hilltop I but a high *positive* relationship (.80) on Hilltop II. The Hilltop I results make good sense; the Hilltop II results are puzzling.

Thus far, in talking about differences between individuals, we have been dealing with differences between patients in amount of agreement and other characteristics which may be associated with them. Now we turn to differences between staff members and consider them in the same way. The first point to be noted is that never agreement and non-zero agreement are even more distinct from one another among staff members than among patients, since there appears to be a slight negative correlation. In other words, there is some tendency for staff members who are higher than average on one kind of agreement to be lower than average on the other. This suggests that an individual's accuracy in using one kind of category has quite a different basis from his accuracy in using the other kind. Perhaps other characteristics which are related to one or the other kind of agreement may give us some clues to the reasons for this.

One obvious consideration is the role of the individual in the hospital. Of the 24 staff members in the group for whom we have data, there are two administrators, three head nurses, five student nurses, 13 aides, and one graduate student nurse. The most obviously different group is that of the student nurses (all on Hilltop II), who do extremely poorly on non-zero agreement. Four of them have the four lowest proportions of non-zero agreement and the fifth one is only slightly higher. However, they are just about average on agreement about the never category, the median point for the five of them being just one point above the median for the entire group.

The two head nurses on Hilltop I do quite well on non-zero agreement, both being well above the median and one having the second highest score of all. The head nurse on Hilltop II is just a shade below the median on non-zero agreement (but well above the median for her unit only, which includes the students) and well above the median on agreement about the never category.

The two administrators are pretty close to the medians of both kinds of agreement. They are among the four people who are closest to the middle of the entire distribution.

The aides vary quite considerably, as might be expected. However, all but one of them are higher than all of the students on non-zero agreement. Six aides (three from Hilltop I and three from Hilltop II) are among the seven people who are highest on non-zero agreement.

Another characteristic of staff members which might be related to agreement is the amount of time they spend with patients. There may be some question about whether to use the total reported by patients for a given staff member or the total reported by the staff member himself. When dealing with amounts of time spent by patients we used the total reported by all the staff members for each patient, partly because this would balance out variations in the use of scales, and partly because staff members might be expected to be more accurate than patients (at least, more accurate than disturbed patients). However, when trying to get accurate totals for the staff members, the advantages of balancing out variations would argue for the use of pooled scores by the patients, whereas the possible greater accuracy of staff members would argue for the use of the staff members' own scores. But perhaps it does not matter which are used. In order to check on this, rank correlations were computed between the two kinds of totals. On Hilltop I there is considerable agreement between the two kinds of totals (correlation = .68), but on Hilltop II there is no agreement whatever (correlation = −.12). It occurred to us that the latter result might be due to the inclusion of data from the student nurses, with whom most of the patients report spending little or no time. We therefore recomputed the correlation, omitting the students, and the result was slightly worse (−.29). Therefore, at least for Hilltop II, it obviously makes considerable difference which measure of time spent is used; for that reason we decided to try both. Using the Hilltop II patient reports on time spent by staff members, the correlation between time spent and non-zero agreement is .77, while the correlation between time spent and agreement about the never category is −.48. Using the staff reports, the correlations have the same signs but are much smaller, the first being .32 and the second −.26. The same correlations were computed for Hilltop I. Using the patient reports on time spent, the correlation between time spent and non-zero agreement is $-.09$ and that between time spent and never agreement is $-.51$. Using the staff reports, the first correlation is $-.03$ and the second $-.19$. We see that the negative correlation between time spent and non-zero agreement is consistent on both units and has a higher value when patient reports are used, suggesting that the pooled patient reports may be more accurate than the unpooled staff reports of time spent. The positive correlation between time spent and non-zero agreement appears only on Hilltop II, while on Hilltop I there is essentially no correlation.

Another staff characteristic that might be related to agreement is the tendency to give uniform answers to questions. Staff members tended to do much less of this than patients, but there were a few who did, especially on Hilltop II, where one staff member gave uniform answers to 29 questions. The correlations with accuracy were quite low. (Between uniform answers and non-zero agreement: .36 on Hilltop I, .12 on Hilltop II. Between uniform answers and never agreement: .23 on Hilltop I, $-.28$ on Hilltop II). The low correlations may very well be due to the fact that there is relatively little difference among the staff members in this respect, much less than among the patients.

Differences between pairs of individuals. In examining the data for ways in which relationships (i.e., patient-staff pairs) differ, there are two complications that have to be dealt with. One is the fact that a large number of relationships are included (55 on Hilltop I, 65 on Hilltop II), so that some selection among them is necessary. The second complication is the problem of differences in use of answer categories. One way to deal with the answer category problem is by a kind of matching procedure. If we want to compare two kinds of relationships we choose pairs of relationships, such that the same individual is involved in both members of a pair, but one relationship is of one kind and the other of the second kind. An example should make this clearer:

In order to examine how relationships in which there is much agreement between the partners differ from those in which there is little agreement, we picked out two staff members for each patient on Hilltop I. One was the person with whom the patient agreed on the largest number of questions (this varied from 31 to 43 out of the 63 questions). The other was the person with whom the patient agreed on the fewest questions (this varied from 7 to 16). In this way we secured a group of five high-agreement relationships and another group of five low-agreement relationships, but with exactly the same patients involved in both groups. (This can also be done by selecting a pair of relationships for each staff member). Similarly, we secured five relationships in which there was most agreement about the never category and five in which there was least agreement about the never category, also a set with high non-zero agreement and a set with low non-zero agreement. (In two instances there was more than one staff member who had the highest, or lowest, amount of a given amount of agreement. In such instances, we averaged the scores of the staff members on whatever variable was under examination.)

Having secured these groups we compared them with respect to the expression of positive feelings by both patients and staff members, thinking that high agreement might indicate a friendly relationship in which the participants enjoy each other's company, or a close relationship in which the participants freely express both positive and negative feelings to each other. As expected, the patients reported expressing considerably more positive feeling toward the staff members with whom they had the most non-zero agreement (the totals were 176 and 128). For agreement about the never category, the relationship was reversed; patients expressed *less* positive feeling toward those with whom they had the most agreement about the never category (totals: 93 to 152.5). The patients also expressed more *negative* feelings toward staff members with whom they had the most non-zero agreement (73 to 53), but there was not much difference in expression of negative feeling with respect to agreement about the never category (57 to 61.5). The results are similar for the expression of feelings by staff members (according to patient reports). Staff members express positive feelings more often to patients with whom they have high non-zero agreement (124 to 82) and less often to patients with whom they have high agreement about the never category (72 to 115.5). Exactly the same is true for the expression of negative feelings (40 to 31 for high vs. low non-zero agreement; 28 to 42.5 for high vs. low agreement about the never category.)

When we had gotten this far it occurred to us that these results could be accounted for by variations in the amount of time various pairs of patients and staff members spend together. In other words, those pairs who have high agreement about categories 3 to 9, and low agreement about the never category may simply be people who spend some time together (regardless of the quality of the relationship), and those pairs for whom the reverse is true may be the people who spend little or no time together. (This possibility is related to the fact that a different basis for measuring agreement was used in dealing with relationships. In the previous section of this report we refer to measures of agreement based on *proportions* of total answers of a given kind; thus, agreement about the never category by a given individual was taken as the proportion of all his answers in the never category which were agreed to by his various partners. These proportions could be high or low quite independently of whether the individual made many or few checks in the never category. However, when dealing with a relationship it would not be appropriate to measure agreement as a proportion of the answers made by *one* partner. Various alternatives are possible, but the simplest is to use absolute amounts of agreement instead of proportions.)

In order to check on the effect of variations in amount of time spent together, we decided to compare relationships in which the partners spent much time together (at least category 7, which is two hours per day) with relationships in which they spent less time together but at least some (at least category 3, which is half an hour per day). For most of the patients on Hilltop I it was not possible to find a pair of relationships meeting these requirements, because they reported spending relatively little time with staff members. Then we tried to find such a pair for each staff member, with slightly more success. We found pairs for four staff members which met the above requirements (and where patients, as well as staff members, marked at least category 3 for time spent). Comparing the two kinds of relationships, it turned out that there is about twice as much agreement about the never category for the relationships in which less time is spent together (38.5 to 18.5). This seems very reasonable, but surprisingly we also find more non-zero agreement, although not very much more, for the relationships with less time spent together (63 to 54). At any rate, these results certainly suggest that non-zero agreement is not simply a matter of amount of time spent together, provided that the participants spend some minimum amount of time together.

Lastly we examined the relations between staff member preference and agreement. For each staff member we selected his most and least preferred patient, choosing only from those patients with which he spent at least a half hour a day, according to both the staff member's and patient's reports. (We were able to find such a pair for every staff member on Hilltop I, except the administrator, who naturally spent less time with patients). The staff members had almost exactly the same amount of non-zero agreement with the patients they liked more as with the patients they liked less (182 to 181), but somewhat greater agreement about the never category for the better liked patients (79 to 61). Even the latter difference is not very significant, since it works out to an average of 1.8 questions out of the 63 (whereas the number of questions in which the partners agreed in answering "never" varied from 0 in one relationship to 37 in another).

Summary. It may be helpful to summarize briefly the findings from the patient-staff questionnaire comparison which have just been presented. Some of these findings are of mainly methodological significance, which is why the material has been included in this part of the report, but others are mainly substantive.

Differences in the frequency with which particular kinds of behavior are reported by patients and by staff members point to differences between the two groups in their conceptions of the interaction or to differences in what they are willing to report and the impression they wish to create. Taking just the items for which the frequency differences are greatest, we find that patients report less time spent in interaction and less effort on both sides to initiate or maintain interaction. Patients also report more frequent avoidance behavior and expression of unhappiness by themselves and more use of control techniques by staff members, than do staff members.

Differences in the extent of agreement about particular items may indicate the validity of those items. In the next section of this report extremes of high and low agreement will be used as part of the evidence concerning the satisfactoriness of particular items and scales.

In analyzing agreement it was found necessary to distinguish between agreement about the "never" category and agreement about other categories. This is an important distinction which deserves further investigation. The diagnosis and functional intelligence of the patient are related to his extent of agreement with staff members, especially non-zero agreement. This supports the assumption that agreement is related to accuracy. The role position of staff members and the amount of time they spend with patients are also related to agreement.

The relation of the two kinds of agreement to the expression of positive and negative feelings was examined. More expression of positive and negative feelings by both patients and staff members is reported for relationships in which non-zero agreement is high. This does not seem to be due simply to more time being spent together but indicates that consensus and freedom of emotional expression (and perhaps greater emotional involvement) do go together.

G. Discussion and Conclusions

In this section the major findings of the evaluation studies will be reviewed, first assembling them for each scale and for a few particular items, and then discussing their general implications for the use of the Relationship Questionnaire.

The scale for Approach by the patient had the lowest reliability coefficients of the 12 scales studied and the second lowest validity coefficient of the six scales for which a reasonable number of instances were observed. The range of scores on this scale was among the lowest of all the scales. By changing the answer categories or rewriting items, it might be possible to increase the difference in the scores which different patients receive, which might increase the reliability and validity. However, it is also possible that approach behavior does actually vary more from week to week than any other kind of behavior dealt with by the questionnaire. If so, the lower reliability coefficient of this scale would not represent inaccuracy. A special study would be needed to check on this, but it is a plausible idea and is certainly consistent with the near-zero coefficient (Table 1) for a four-month period which shows that approach behavior changes even more over a longer period. Two of the items (13, 14) were among those which caused staff members difficulty in answering. Item 13 had a correlation of .04 between questionnaire and observation (out of 28 items). Item 13 was one of the four items for which there was the highest amount of agreement between patients and staff members. However, most of this agreement involved the extreme high category, indicating that these patients responded to approach most of the time, so that the item did not discriminate very well among these patients either.

The scale for Avoidance by the patient was not yet in the questionnaire at the time of the reliability and validity studies. Three of its four items were among those which staff members had difficulty in answering and all four of the items were among those to which patients gave higher answers than staff members.

The scale for Personal Communication by the patient had a reliability coefficient over .90, which may be taken as quite satisfactory. Not enough instances were observed to provide an adequate test of its validity. No items from this scale emerged as troublesome in the tabulation of comments and omissions, nor were any especially noted in the comparison of patient and staff questionnaires.

The scale for Clarity of Communication by the patient had a satisfactory reliability coefficient and the second highest validity coefficient (.83). Four of the items were noted in the tabulation of comments and omissions. None of the items were outstanding for either agreement or disagreement in the patient-staff comparison. In view of the many comments and questions and also our failure to establish a clear-cut discrimination between confused speech and delusional speech, this scale seems to be based on a very crude distinction between normal and "crazy" speech. However, the large and striking differences among patients make it possible for this scale to discriminate between patients quite adequately.

The scale for Problem Behavior by the patient had the highest reliability coefficient (.99) and the third highest validity coefficient (.74). Only one of its items (#72) appeared in the group of troublesome items. This scale appears to be measuring fairly adequately a kind of behavior with which staff members are much concerned and about which they are in reasonable overall agreement.

The scale for the Expression of Positive Feelings by the patient had a satisfactory reliability coefficient and the highest validity coefficient (.90). None of its items were in the group of troublesome items, but in the patient-staff comparison there was high disagreement about item 25. With the possible exception of this item, the scale is highly satisfactory.

The scale for the Expression of Negative Feelings by the patient had a satisfactory reliability coefficient, but the validity coefficient was only .21, which was the lowest of the lot and is especially striking in view of the relatively large number of instances which were observed of behavior related to this scale. However, two items from this scale showed up much more favorably when separately compared with observation data. These were items 28 and 30 ("How often did he show or express the following feelings: [28] Unhappy [30] Angry, annoyed"); their validity coefficients were .59 and .56. (Slightly revised versions of these items appear in the latest revision of the questionnaire as items 27 and 29.) Since these two items between them account for 62 of the 65 instances which were observed, it is clear that the observations were not an adequate check on the scale as a whole and therefore judgment on this scale should probably be suspended.

The scales for Active Activities and Passive Activities were added to the questionnaire after the studies of reliability and validity had been done. No items from either scale appeared in the group of troublesome items nor were any of them the source of high disagreement between patients and staff members.

The scale for Approach by the staff member had a reliability coefficient of .79, which was the second lowest. Thus the two approach scales have the lowest reliabilities of all the scales tested. As mentioned earlier, this may simply mean that approach behavior is more variable than other kinds of relationship behavior, but this might well be checked by an observational study. One item from this scale was among those checked by direct observation. This was item 47, which had a validity coefficient of .93, the highest for that whole group of items.

The scale for Personal Communication by the staff member had a satisfactory reliability coefficient. It was among the scales whose validity was tested by direct observation, but so few instances were observed (15) that the resulting validity coefficient (.53) probably means very little. The small number of instances suggests that these staff members did not engage in much personal communication with patients. In the Hilltop patient-staff questionnaire comparison, two items from this scale were given markedly higher ratings by staff members than by patients, suggesting that staff member reports on the questionnaire may exaggerate the amount of personal communication they engage in with patients.

The scale for the Expression of Positive Feelings by the staff member had a satisfactory reliability coefficient. As with the preceding scale not enough instances were observed for a satisfactory validity test. (Actually, we observed four instances.) One of the items from this scale (#33) was among the four items with the highest amount of patient-staff disagreement. This item is quite similar to item 25, which, as mentioned above, was another one of the high disagreement items. The wording or content (or both) of these items may suggest different things to different people or this may be a particularly sensitive area for these patients.

The scale for the Expression of Negative Feelings by the staff member had a satisfactory reliability coefficient. Not enough instances were observed (only two) for a validity check. One item from this scale was among the troublesome items (#34). Use of this scale clearly involves two problems: (1) that the behavior does not occur very often, and (2) what does occur is probably under-reported.

The scale for the Use of Control Techniques by the staff member had a satisfactory reliability coefficient. Its validity coefficient was .67, the fourth highest. Separate validity coefficients for the three items of this scale were computed from the observation data. The coefficients for items 78 and 81 are $+.69$ and $+.81$, but the coefficient for item 77 was $-.07$, which probably lowered the validity of the scale as a whole. Item 77 (now #37) has been revised. One of the items of this scale was among the four highest disagreement items in the patient-staff comparison (#39). On the other hand, another item was among the four highest agreement items (#42), but this may be mainly because force was rarely used with this group of patients.

The scale for Compliance by the patient was not yet included in the questionnaire at the time of the reliability and validity checks. Item 38 was one of the four which elicited highest disagreement in the patient-staff comparison. All three items of this scale were among the troublesome items according to comments and omissions. This scale clearly needs further work, and results from it should be interpreted with caution.

Data from the various methodological studies also bear on the satisfactoriness of individual items which are not included in scales. In the latest version of the questionnaire there are six such items about which there may be some problems. Five of these (1, 42A, 42B, 46, 52) are in the group of troublesome items as indicated by frequent comments and questions during administration. The remaining one (#5) had a validity coefficient of .51 which seems somewhat low in view of the fact that 109 instances were observed, the fourth largest frequency for a single item. In the patient-staff comparison this item was one of the six for which the staff reports exceeded the patient reports by the greatest amount.

In reviewing these methodological studies from the viewpoint of the questionnaire as a whole, the most important point is the unsatis-factoriness of the questionnaire for the study of individual patient-staff relationships because of the variations in style of answering by different staff members. This was made clear by examination of the use of answer categories and emphasized by the study of validity through direct observation. It is only when the data from different staff members are pooled that we can get scores which are reasonably comparable with those for other patients and which have satisfactory validity coefficients. This means that the questionnaire tells us about the general relationship style of a patient, how he behaves on the average or in most of his relationships with staff members. This also raises serious questions about the attempt to use questionnaires on an individual basis with administrators and therapists, who are undoubtedly also subject to idiosyncratic variations in ways of answer-ing. We did develop a simple method for obtaining some information about an individual relationship by noting extreme scores as compared with other relationships of the same staff member. This method will be described and discussed in more detail later (see section 4E) but it is worth mentioning here that it accomplishes only part of what we orig-inally anticipated with the questionnaire.

The reliability and validity studies indicate that the questionnaire is a basically satisfactory instrument in our setting (when data from various staff members are pooled), although particular items and scales need to be revised or to be further checked. However, these reliability and validity studies were done with a very small group of patients and staff members in a single clinical setting, which means we don't really know about the usability of the questionnaire in other settings. The questionnaire is more likely to be suitable in hospitals with high staff-patient ratios and with levels of staff-patient interaction which are comparable to those at Chestnut Lodge.

The correlation analyses of the observation data indicate that some interscale correlations from the questionnaire data may be inflated, presumably by the preconceptions and stereotypes of staff members (and also that it is possible for such correlations to be deflated at times).

The findings about the variation in response styles of different staff members and about the inflation and deflation of correlations from questionnaire data have serious implications for other studies besides our own. They raise questions about behavior ratings of mental patients made by one or two individuals and about intercorrelations among such ratings.

4. USES OF THE QUESTIONNAIRE

In this part of the report will be found descriptions of the studies made with the questionnaire whose aim has been primarily substantive rather than methodological. Not all of these attempts at use of the questionnaire have been successful, but something can be learned from the failures as well as from successes. (The cluster analyses will not be described here since they have already been dealt with in sections 2B and 2C and in Chapter V).

A. The Study of Change

Change can be studied in an individual relationship, in the relationship pattern of a particular patient, and in the overall relationship behavior of a whole group. For reasons already discussed, we made little use of the questionnaire to study changes in individual relationships. The study of change in particular patients was one of our important objectives in developing the questionnaire. We hoped to measure changes in the relationship behavior of each patient and to look for connections between such changes and events in psychotherapy and in other significant relationships of the patient.

The most intensive study of changes in particular patients was done with six successive administrations of the questionnaire (January 1959 through March 1960) and with nine patients who were present for all six administrations. The findings will be summarized here quite briefly. The reports on three patients indicate a worsening of their conditions and of their relationships with nursing personnel; one of these was Harrashaw. Richter showed an increase in interaction with nursing personnel when he was restricted to the unit in September 1959, followed by a decline to his previous level of interaction. Feldman showed a slight improvement in social behavior from January to June 1959, followed by a gradual worsening, so that by March 1960 he was somewhat below his level on the first questionnaire. Nursing personnel reports indicated little change in Glen's relationship behavior over the period covered; he decreased in Personal Communication and the Expression of Negative Feelings. We were disappointed to find so little improvement. Having discovered this, we pretty well abandoned our hope of studying change in patients (since we were really more interested in studying improvement than decline). However, the difficulty seems clearly due not to the questionnaire, but to the setting; the questionnaire seems quite capable of picking up the changes that do occur.

The data from the six successive administrations of the questionnaire were also examined from the viewpoint of the whole group, by looking at the overall averages for each scale. No large changes in any scale were noted for this period, indicating that the overall relationship behavior (the general social atmosphere of Third Floor) did not change very much.

Another examination for possible changes was made with data from the March and December 1960 questionnaire administrations. Between those two administrations both the administrator and the head nurse of Third Floor were changed. There were eight patients (including Appleton, Dan, and Glen) and six nursing staff members who were present on both occasions, so we tabulated the average scale scores of these staff members reporting on these patients, as well as the scale scores of the old and new administrator and head nurse for the same eight patients. In the overall averages of the six staff members there was little change; in none of the scales was there a change as large as 20 percent. There was a slight rise in Avoidance by the patients and in the Expression of Negative Feelings by the patients, together with a slight drop in the Expression of Positive Feelings by both patients and staff members. There was also a slight drop in Problem Behavior by the patients and the Use of Control Techniques by the staff members, together with a slight rise in Compliance by the patients. In the administrator and head nurse questionnaires the differences were much greater. For both the administrators and the head nurses there were differences of 20 percent or greater on 12 out of the 16 scales for which comparisons were made, with changes ranging up to nearly 150 percent for the administrators and nearly 200 percent for the head nurses. However, 10 of the 12 differences between the two administrators and 11 of the 12 differences between the two head nurses were increases, which strongly suggests that a good part of the differences between the members of each pair was in the use of answer categories with the later administrator and the later head nurse both tending to use larger categories. This apparent difference in the use of answer categories makes the comparison much more difficult, but examination of the more extreme differences may give some clues as to the actual change. The two largest differences between the administrators are in Avoidance by the patients and the Expression of Negative Feelings by the administrator, the second administrator reporting much larger amounts of both. The two largest differences between the head nurses are in the Expression of Negative Feelings by the patients and the Expression of Negative Feelings by the head nurse, the second nurse reporting much larger amounts of both. The only scale for which the second nurse reported lower amounts was Compliance by the patients and the only two scales for which the second administrator reported lower amounts were Active Activities and Clarity of Communication by the patients. These differences suggest that the second head nurse and administrator were on somewhat poorer terms with these eight patients in December than their predecessors had been the previous March.

The same data (March-December 1960) were also examined for indications of change in individual patients by noting changes of 20 percent or more on each scale. Dan showed such changes on eight of the 16 scales and the changes indicated a general worsening of social behavior. Glen showed changes on five scales, three of which showed poorer social behavior. Appleton also showed poorer behavior on three scales.

For purposes of comparison we also examined changes over the period from April 1959 to March 1960, during which the same administrator remained in charge of Third Floor. Nine patients and five nursing staff members were on hand on both occasions; data were tabulated from their questionnaires with respect to 11 scales (since fewer of the scales were represented in the earlier questionnaire). We found overall changes of 20 percent or more on three of these scales (an increase of over 20 percent in Approach by the staff members, an increase of over 55 percent in the Expression of Negative Feelings by the staff members, and an increase of nearly 30 percent in the Use of Control Techniques by the staff members). As the foregoing changes suggest, an increase in Problem Behavior by the patients was also reported over this period (but it was less than 20 percent).

B. Variability and Differentiation

Our interest in differentiation and in comparing the relationship patterns of different patients led us to wonder whether we could measure the extent to which a patient's relationships were differentiated. The variability of scores on the scales of the questionnaire might provide such a measure of differentiation. If staff reports on patient A vary more from one another than do their reports on patient B, this should indicate that their interactions with patient A vary more from one another and hence that patient A has more differentiated relationships.

We attempted to secure an overall measure of differentiation. Using data from the January 1960 administration of the questionnaire, the standard deviation was computed for each patient's scores on each of 14 scales. The patients were then ranked in order of variability on each scale and the ranks were averaged to give a rough measure of overall variability for each patient. The results did not correspond to our expectations about which patients would have most and least differentiated relationships. Further examination of the data led us to question the assumption that variability on different scales was related. (Without this assumption an overall measure of variability is meaningless.) Correlations of variability of different scales were computed with data from two administrations of the questionnaire; most of them were quite small. It is still conceivable that the variability of some particular scales may be related to differentiation, but we decided not to pursue this any further.

C. Symmetry of Relationship Behavior

We became interested in the question of symmetry of behavior (the extent to which patient and staff member behave in the same way toward each other) because it seemed that this might be an indicator of mutuality in relationship. We felt that a more mutual relationship might indicate greater intimacy or more normal behavior on the part of the patient or freer and more accepting behavior by the staff member, or perhaps some combination of these.

Using data from the March 1960 administration of the questionnaire, we made tabulations for 14 pairs of items. In each pair one item asked about patient behavior and the other about staff behavior in words that corresponded exactly except for the person referred to. (The 14 pairs of items included all items in the questionnaire at that time which met these conditions.) A table was made for each staff member containing a column for each patient and a row for each pair of questions. In each box was entered a zero, a plus, or a minus to indicate whether there was roughly no difference, or the patient was reported higher than the staff member, or the patient was reported lower than the staff member on that pair of items. (Only discrepancies of two or more answer categories were counted as differences). From these tables a summary table was prepared, showing for each patient the number of times he was reported higher than, lower than, or approximately the same as the staff member on each pair of items. Only data from this summary table will be discussed here. (Individual differences in style of filling out the questionnaire, already discussed, obviously create difficulties in interpreting the data for individual staff members).

Of the 14 patients who were reported on at this time, Richter was second highest in most agreement (88 out of 126 comparisons) on these 14 pairs of items (indicating high symmetry or mutuality). The patient with the lowest agreement was Harrashaw (51 out of 125 comparisons). Whether the patient is generally reported higher or lower may also be of interest. Thus Harrashaw, who was in a very regressed state, was reported higher only 11 times and lower 63 times.

Totals were also tabulated by pairs of items. The pair with the highest total symmetry was 60-68 ("He talked to me about the relationship between the two of us (how we get along)." "I talked to him about . . ." Proportion of agreement: 100/126), followed by 58-65 ("He talked to me about my personal life (my thoughts, feelings, personal affairs, past life, etc.)" "I talked to him about his personal life . . ." Proportion: 85/125) and 28-35 ("When he was with you, how often did he show you or let you know that he felt suspicious or distrustful?" Proportion: 84/127). At the other extreme, the pair with the lowest symmetry was 27-34 ("When he was with you, how often did he show you or let you know that he felt unhappy?" Proportion: 32/125), followed by 14-16 ("When you were with him, how often did he try to get you to stay longer with him?" Proportion: 54/123) and 24-32 ("When he was with you, how often did he show you or let you know that he felt active or energetic (lively and interested)?" Proportion: 60/124). As with particular patients there were also considerable differences between pairs of items in whether the patient was generally reported higher or lower. Thus for items 24-32 the patient was reported lower 55 times and higher only nine times, whereas for items 27-34 the patient was reported lower only three times and higher 90 times. The high symmetry kinds of behavior do generally seem to be activities in which mutual participation is necessary or expected. Thus we expect conversation about the relationship to involve both participants, and conversation about the personal life of the other is usually expected to be reciprocated. Distrust is often reciprocal also. On the other hand, the low symmetry items are those in which mutuality and reciprocity are not expected; quite the contrary, we expect discrepancies between patients and staff members in such things as expressing unhappiness or being active and interested.

Related to the foregoing pair comparisons are two series of intrapair correlations computed with data from the April and September 1959 questionnaire administrations. Rank correlations were computed for 13 pairs of corresponding items which were in the questionnaire on those two occasions, approximately the same items as the 14 pairs studied in the March 1960 data. Perhaps it should be pointed out that correlations are not the same as measures of symmetry; for example, it is possible to have a high correlation with low symmetry if the rankings on the two items correspond fairly well. However, that would suggest some responsiveness, even without exact mutuality. Furthermore, we would expect symmetry and correlation to be more closely related a good deal of the time. Most of the 13 correlations were fairly consistent between April and September; the largest change was .69 but most of the changes were far smaller than that. (There were nine patients who were present on both occasions; six who were present only one time or the other.) The five pairs of items with high correlations (.70 or above) on both occasions were: 46-49, 54-62, 56-64, 57-65, and 58-66. The four pairs of items with low correlations (.40 or less) on both occasions were: 45-48, 14-16, 55-63, and 61-69.

If measures of symmetry are to be used as indicators of mutuality for individual patients it would be desirable to distinguish mutual abstention from mutual participation, since mutual abstention does not really show mutuality. This corresponds to the distinction between agreement about the never category and agreement about other categories, already discussed (section 3F).

D. Characterization of Individual Patients

One use of the questionnaire for the description of individual patients has already been illustrated in the section on the study of change. Changes in scale scores for nine patients corresponded with clinical impressions of the courses of those patients.

Another way of describing patients is based on the cluster analyses. The clusters found have been reported and described in Chapter V and in section 2B of this appendix. Third Floor patients were classified on the basis of these clusters, using data from the January and December 1960 questionnaire administrations.

Patients were placed in categories in the following way: The median score for each scale with the particular group of patients was found. A patient was assigned to the Low group if his scores on all the scales in a cluster were below the median or just at the median. Similarly for the High group. If a patient had scores on both sides of the median, he was put in the Medium group. If a patient in the medium group had scores on different scales whose ranks differed from one another by more than six (roughly half the range), he was classified as Mixed, indicating that the cluster does not fit him as well as it does most patients.

Only one patient (out of 19) was High on both clusters or Low on both clusters at the same time. For most patients, the two patterns of behavior were alternatives. In other words, most patients did mainly one or mainly the other or some of each, but neither a great deal of both nor hardly any of either. In January 1960 Appleton and Glen were both high on Problem Behavior and medium on Friendly Overtures, Dan and Feldman were both high on Friendly Overtures and low on Problem Behavior, and Richter was medium on Problem Behavior and low on Friendly Overtures. In December 1960 Appleton was mixed on Problem Behavior and low on Friendly Overtures, Dan was medium on Problem Behavior and low on Friendly Overtures, and Glen was medium on both Problem Behavior and Friendly Overtures.

In Chapter V another cluster was mentioned, which was found in that data from Third Floor in December 1960 but not in January 1960. This cluster included four scales: Personal Communication by both patient and by staff and the Expression of Negative Feelings by patient and by staff. On this cluster, Appleton was low, Dan was mixed, and Glen was high.

E.   Characterization of Individual Relationships

We have already emphasized the difficulties facing the questionnaire as a device for studying individual relationships, difficulties which we did not succeed in overcoming. However, it is possible to extract from the questionnaire some data about an individual relationship which seem likely to be valid. This method is based on the assumption that a staff member's idiosyncrasies in filling out the questionnaire are likely to affect his reports on all patients, so that comparison of these reports with one another may be relatively unbiased. In other words, if staff member A reports spending more time with patient X than with patient Y we should be more justified in accepting this as true than in accepting staff member A's report that he spends more time with X than staff member B does. Making use of this assumption we can proceed as follows: To discover the special characteristics of A's relationship with X, examine A's questionnaire reports (on all patients) and select those items for which A gave X the highest score or the lowest score that he gave anyone on that item. These items are the ones for which X's behavior (or A's behavior toward X) are extreme (in terms of A's perception of the extremes of this kind of behavior) and this may be a significant fact of the relationship or may indicate an important way in which this relationship differs from A's other relationships. (It is of interest to know that this is the patient toward whom A expresses the most anger, or the least anger.) This method was used in examining the relationships of Baxter, Grabble, and Wallace with Harrashaw (the results will be found in Chapter X).

F. Differences in Relationship Behavior According to Staff Role

Using data from the December 1960 all-hospital administration of the questionnaire, the scale scores of administrators, therapists, ward staff, and student nurses were compared. On most of the comparisons administrators gave lower reports than therapists and ward staff. At least part of this difference must be due to the difference in the amount of time spent with patients. Since we could not find any simple and satisfactory way of allowing for this, the comparisons involving administrators are omitted here.

In the comparisons between therapists and ward staff (nurses and aides) we find the following differences on most or all units: Therapists report more Personal Communication both by the patients and by themselves, more Clarity of Communication by the patients, and more Expression of Negative Feelings by both the patients and themselves. Ward staff report more Expression of Positive Feelings by patients and by staff and more Use of Control Techniques by staff.

Comparisons between student nurses and ward staffs were made only for three of the seven nursing units, since there were not enough student nurses on other units to justify averaging their scale scores. Student nurses reported higher amounts of Clarity of Communication by patients and of the Expression of Positive Feelings by staff. Ward staff reported higher amounts of Approach by the patients, Personal Communication by both patients and staff, Problem Behavior, Use of Control Techniques, Expression of Negative Feelings by staff, and Passive Activities. These differences suggest that student nurses had somewhat less to do with patients than regular ward staff, perhaps that they spent more time observing and less time actively participating. The student nurses may also have tried to present the situation in a more favorable light, as suggested by their reporting greater clarity of patient communication and more expression of positive feelings by themselves.

G. Behaviors Related to Time Spent with Patients

Using the January 1960 data, correlations were computed between each of the scales and item 1 ("In the past week, how much time did you usually spend with each patient during a shift?"). The following scales had correlations with this item that were over .50:

Passive Activities	+.69
Use of Control Techniques by staff	+.59
Approach by staff	+.57
Active Activities	+.57

Similar correlations were computed for each of the seven units of the hospital with the December 1960 data. Three of the foregoing scales (all but the Use of Control Techniques) had correlations with item 1 that were over +.50 on at least five out of the seven units, and this was also true for another scale, Personal Communication by the staff. In December 1960 the correlations with item 1 which were over .50 in the data from Third Floor were:

Approach by the patient	+.83
Approach by the staff	+.71
Avoidance by the patient	−.70
Personal Communication by the patient	+.70
Active Activities	+.70
Personal Communication by the staff	+.67
Clarity of Communication by the patient	+.54
Passive Activities	+.53

Thus we see that there are differences both from one time to another and from one unit to another in the kinds of behavior associated with the amount of time spent with patients by staff members. The four scales which are most consistently associated with time spent are the two activities scales (which may be thought of as more detailed ways of asking the question about how much time is spent with a particular patient) and two scales having to do with staff behavior (Approach and Personal Communication). The relatively consistent relation of the staff behavior scales to time spent suggests that staff interest and initiative are usually of great importance in determining which patients get the most attention. The correlation of Approach by staff with time spent is higher on five out of the seven units than the correlation of Approach by patient with time spent. At particular times on a given unit other kinds of behavior may assume importance. Thus, on two out of the seven units Problem Behavior has fairly high correlations with time spent (+.70 and +.65), whereas on the other five units they are much closer to zero (ranging from −.38 to +.38). The same two units with the high Problem Behavior correlations also show the highest correlations of the Use of Control Techniques and the Expression of Negative Feelings by staff with amount of time spent.

H. The Study of Disagreement

In connection with the December 1960 questionnaire administration we attempted to investigate further the connection between hidden staff disagreement and pathological excitement which was reported by Stanton and Schwartz (1954). This attempt has already been reported (Gladstone & Burnham, 1966), so we will simply describe here the use of the questionnaire to study disagreement among staff members.

We distinguished actual disagreement from acknowledged disagreement. Actual disagreement refers to differences between staff members in what they actually reported about a given patient on the questionnaire. For each scale the highest and lowest ranking that the patient had received on that scale was determined and the difference between the two found. The sum of these differences for all scales for a given patient was the actual disagreement score for that patient.

Acknowledged disagreement refers to disagreement which staff members are aware of and willing to report on the questionnaire. A measure of it was derived from items (42-A, B, C, D) asking how often the respondent's "ideas about how to handle this patient" were in agreement with those of other staff members. Scores on this item indicated agreement and they could simply be reversed to indicate disagreement.

Stanton and Schwartz talk about hidden disagreement. While this cannot be determined directly, an indication of it can be obtained by comparing the measures of reported and actual disagreement. If actual disagreement is higher than reported disagreement, this suggests that here is some hidden disagreement. In order to make actual and reported disagreement commensurate, they were ranked and the difference between their ranks was taken as an indicator of hidden disagreement.

A finding of some interest which emerged from this investigation is that reported and actual disagreement do not seem to be related to one another. Measures of two kinds of disagreement correlated $-.14$ on one unit and $-.20$ on another unit. This may deserve further investigation. One possibility would be to see whether the same extremely low correlations are found with the data from the other five nursing units. Another possibility would be to examine more closely what the disagreements are about and whom they are between, and to see whether either of these appears to be related to the reporting of disagreement.

5. THE THERAPIST FORM OF THE RELATIONSHIP QUESTIONNAIRE

The first form of the therapist questionnaire was developed in January 1959 and it was administered for the first time in February 1959. Because of the way in which contacts with therapists are structured and what the therapists attempt to do in their hours with the patients, the therapist form differed in some important respects (such as the approach items) but corresponded to the ward staff form of the questionnaire in other respects (such as items dealing with the expression of feelings). Starting in April 1959 the therapist questionnaire was administered at approximately the same time as the questionnaire for ward staff on all succeeding occasions. As far as possible, revisions in both forms were made at the same times and in the same or equivalent ways.

On the basis of data from the January 1960 administration, scales were formed which were intended to correspond with the scales of the ward staff questionnaire. Because of the differences in item wording and item inclusion, as well as differences in the values of correlations between items, none of the scales for the therapist version corresponded exactly to scales for the ward staff version although some came pretty close, the closest correspondence probably being for the Problem Behavior scales. Correlations were computed among the 17 scales of the therapist questionnaire, using data from the January 1960 administration. Cluster analysis of these intercorrelations yielded five clusters, which are presented and discussed in Chapter V. Table 7 shows how the six patients who were studied intensively fitted into these five clusters. (The criteria for assignment to a particular category are the same as those described earlier, section 4D).

TABLE 7

Cluster Placement—Third Floor Patients—January 1960
Therapist Questionnaire

	Low	Medium	High	Mixed
Mutual friendlines	Appleton		Dan Glen	Feldman Harrashaw Richter
Approach (pt.) & *Personal Communication*	Appleton Dan	Feldman Harrashaw	Glen Richter	
Problem Behavior *& Contentiousness*	Dan Glen	Richter	Appleton Feldman	Harrashaw
Problem Behavior *in Therapy*	Dan Glen	Richter	Appleton Feldman Harrashaw	
Patient & Therapist *Dissatisfaction*	Dan Glen	Harrashaw	Appleton Feldman Richter	

Interitem correlation analyses to check the generality of scales were performed with questionnaires from therapists of patients on three nursing units filled out in December 1960. Of the 11 scales checked, the following five had satisfactory intercorrelations among their items: Approach by the patient, Personal Communication by the patient, the Expression of Positive Feelings by the patient, the Expression of Negative Feelings by the patient, and Personal Communication by the therapist.

No reliability or validity or other methodological studies have been done with the therapist version of the questionnaire; these would be desirable if further use of it were comtemplated. In particular, the problem of individual differences in style of answering questions (which we found such a difficult problem in the ward staff version) needs to be faced.

6. THE LATEST REVISION OF THE RELATIONSHIP QUESTIONNAIRE

In this section we present the latest revision of the Relationship Questionnaire with suggestions for its administration. The questionnaire is intended for use in clinical settings, especially with disturbed and psychotic patients. At this stage it should be used for research purposes only. The results and implications of our evaluative studies (as summarized in section 3G) should be kept in mind.

A. Items

Each item of the questionnaire is presented on a separate sheet, in the following format:

His talk was mixed up, confused and hard to figure out.

Patient	Most of the time		½ of the time		¼ of the time		Hardly ever		Never
Armstrong									
Becker									
Caruso									
Doyle									
Etc.									

The answer categories are not the same for all items. The categories shown above are used with many of the items. The other set commonly used is Many times a day, five or six times a day, a few times in past week, once or twice in past week, never in past week. In the following list of items the set of answer categories used is indicated in brackets following each item. If the item uses one of the two sets already given, only the first category label is shown. Otherwise, all five are shown.

ITEMS FOR RELATIONSHIP QUESTIONNAIRE

(Wherever a number is omitted in the chronological order, it means that a question once having that number has been discarded from previous runs of the questionnaire).

1. In the past week, how much time did you usually spend with each patient *during a shift?* [3 or more hours, 2 hours, 1 hour, ½ hour, 0]

2. During the whole week, what was the total time you spent giving *nursing care?* (Dressing, bathing, changing clothes, feeding, doing things which the patient didn't do for himself, etc.) [10 or more hours, 5 hours, 1 hour, ½ hour, 0]

4. During the whole week, how much time did you spend *just being together without talk?* (Sitting quietly, listening to music, looking at a magazine, smoking, watching TV, etc.) [10 or more hours, 5 hours, 1 hour, ½ hour, 0]

5. During the whole week, how much time did you spend in *conversation?* (Talking of any sort.) [10 or more hours, 5 hours, 1 hour, ½ hour, 0]

6. During the whole week, how much time did you spend in *horseplay?* (Teasing, wrestling, etc.) [10 or more hours, 5 hours, 1 hour, ½ hour, 0]

7. During the whole week, how much time did you spend in *pleasure trips off the ward?* (Walks, rides, movies, Kiosk, parties, psychodrama, etc.) [10 or more hours, 5 hours, 1 hour, ½ hour, 0]

8. During the whole week, how much time did you spend in *activities in which you and the patient did something together* such as playing a game, making some craft or art project, doing some work, playing music or singing, reading aloud, etc.?) [10 or more hours, 5 hours, 1 hour, ½ hour, 0]

9-A. During the whole week, how much time did you spend with the patient doing things in which he took an active part and showed interest? [5 hours, 2 hours, 1 hour, ½ hour, 0]

10-A. During the whole week, how much time did you spend with the patient in activities which he himself suggested? [5 hours, 2 hours, 1 hour, ½ hour, 0]

11-A. During the whole week, how much time did you spend with the patient doing things in which he showed little interest and just went along rather passively? [5 hours, 2 hours, 1 hour, ½ hour, 0]

13. When you approached him, how often did he respond by words or gesture? [Most of the time, etc.]

14. When you were with him, how often did he try to get you to stay longer with him? [Most of the time, etc.]

15. When you were with him, how often did he try to keep the time short and to leave soon? [Most of the time, etc.]

16. When you were with him, how often did you try to get him to stay longer with you? [Most of the time, etc.]

17. His talk was mixed up, confused and hard to figure out. [Most of the time, etc.]

18. The things he said to me were unrealistic (imaginary, delusional, outlandish.) [Most of the time, etc.]

19. When I talked to him he made sensible replies which had to do with what I was saying. [Most of the time, etc.]

20. He showed by his actions that he understood what I said. [Most of the time, etc.]

21. His replies showed that he twisted or distorted what I said. [Most of the time, etc.]

22. When he was with you, how often did he show you or let you know that he felt *cheerful* (in a good mood)? [Most of the time, etc.]

23. When he was with you, how often did he show you or let you know that he felt *friendly* (seemed to like being with you)? [Most of the time, etc.]

24. When he was with you, how often did he show you or let you know that he felt *active* or *energetic* (lively and interested)? [Most of the time, etc.]

25. When he was with you, how often did he show you or let you know that he felt *admiring* or *praising* (complimented you on appearance, behavior, accomplishments, belongings)? [Most of the time, etc.]

26. When he was with you, how often did he show you or let you know that he felt *grateful* or *appreciative* (said "thank you" or appeared to be grateful)? [Most of the time, etc.]

27. When he was with you, how often did he show you or let you know that he felt *unhappy?* [Most of the time, etc.]

28. When he was with you, how often did he show you or let you know that he felt *suspicious* or *distrustful?* [Most of the time, etc.]

29. When he was with you, how often did he show you or let you know that he felt *angry* or *annoyed?* [Most of the time, etc.]

30. When he was with you, how often did he show you or let you know that he felt *fearful* or *cautious?* [Most of the time, etc.]

31. When you were with him, how often did YOU show or let him know that YOU felt *especially friendly* (particularly liked to be with him)? [Most of the time, etc.]

32. When you were with him, how often did YOU show or let him know that YOU felt *active* or *energetic* (lively and interested)? [Most of the time, etc.]

33. When you were with him, how often did YOU show or let him know that YOU felt *pleased with him* (approving, grateful, or admiring)? [Most of the time, etc.]

34. When you were with him, how often did YOU show or let him know that YOU felt *unhappy?* [Most of the time, etc.]

35. When you were with him, how often did YOU show or let him know that YOU felt *suspicious* or *distrustful?* [Most of the time, etc.]

36. When you were with him, how often did YOU show or let him know that YOU felt *angry* or *annoyed?* [Most of the time, etc.]

37. How often did you *ask* or *suggest* that he do, or stop doing something? [Many times a day, etc.]

38. How often did you succeed in getting him to do, or stop doing something *just by* asking him? [Most of the time, etc.]

38-A. How often does he refuse to do what you ask him? [Most of the time, etc.]

38-C. How often does he ignore what you ask him to do? [Most of the time, etc.]

39. In trying to get him to do, or stop doing something, how often did you reason, coax, or *explain*? [Most of the time, etc.]

40. In trying to get him to, or stop doing something, how often did you *watch* him and *keep after* him? [Most of the time, etc.]

41. In trying to get him to do, or stop doing something, how often did you *command, warn,* or *give ultimatum*? [Most of the time, etc.]

42. In trying to get him to, or stop doing something, how often did you *use force* (interfere in a fight, seclude him, force him to do something)? [Most of the time, etc.]

42-A. How often do you think your ideas about how to handle this patient agree with those of *his therapist*? [Most of the time, etc.]

42-B. How often do you think your ideas about how to handle this patient agree with those of the *ward administrator*? [Most of the time, etc.] (Only ward personnel have this question and 42-C.)

42-C. How often do you think your ideas about how to handle this patient agree with those of *the other ward personnel* (other nurses and aides)? [Most of the time, etc.]

42-D. [This question for ward administrator only]
How often do you think your ideas about how to handle this patient agree with those of *your ward personnel* (nurses and aides)? [Most of the time, etc.]

43. He spoke to me. [Many times a day, etc.]

44. He spoke (sang, chanted, etc.) to himself without directly addressing anyone. [Many times a day, etc.]

45. He actively sought me out. [Many times a day, etc.]

46. He stayed around me but didn't speak to me unless I spoke first. [Many times a day, etc.]

48. I actively sought him out. [Many times a day, etc.]

49. I stayed around him ready to talk or do something he wanted (but waiting for him to make the first move). [Many times a day, etc.]

50. He directly asked me for something (help, permission, advice, information, food, other items). [Many times a day, etc.]

51. He let me know he wanted something without expressing it clearly in words. [Many times a day, etc.]

52. He nagged or made persistent demands. [Many times a day, etc.]

53. He tried to give logical reasons why his requests should be granted. [Many times a day, etc.]

54. He talked to me about impersonal topics (such as news events, weather, sports, politics, etc.). [Many times a day, etc.]

55. In talking to me he made *complaints* (criticism, accusations). [Many times a day, etc.]

56. In talking to me he *joked and kidded*. [Many times a day, etc.]

57. He talked to me about *his personal life* (his thoughts, feelings, personal affairs, past life, etc.). [Many times a day, etc.]

58. He talked to me about *my personal life* (my thoughts, feelings, personal affairs, past life, etc.). [Many times a day, etc.]

59. In talking to me he expressed *agreement or disagreement* with what I said. [Many times a day, etc.]

60. He talked to me about the *relationship between the two of us* (how we get along). [Many times a day, etc.]

61. In talking to me he expressed concern about understanding what I said and about my understanding what he said (asking me to explain something, asking if I knew what he meant, etc.). [Many times a day, etc.]

62. [NOTE that this item and the following 7 items ask about what YOU said.]
I talked to him about impersonal topics (such as news events, weather, sports, politics, etc.). [Many times a day, etc.]

63. In talking to him I made *complaints* (criticisms, accusations). [Many times a day, etc.]

64. In talking to him, I *joked* and *kidded*. [Many times a day, etc.]

65. I talked to him about *his personal life* (his thoughts, feelings, personal affairs, past life, etc.). [Many times a day, etc.]

66. I talked to him about *my personal life* (my thoughts, feelings, personal affairs, past life, etc.). [Many times a day, etc.]

67. In talking to him I expressed *agreement or disagreement* with what he said. [Many times a day, etc.]

68. I talked to him about the *relationship between the two of us* (how we get along). [Many times a day, etc.]

69. In talking to him I expressed *concern about understanding* what he said and about his understanding what I said (asking him to explain something, asking if he knew what I meant, etc.). [Many times a day, etc.]

70. How often did you notice self-neglect (poor eating, personal appearance, or hygiene)? [Many times a day, etc.]

71. How often did you notice attempts at or talk about *suicide or self-injury?* (self-mutilation or frequent minor injuries)? [Many times a day, etc.]

72. How often did you notice him making *threats or attacks on others or yourself?* [Many times a day, etc.]

74. How often did you notice him showing *socially unacceptable behavior* nudity, messiness, noisiness, demanding attention)? [Many times a day, etc.]

75. How often did you notice him *breaking rules or ward routine* (escape attempts, unauthorized phone calls, refusal to go to dining room or to return to ward, etc.)? [Many times a day, etc.]

76. How often did you notice him being destructive (tearing clothes, breaking things)? [Many times a day, etc.]

77. He keeps to himself. [Most of the time, etc.]

78. When I ask him to go somewhere or do something with me he refuses. [Most of the time, etc.]

82. He shows that he doesn't want to be with me. [Most of the time, etc.]

87. In this question we want to find out which patients you most like to work with and spend time with. Put a 1 after the name of the patient you like most to be with, a 2 after the patient who is your second choice to be with, and so on. Be sure to put a number after the name of each patient.

B. List of Items in Each Scale

Scale	Item Numbers*	First Run on which all Items on Scale appeared
1. Approach (pt.)	13, 14, 43, 45	Jan. 1959
2. Avoidance (pt.)	15, 77, 78, 82	Jan. 1960
3. Communication, Impersonal (pt.)	53, 54, 59	Apr. 1959
4. Communication, Personal (pt.)	56, 57, 58, 60	Apr. 1959
5. Communication, Clarity (pt.)	—17, —18, 19, 20, —21, —44	Jan. 1959
6. Problem Behavior (pt.)	70 thru 72, 74 thru 76	Apr. 1959
7. Positive Feelings (pt.)	22 thru 26	Apr. 1959
8. Negative Feelings (pt.)	27 thru 30	Apr. 1959
9. Active Activities	8, 9-A, 10-A	Jan. 1960
10. Passive Activities	2, 4, 11-A	Jan. 1960
11. Approach (stf.)	16, 48, 49	Jan. 1959
12. Communication, Personal (stf.)	64, 65, 66, 68	Apr. 1959
13. Positive Feelings (stf.)	31, 32, 33	Apr. 1959
14. Negative Feelings (stf.)	34, 35, 36	Apr. 1959
15. Use of Control Techniques (stf.)	37, 39, 42	Jan. 1959
16. Compliance (pt.)	38, —38A, —38C	Jan. 1960
	61 Scale Items	

Single Items not incorporated into the Scales: (22 Items)

```
 1   3   5   6   7
40  41  42-A 42-B  42-C  42-D
46  50  51  52  55
61  62  63  67  69  87
```

* Minus sign in front of item number means that scores on that item were reversed (by subtracting the actual score from 10).

C. Administration

The following instructions are suggested. This is a revised version of instructions which were used at Chestnut Lodge:

This questionnaire deals with some of the things that patients and staff members do. We want to find out about the relationships *during the past week* between you and the patients with whom you work.

Each item describes a single action, which is to be marked to show how often it happened. Here is an example:

He spoke to me

	Many times a day		5 or 6 times a day		A few times in past week		Once or twice in past week		Never in past week
Adams									
Bond									

On each line you are to put a check mark in the box which shows how often that patient spoke to you during the past week. If the answer is between two of those given, put your check in the box between them.

Work rapidly and try not to spend a lot of time on any one item. Feel free to write comments on the questionnaire if you want to. When you are finished, please make sure you have put a check for each patient on each page.

At least the first time that someone fills out the questionnaire it is desirable that the researcher or an assistant be present to answer questions and note comments.

BIBLIOGRAPHY

Gladstone, A. I. & Burnham, D. L. (1966), A Method of Studying the Relationship between Pathological Excitement and Hidden Staff Disagreement. *Psychiat., 29*:339-343.

LaForge, R. & Suczek, R. F. (1955), The Interpersonal Dimension of Personality: 3, An Interpersonal Check List. *J. Personal., 24*:94-112.

Lorr, M. (1953), *Multidimensional Scale for Rating Psychiatric Patients, Hospital Form.* Veterans Administration Technical Bulletin, T B 10-507. Washington, D.C.: Veterans Administration.

Newcomb, T. (1931), An Experiment Designed to Test the Validity of a Rating Technique. *J. Educ. Psychol., 22*:279-289.

Stanton, A. H. & Schwartz, M. S. (1954), *The Mental Hospital.* New York: Basic Books.

NAME INDEX*

* The italicized figures are the page numbers of bibliographic references.

SUBJECT INDEX